A Catalogue of

The African Collection

in

The Moorland Foundation
Howard University Library

Compiled by

STUDENTS IN
THE PROGRAM OF AFRICAN STUDIES

Edited by

DOROTHY B. PORTER

Published for The Moorland Foundation
and The Program of African Studies
by
The Howard University Press
Washington, D. C.
1958

Printed at Baltimore, Maryland, by
The Collegiate Publishing Company

The following corrections should be made in the index:

The following corrections should be made in the Index:

			should read	
p. 373	Cush, 576		"	578
	Dodoye, 577		"	579
p. 374	Delafosse, 578		"	580
	Dictionary of the Yoruba			
	language, 579, 580		"	581, 582
	Dillman, 581-583		"	583-585
	Doles, 584-589		"	586-591
	Douglas, 590		"	592
p. 375	Deap, R. ..., 591		"	593
	Sahagun, 592		"	594
p. 376	Wilkinson, 593, 594		"	595, 596
	Foch, 595		"	597
	Forlong, 596		"	598
p. 377	Gaston, 597		"	599
	Gardiner, Alan, 598		"	600
p. 378	Grout, 602		"	601
	Guthrie, 603-605		"	602-607
p. 379	Hamlyn, 606		"	608
	Hinde, H., 607		"	609
p. 380	Hollis, 608, 609		"	610, 611
	Hemingway, 610		"	612
	Howitt, 611		"	613
	International Institute, 612		"	614
p. 381	Inter-territorial, 613		"	615
	Jabavu, 614		"	616
	Jacottet, 615		"	617
	Johnston, 616		"	618
	Jones, Daniel, 617		"	619
p. 382	Kenita, 618, 618		"	620, 621
	Kelne, 619		"	622
	Kral, 621		"	623
	Ioonia			Nouria
p. 383	Labouret, 622		"	624
	Laverrs, 623		"	625
p. 384	Luke, 625		"	626
	Heckmann, 627		"	629
p. 385	Meinhof, 626, 629		"	620, 621

PREFACE

It is the purpose of this publication to provide a list of the materials relating to Africa which are located in the Moorland Foundation, of the Howard University Library and which were received prior to June 1957. Few bibliographies are ever complete and the present one is no exception. By the time this list is published more books and periodicals will have been added to the collection, and within a few years a supplement may seem desirable.

The arrangement of the 4,865 book entries included adheres to an alphabetical scheme by countries, or other political units, which are in turn grouped under six main regions, i.e., Northern Africa, North-Eastern Africa, Western Africa, Central Africa, Eastern Africa and Southern Africa. A general section arranged by subject precedes the listing by country divisions.

No attempt has been made to annotate the book and pamphlet titles. Periodicals have been listed alphabetically by title and newspapers by geographic area. No attempt has been made to include the exact holdings for each title, some of which are incomplete. An index primarily of authors, but containing some subjects, has been added to facilitate the use of the bibliography.

Since there has not been time to recheck all titles, occasional error, or inconsistency may have crept in. The editor hopes to be forgiven any serious failings of this kind.

The work of compiling this bibliography has been carried out chiefly by students in the Program of African Studies, at Howard University— the Misses Myrtle Gilbert, Addie Collins, Carol Russell, Daphne Pitt, Gladys M. Clark and Mrs. Enid W. Gordon. Special thanks are due Miss Gladys M. Clark and Miss Dolores C. Leffall, assistants in The Moorland Foundation who gave invaluable aid during the final stages of the preparation of the bibliography.

This publication has been made possible through grants from the Ford Foundation to the Program of African Studies at Howard University. Grateful acknowledgment is made to Dr. E. Franklin Frazier, Director of the Program of African Studies, who first suggested the bibliography and encouraged its completion.

It is hoped that the results of this cooperative undertaking will prove of real value to students of African life and history. Certainly, it should make the collection of African works in The Moorland Foundation better known and encourage more students to use the resources of the Foundation.

Howard University Library   DOROTHY B. PORTER, *Editor*

CONTENTS

6

AFRICA: GENERAL

BIBLIOGRAPHIES

1 The African Press and Advertising Annual, 1953-1954, 1956. Cape Town, Boston House, 1954-1957. (MO79Ad9)

2 Afrique Equatoriale Française. Service de statistique. Bibliographie ethnographique de l'Afrique Equatoriale Française, 1914-1918. Paris, Imprimerie Nationale, 1949. 107p. (AMO1Af8b)

3 Appleyard, Margaret Elizabeth. Dr. David Livingstone: a bibliography. [Cape Town] University of Cape Town, School of Librarianship, 1949. 50p. (AMO12Ap5)

4 Baker, Mary. Sir Benjamin D'Urban's Administration, 1834-1838. Capetown, University of Cape Town, School of Librarianship, 1946. 31p. (AMO16B24)

5 Bee, Barbara M. Historical bibliography of the city of Durban; or, Port Natal. [Cape Town] University of Cape Town, 1946. (AMO16B39)

6 Bibliographie d'histoire coloniale. (1900-1930). Publiée par les soins de Mm. Alfred Martineau . . . Roussier . . . Tramand . . . delégnes par le congrès. Paris, Société l'Histoire des colonies françaises, 1932. 667p. (MO16.325B47)

7 Bielschowsky, Ludwig. List of books in German on South Africa and West Africa published up to 1914 in the South African public library, Cape Town, compiled by Ludwig Bielschowsky. Cape Town, School of Librarianship, 1949. 48p. (AMO16B771)

8 Blum, P. Union native policy as reflected in government legislation and publication, 1910-1948; a bibliography. Cape Town, University of Cape Town, School of Librarianship, 1950. 281p. (MO16.968B62)

9 Brownlee, Margaret. The lives and work of South African missionaries; a bibliography. Cape Town, University of Cape Town, School of Librarianship, 1952. (AMO16B81)

10 Cardinall, Allan Wolsey. Bibliography of the Gold Coast 1496-1931. Accra, Government Printer, 1932. 384p. (MO1C17)

11 Carpenter, Olive. The development of Southern Rhodesia from the earliest times to the year 1900; a bibliography. Cape Town, University of Cape Town, School of Librarianship, 1946. 20p.

12 Comhaire, J. Urban conditions in Africa: select reading list on urban problems in Africa. New and revised edition. London, Pub-

lished for the Institute of Colonial Studies by Oxford University Press, 1952. 48p. (MO16.96C73u)

13 Conover, Helen F. Africa South of the Sahara; a selected, annotated list of writings, 1951-1956. Washington, Library of Congress, 1957. 269 p.

14 Conseil Scientifique pour l'Afrique au Sud du Sahara. Cartographie de l'Afrique au Sud du Sahara. Bukavu, Congo Belge, 1953. 122p. (MO16.968C76c)

15 Cox, Diedre L. A bibliography of the federation of the Rhodesias and Nyasaland, up to June 30, 1949. Compiled by D. L. Cox. Cape Town, University of Cape Town, School of Librarianship, 1949. v. 23 (AMO16C83b)

16 Craig, Barbara June. Rock paintings and petroglyphs of South and Central Africa. Cape Town, University of Cape Town, School of Librarianship, 1947. Mimeographed. 58p. (AMO1C84r)

17 Edwards, Francis. Catalogue of books, pamphlets, views, maps, and transactions of societies, relating to Africa and African islands. London, Francis Edwards, 1902. 224p. (MO17.4Ed9)

18 Fox, Vivienne Christine. Prisons and penal reform in South Africa, 1938-1948. Cape Town, University of Cape Town, School of Librarianship, 1949. 251p. (MO16.365F83p)

19 France. État-major de l'Armée. L'Afrique française du nord. Bibliographie militaire des ouvrage française ou traduits en français et des articles des principales revues françaises relatifs à l'Algérie, à la Tunisie et au Maroc de 1830 à 1926. Paris, Imprimerie nationale, 1930. vols. 1, 3, 4. (MO16.961F84)

20 France. Ministère de la France d'outre-mer. Service des statistiques. Bulletin bibliographique. no. 1- aout 1948. Paris, Jan. 1949. no. 4. (MO16325F84)

21 Galloway, Margaret H. Zululand and the Zulus: a bibliography. Cape Town, 1944. 16p. (MO16.968G13z)

22 Great Britain. Colonial Office. Bibliography of published sources relating to African land tenure. London, H. M. Stationery Office, 1950. 156p. (AMO1G79b)

23 Greshoff, N. M. Some English writings by South African Bantu. Cape Town, 1943. 11p. (Bibliographical series). (MO1G86S)

24 Groen, Julie. Bibliography of Basutoland. Cape Town, University of Cape Town, School of Librarianship, 1946. (MO16.968-G89b)

25 Hambly, Wilfred D. Bibliography of African anthropology, 1937-

1949. Chicago Natural History Museum, 1952. 292p. (AM572-H1750)

26 Hampton, Va. Normal and Agricultural Institute. Collis P. Huntington library. A classified catalogue of the Negro collection in the Collis P. Huntington library, Hampton Institute. Compiled by workers of the Writers' program of the Works projects administration in the state of Virginia. Sponsored by Hampton Institute. n.p., 1940. 255p. (MO1H18)

27 Heyse, Théodore. Bibliographie du Congo Belge et du Ruanda-Urundi (1939-1951) Documentation générale: bibliographies et centres d'etudes, expositions, presse et propaganda. Répetoire suivi d'un complément à la "Politique Indigène," Période antérieure à 1940. Bruxelles, G. van Campenhout, 1952. 57p. (MO16.967H51b)

28 Heyse, Théodore. Bibliographie du Congo Belge et du Ruanda-Urundi (1939-1951) Documentation générale. Folklore philatélie, sports, tourisme; répertoire suivi d'un complément final a la "Politique indigène," période antériure à 1940. Bruxelles, G. van Campenhout 1952. 40p. (MO16.967)

29 Heyse, Théodore. Bibliographie du Congo Belge et du Ruanda-Urundi (1939-1951) Sciences coloniales. Répertoire suivi d'un complément a la "Politique indigéne" période antérieure a 1940. Bruxelles, G. van Campenhout, 1952. 71p. (Chaiers belges et congolais, no. 18) (MO16.967H516s)

30 Holden, A. and Jacoby, A. Supplement to Schapera select bibliography of South African native life and problems: modern status and conditions. Capetown, University of Capetown, School of Librarianship, 1949. 32p. (AMO16Schl)

31 Howard University. Founders Library. Liberia: her history and people; a selected list of books, pamphlets and periodical articles in the Moorland Foundation. Washington, The Moorland Foundation, Howard University, 1951. 12p. (Mimeographed)

32 Ibrahim-Hilmy, Prince. The literature of Egypt and the Soudan from the earliest times to the year 1885 (i.e. 1887) inclusive. London, Trübner and Co., 1886-87. 2 vols. (MO16Ib7)

33 Inskip, Catherine. List of guide-books and handbooks dating from 1800 to the present day, dealing with South Africa and with the Western Province. [Cape Town] University of Cape Town, 1948. mimeographed. v. 18 (MO16.968In7s)

34 Institut Français d'Afrique Noire. Conseils aux Chercheurs, une brochure a conserver, 2nd ed. Dakar, I F A N, 1943. 61p. (MO16.96In8)

35 Institut Français d'Afrique Noire. Conseils aux Chercheurs, une brochure a conserver, 3d. ed., 1948. p. 78

36 Institut Français d'Afrique Noire. Conseils aux Chercheurs, une a conserver, 4th ed., 1953. 74p.

37 International African Institute. Select annotated bibliography of tropical Africa, compiled under the direction of Daryll Forde. New York, the Twentieth Century Fund, 1956. (MO16.916In8s)

38 Joucla, Edmond. Bibliographie de l'Afrique Occidentale Française. Paris, Société d'Editions Geographiques, 1937. 704p. (MO16.-966J82)

39 Joucla, Edmund. Bibliographie de l'Afrique Occidentale Française. Paris, Bibliothèque Internationale d'Edition, 1912. 275p. (MO16.966J82)

40 Journal de la Société des Africanistes. Paris, Musee de l'homme, 1931.

41 Leslau, Wolf. Bibliography of the Semitic languages of Ethiopia, by Wolf Leslau. New York, New York public library, 1946. 275p. (MO1L56b)

42 Library of Congress. Division of Bibliography. British West Africa: a selected list of references, compiled by Helen F. Conover under the direction of Florence S. Hellman. December 1, 1942. 32p. (MO1L61b)

43 Loening, L. S. E. A bibliography of the status of South-West Africa up to June 30, 1951. Cape Town, University of Cape Town, School of Librarianship, 1951. 32p.

44 Luke, Harry Charles Joseph. A bibliography of Sierra Leone, preceded by an essay on the origin, character and peoples of the colony and protectorate, by Harry Charles Luke. 2nd enl. ed. London, H. Milford, Oxford University Press, 1925. 230p. (AMO1L96)

45 Mandelbrote, Joyce C. The cape press, 1838-1850: bibliography. Cape Town, University of Cape Town, School of Librarianship, 1945. 65p. (MO16.968M31c)

46 Meek, C. K. Colonial law, a bibliography with special reference to native African systems of law and land tenure. London, Oxford University Press, 1948. 58p.

47 Morris, G. R. A bibliography of the Indian question in South Africa Cape Town, School of Librarianship, 1946. 17p.

48 New York Public Library. Ancient Egypt 1925-1941. A supplement to Ancient Egypt: Sources of information in the New York

public library. 1925. Compiled by Ida A. Pratt. New York, The New York public library, 1942. 340p. (MO15.32N48)

49 Perry, Ruth. A preliminary bibliography of the literature of nationalism in Nigeria. Stanford, Calif., Hoover Institute & Library on War, Revolution and Peace, 1956. 38p.

50 Robinson, A. M. Lewin, comp. A bibliography of African bibliographies covering territories south of the Sahara. Cape Town, South African Public Library, 1955. 169p. (MO16.916R56b)

51 Rossouw, Dorothea E. Catalogue of African languages (1858-1900) in the Grey collection of the South African Library. Cape Town, University of Cape Town, School of Librarianship, 1947. (mimeographed) (MO16.496R73c)

52 Royal empire society, London. Library. A select list of recent publications contained in the library of the Royal colonial institute illustrating the constitutional relations between the various parts of the British Empire. Compiled by Evans Lewin. London, Royal colonial institute (Heaton Mersey, near Manchester, The Cloister press limited) 1926. 30p. (MO16R81s)

53 Royal empire society, London. Library. Annotated bibliography of recent publications of Africa, south of the Sahara, with special reference to administrative, political economic and sociological problems, by Evans Lewin, M.B.E., librarian of the Royal empire society. London, The Royal empire society, 1943. 104p. (MO16R81a)

54 Ruth Sloane Associates. Washington, D.C. The Press in Africa. Edited by Helen Kitchin. Washington, The Associates, 1956. 96p.

55 Saul, C. Daphne. South African periodical publications, 1800-1875. Cape Town, School of Librarianship, University of Cape Town, 1949. 45p. (AMO16Sa8s)

56 Schapera, Isaac. Select bibliography of the South African native life and problems, London, Oxford University Press. H. Milford, 1941. 249p. (MO16Schl)

57 Schumann, E. W. A bibliography of South African grammar books, compiled by E. W. Schumann. Cape Town, School of Librarianship, 1946. 47p. (AMO16Sc8b)

58 Smith, Anna H. Catalogue of Bantu Khoisan and Malagasy in the Strange Collection of Africana, ed. by Anna H. Smith. Johannesburg, Public Library, 1942. 232p. (mimeographed) (MO16.492-Sm5c)

59 South African Institute of International Affairs. Africa Library.

Johannesburg, 1951. 20p.

60   South African Public Library, Cape Town. A bibliography of African bibliographies. Rev. to Feb., 1948. Cape Town, South African Public Library, 1948. 52p. (AMO16So8)

61   South African Public Library. Cape Town. Union list of South African newspapers. November, 1949 with a foreword by Ralph Kilpin. Cape Town, South African Public Library, 1950. 99p. (MO1So8u)

62   Spain. Dirección General de Marrucecos y Colonias. Biblioteca. Catálogo de libros espanoles sobre geografía y via jes en Africa, por M. Asunción del Val directora de la biblioteca. Madrid, Instituto de Estudios Africanos, 1948. 120p. (MO16.96Spl)

63   Spain. Dirección General de Marrucecos y Colonias. Biblioteca. Catálogo de materias por M. Asunción de Val. Madrid, Impr. de Sucesores de Rivadeneyra, 1949. 380p. (AMO16Spl)

64   Spohr, Otto H. Catalogue of books, pamphlets and periodicals published in German relating to South Africa. Cape Town, School of Librarianship, University of Cape Town, 1950. 71p. (AMO-16Sp6c)

65   Starr, Frederick. A bibliography of Congo languages. Chicago, The University of Chicago Press, 1908. 97p. (MO1St2)

66   Stevens, P. M. Zimbabwe culture: A bibliography. Cape Town, University of Cape Town, School of Librarianship, 1946. 47p.

67   Streit, R. and Dindinger, J. Biblioteca missionum: Afrikanische missionsliteratur, 1053-1940. Freiburg, Herder, 1951-54. 5v.

68   Tervueren. Musee du Congo Belge. Bibliographie Ethnographique du Congo Belge et des regions avoisinantes, 1925-1930. Bruxelles, En Vente Chez Falk Fils, 1925, 1938. (MO1T27)

69   Thomson, Daphne W. Cecil John Rhodes, a bibliography, compiled by Daphne W. Thomson. Cape Town, School of Librarianship, University of Cape Town, 1947. 29p. (AMO12T38c)

70   Tuaillon, Jean Lois Georges. Bibliographie critique de l'Afrique occidentale française. Paris, etc., Charles Lavauzelle and Cie, 1936. 49p. (AMO16T79b)

71   Turest, E. N. A bibliography of National health services in South Africa from 28th August, 1942 - July, 1945, compiled by E. N. Turest. Cape Town, University of Cape Town, 1945. 23p. (AMO1T84b)

72   U. S. Dept. of State. Office of Intelligence. Research. Unpublished research on Africa, completed and in progress. Compiled and

distributed by External Research Staff. Washington, 1953. 11p. (MO16.96Un3su)

73 U. S. Library of Congress. Census library Project. Population censuses and other official demographic statistics on British Africa; an annotated bibliography, prepared by Henry J. Dubester, Chief. Census Library Project, Washington, U. S. Government Printing Office, 1950. 78p. (MO16.3D85p)

74 U. S. Library of Congress. Reference Dept. African newspapers currently received in selected American libraries. Washington, 1956. 16p.

75 U. S. Library of Congress. Reference Dept. Periodicals on Africa currently received in selected American libraries. Washington, 1956. 34p.

76 U. S. Library of Congress. Reference Dept. Research and information on Africa: continuing sources. Washington, 1954. 70p. (M01L61r)

77 U. S. Library of Congress. Division of Bibliography. French colonies in Africa: a list of references. Compiled by Helen F. Conover, under the direction of Florence S. Hellman, chief bibliographer. Washington, U. S. Government Printing Office, 1942. 89p. (MO16Un3f)

78 U. S. Library of Congress. European Affairs Division; Introduction to Africa: A selected guide to background reading. Washington, University Press of Washington, 1952. 237p. (MO-16.96Un3i)

79 Varley, Douglas Harold. African native music: an annotated bibliography. London, The Royal empire society, 1936. 116p. (AMO1V42a)

80 Varley, Douglas Harold. A bibliography of Italian colonization in Africa. London, The Royal empire society and the Royal institute of international affairs, 1936. 92p. (AMO1V42)

81 Wieschhoff, Heinrich A. Anthropological bibliography of Negro Africa. New Haven, Conn., American Oriental Society, 1948. 461p. (MO16.960W63)

82 Welch, Floretta H. South-West Africa: a bibliography. Cape Town, University of Cape Town, School of Librarianship, 1946. 33p. (MO16,968W44s)

83 Whyte, Morag. Bibliography of the works of Sarah Gertrude Millin. [Rondebosch] School of Librarianship, University of Cape Town, 1952. (MO12W62)

84 Woodward, Sarah C. A bibliography of Africa. Hartford, Conn., Church Missions Publishing Co., 1909. 63p. (AMO1W87)

85 Wookey, D. M. A bibliography of physical anthropology in South Africa (1936-1947). Cape Town, University of Cape Town, 1947. 45p. (AMO1W87b)

86 Work, Monroe Nathan. A bibliography of the Negro in Africa and America. New York, The H. W. Wilson Co., 1928. 698p. (MO1W98)

GENERAL WORKS

87 Africa, past and present . . . by an old resident. New York, American Tract Society (pref. 1879). 387p. (M960Af8)

88 African academy of arts and research, New York. Africa, today and tomorrow. April, 1945. [New York] African Academy of arts and research [1945] 80p. (M960Af8a)

89 African World Annual. London, The African World, 1904-1956. (M960Af83)

90 Association for promoting the discovery of the interior parts of Africa. Proceedings. London, C. Macrae, 1790. 215p. (AM960As7p)

91 Baker, Helen E. More about Africa. New York, Friendship Press, 1945. 122p. (AM960B17m)

92 Balm, Catherine Miller. Fun and festival from Africa. New York, Friendship Press, 1936. 43p. (AM960B21f)

93 Barber, D. H. Africans in Khaki. London, Edinburgh House Press, 1948. 120p. (M960B14a)

94 Bartlett, Vernon. Struggle for Africa. London, Frederick Muller, Ltd., [1953] 251p. (M960B28)

95 Batten, Thomas Reginald. Africa, past and present. London, Oxford University Press, 1943. 108p. (AM960B32)

96 Batten, Thomas Reginald. Problems of African Development. London, Oxford University Press, 1947-48 2v. (M960D32p)

97 Batten, Thomas Reginald. Thoughts on African Citzenship. [London] Oxford University Press [1945] 77p. (M960B32t)

98 Beer, George Louis. African questions at the Paris Peace Conference, with papers on Egypt, Mespotamia, and the colonial settlement. New York, The Macmillan Company, 1923. 628p. (M960B39)

99 Blanchod, Frederic Georges. Os estranhos costumes do continente

Negro. Porto, Livraria Tavares Martins, 1946. 397p. (AM-960B59e)

100 Booth, Joseph. Africa for the Africans. Baltimore, Md., Morgan College Printer. 16p. (M960B64)

101 Bowles, Chester. Africa's Challenge to America. Berkeley, University of California Press, 1956. 134p. (M960B68a)

102 Brawley, Benjamin Griffith. Africa and the war. New York, Duffield & Co., 1918. 94p. (M916B73a)

103 Brown, William O., ed. Contemporary Africa, trends and issues. (The Annals of the American Academy of Political and Social Sciences.) Philadelphia, The American Academy of Political and Social Science, 1955. 248p. (M960B81)

104 Buell, Raymond Leslie. The native problem in Africa. New York, The Macmillan Company, 1928. 2v. (M960.323B86)

105 Cameron, N. E. The evolution of the Negro. Georgetown, Demerara, "The Argosy" Co., 1929-34. (AM960C14e)

106 Campbell, Alexander. Empire in Africa. London, V. Gollancz, Ltd., 1944. 160p. (AM960C15e)

107 Campbell, Alexander. It's your empire. London, V. Gollancz, Ltd., 1945. 223p. (AM325.342C15)

108 Campbell, William Kenneth Hunter. Practical cooperation in Asia and Africa. Cambridge, England, W. Heffer, 1951. 275p. AM334C15p)

109 Carter, Gwendolen M. Africa, south of the Sahara; outline for study with suggested reading. Washington, D. C., American Association of University Women, 1955. 8p.

110 Cary, Joyce. The case for African freedom. London, Secker and Warburg, 1941. 127p. (AM960C25c)

111 Catholic Association for International Peace, Subcommittee on Africa. Symposium of Africa. Washington, 1947. 32p. (AM960C28s)

112 Chukwuemeka, Nwankwo. International cooperation in Africa. Reprinted from Social Research, 1951. 75p. (AM960C47i)

113 Cirpiani, Lidio. A traves de Africa, Buenos Aires [Sociedad Geografica Americana, Editorial y Cultural] 1946. 186p. (M960-C49t)

114 Committee on Africa, the war, and peace aims. The Atlantic charter and Africa from an American standpoint, a study by the Committee on Africa, the war, and peace aims. The ap-

plication of the "eight points" of the charter to the problems
of Africa, and especially those related to the welfare of the
African people living south of the Sahara, with related material
on African conditions and needs. New York City, 1942. [i.e.
1943] 168p. (M960C73)

115   Conference on Africa. Proceedings of the conference on Africa.
New York, Council on African Affairs, 1944. 52p. (M960C76p)

116   Congress on Africa. Africa and the American Negro. Addresses
and proceedings of the Congress on Africa, held under the
auspices of the Stewart Missionary Foundation for Africa of
Gammon Theological Seminary, in connection with the Cotton
states and international exposition, Dec. 13-15, 1895. Atlanta,
Gammon Theological Seminary, 1896. 242p. (M960C76)

117   Conseil Scientifique pour l'Afrique au Sud du Sahara. Directory
of Scientifique and technical libraries in Africa south of the
Sarah. London. Published under the sponsorship of the Commission for Technical Cooperation in Africa South of the
Sahara, 1954. 71p. (AMO26C76r)

118   Conseil Scientifique pour l'Afrique au Sud du Sahara. Recherches
relatives aux Sciences humaines en Africa au Sud du Sahara.
Bukavu, Congo Belge, Publié sous l'égide de la Commission de
Coopération Technique en Afrique au Sud du Sahara, 1954.
75p. (AM300C76)

119   Cookson, John. Before the African storm. 1st ed. Indianapolis,
Bobbs-Merrill, 1954. 279p. (AM960C66)

120   Coppinger, William. The race for Africa. Hampton, Va., Normal
School Steam Press, 1883. 12p. (M960C79)

121   Council on African Affairs. Conference on Africa—New Perspectives. Proceedings. New York, 1944. 52p. (M910C759)

122   Coupland, Reginald. The destiny of Africa. London, The Anti-
Slavery and Aborigines Protection Society, 1947. 8p. (AM-
960C83d)

123   Crummell, Alexander. The future of Africa; being addresses,
sermons, etc., delivered in the republic of Liberia. New York,
C. Scribner, 1862. 372p. (M960C88f)

124   Davis, Hassoldt. Feu d'Afrique. Paris, A. Fayard, 1945. 350p.
(AM960D29f)

125   Delavignette, Robert Louis Service Africain. Paris, Gallimard,
1946. 281p. (AM960D37se)

126   Deloncle, Pierre. The claim for colonies. Supplement to the

Journal of the Royal African Society, April 1937. 18p. (AM-960D38)

127 DeMarco, Roland R. The Italianization of African Natives. New York, Teachers College, Columbia University, 1934. 150p. (AM960D34i)

128 De Preville, A. Socíetes Africaines leur origine, leur evolution, leur avenir. Paris, Librairie de Firmin-Didot, 1894. 345p.

129 Doucet, Robert. Commentaires sur la colonisation. Paris, Librairie Larose, 1926. 133p.

130 DuBois, William E. B. Africa, its geography, people and products. Girard, Kansas, Haldeman-Julius publications, 1930. 64p. (M960D85a)

131 DuBois, William E. B. The world and Africa. New York, The Viking Press, 1947. 276p. (AM960D85w)

132 Einstein, Carl. Afrikanische Legenden. Berlin, Ernest Rowohlt, 1925. 280p. (AM916E68)

133 L'Encyclopedie Coloniale et Martime. Encyclopedie of Tunisie, Afrique Occidentale Française, Afrique Equatorial Française, Algérie et Sahara, Cameroun Togo, et Maroc. Paris, Editions de l'Union Française, 1948-51. 7v. (M960En19)

134 Fleming, G. D. Blue is the sky. Boutnemouth and London, W. Earl and Co., Ltd., 1947. 183p. (AM960F62B)

135 Ford, James W. Imperialism destroys the people of Africa. New York, Harlem Section of the Communist Party, n.d. 15p. (AM960F75i)

136 Frazier, Edward Franklin. The impact of colonialism on African social forms and personality. Reprinted for private circulation from Calvin Stillman (ed.) Africa in the Modern World, University of Chicago Press, 1955. Pp. 70-96. (M960F86i)

137 Fritchman, Stephen H. The challenge of Africa to the conscience of the world. An address. Los Angeles, n.p., 1955. 11p. (M960F91)

138 Frobenius, Leo. Der schwarze Dakameron . . . Berlin-Charlottenburg, Vita, deutsches verlagshaus, 1910. 387p. (AM960F92s)

139 Gaitskell, Arthur. What have they to defend? The Africa Bureau, Annual Anniversary Address, 1955. Southwick, Sussex, Grange Press, 1955. 32p. (M960G12)

140 Gammon Theological Seminary. Stewart Missionary foundation on Africa. Africa and the American Negro . . . addresses and proceedings of the Congress on Africa . . . Dec. 13-15, 1895.

Atlanta, Gammon Theological Seminary, 1896. 242p. (M960-G14)

141 Garvey, Amy Jacques. Correlative of Africa . . . Jamaica, B.W.I., 1944. 65p. (AM960G19)

142 Ghurye, G. S. Race relations in Negro Africa. Bombay, Calcutta, Asia Publishing House, 1952. 96p. (AM323G34r)

143 Gibbons, H. A. The new map of Africa. New York, The Century Co., 1916. 503p. (AM960G35)

144 Gibbs, Henry. Africa on a tightrope. London, New York, Jarrolds, 1954. 200p. (M960G35a)

145 Goldsmith, J. A general view of the manners, customs and curiosities of Nations. New Haven, John Babock and sons, 1822. 2v. (AM960G57)

146 Goodrich, Joseph King. Africa of Today. Chicago, A. C. McClurg and Co., 1912. 315p. (M960G62)

147 Gunther, John. Inside Africa. New York, Harper, 1955. 952p. (M960G96i)

148 Haardt, Georges-Marie and Dubreuil-Audouin, Louis. The black journey. New York, Cosmopolitan Book Corporation, 1927. 316p.

149 Hailey, William Malcolm Hailey, baron. An african survey; a study of problems arising in Africa south of the Sahara. London, New York, Oxford University Press, 1938. 1837p. (M916H12)

150 Hailey, William Malcolm Hailey, baron. The future of colonial peoples. London, Oxford University Press, 1944. 63p. (AM916H12f

151 Hailey, William Malcolm Hailey, baron. Native administration in the British African territories. London, H.M.S.O., 1950-51. 4v. (AM354H12n)

152 Haines, Charles Grove. Africa today. Baltimore, Johns Hopkins, 1955. 510p. (M960H12a)

153 Hambly, Wilfrid Dyson. Ethnology of Africa. Chicago, Field Museum of Natural History, 1930. 226p.

154 Hambly, Wilfrid Dyson. Source book of African anthropology. Chicago, 1937. 2v. (AM572H17s)

155 Harris, John Hobbis. A new colonial era for dependencies. "Possession" or "Trusteeship." London, Anti-Slavery and Aborigines Protection Society, 1918. 7p. (AM332.14H24)

156 Harroy, Jean-Paul. Afrique terre qui meurt, la degradation des

sols Africains sous l'influence de la colonisation. Bruxelles, M.
Hayes, 1944. 557p. (AM631.45H24)

157 Harvard African Studies. Vol. 1-4. Cambridge, Mass. The African
Department of the Peabody Museum of Harvard University,
1917-1927. 4v. (AM572H26)

158 Haynes, George Edmund. Africa, continent of the future. New
York, Association Press, 1951. 516p. (AM916H32a)

159 Herskovitz, Melville J. The myth of the Negro past. New York,
Harper and bros., 1941. 374p. (AM960H43m)

160 Herskovitz, Melville J.. Program of African studies, the first five
years, 1949-1953. Evanston, Illinois, Northwestern University,
195- 31p. (AM572H53a)

161 Hight, Gladys. African tempo. N.Y.Exposition Press, 1951. 132p.
(M960H53a)

162 Hollis, Christopher. Italy in Africa. London, H. Hamilton, 1941.
253p. (AM960H72)

163 Horlech, Lord. Lord Hailey's African survey. London, Royal
Society, 1939. 70p. (AM960H22)

164 Hoskins, Holford Lancaster. European imperialism in Africa. New
York, Henry Holt and co., 1930. 118p. (AM960H79)

165 Hunton, William Alphaeus. Africa fights for freedom. New York,
New Century, 1950. 15p. (M960H91a)

166 International African Institute. African worlds. London, New York,
Oxford University Press, 1954. 243p. (AM572In8)

167 International Institute of African languages and cultures. A five-
year plan of research. London, Oxford University Press, International Institute of African languages and cultures, 1932. 14p.
(M960In8c)

168 Isaacs, Harold Robert. Africa; new crises in the making. New
York, Foreign Policy Association, 1952. 62p. (AM960Is2)

169 Johnson, Harry Hamilton. The opening up of Africa. . . New York,
H. Holt and co., 1911. 255p. (M960J64)

170 Kahin, George McTurnan. The Asian-African Conference, Bandung, Indonesia, April 1955. Ithaca, N.Y., Cornell University
Press [1956] 88p. (M960K12)

171 Kessie, Ohenenana. Colonies; what Africa thinks. London, The
African Economic Union. 28p. (M960K48c)

172 Khama, Tshekedi. Political change in African Society. A study
of the development of representative government. London,
Africa Bureau, 1956. 16p.

173 Kuczynski, Robert Rene. Colonial population. London, Oxford Uni-
     versity Press, 1937. 101p. (AM312K95)

174 Kuczynski, Robert Rene. Demographic survey of the British Colonial
     Empire. London, New York, Oxford University Press, 1948.
     vols. 1 and 2. (M960K95d)

175 Lagercrantz, Sture. African methods of fire-making. Uppsala
     1954. 77p. (AM571.6L13a)

176 Latimer, Elizabeth Wormeley. Europe in Africa in the Nineteenth
     Century ... Chicago, A. C. McClurg and company, 1896. 451p.
     (M960L34)

177 Leakey, Louis Seymour Bazett. Stone age Africa. London, Oxford
     University Press, H. Milford, 1936. 218p. (AM571.1L47)

178 Lindskog, Birger. African leopard men. Uppsala, 1954. 219p.
     (AM572.7L65)

179 Logan, Rayford Whittingham. The African mandates in world poli-
     tics. Washington, D.C., Public Affairs Press, 1948. 220p.
     (AM960L82a)

180 Logan, Rayford Whittingham. The Operation of the Mandate Sys-
     tem in Africa. Washington, D.C., The Foundation Publishers,
     Inc., 1942. 50p. (AM960L82o)

181 Lugard, Frederick John Dealtry. The dual mandate in British
     tropical Africa. Edinburgh and London, W. Blackwood and
     Sons, 1929. 643p. (M960L96)

182 McClellan, Grant S. Colonial progress in Central Africa, Belgian
     Congo and French Equatorial Africa. In Foreign Policy Re-
     ports, May 15, 1944. 50p. (AM960M13)

183 Mack, Silas Franklin. This is Africa. New York, Friendship
     Press, 1952. unpaged. (AM960M19t)

184 MacLean, Joan Coyne. Africa: the racial issue. New York, Wilson.
     1954. 198p. (AM323M22)

185 Mair, Lucy Philip. Native Policies in Africa. London, G. Rout-
     ledge and sons, ltd., 1936. 303p. (AM960M28m)

186 Maisel, Albert Q. Africa, facts and forecasts. New York, Duell,.
     Sloan and Pearce, 1943. 307p. (AM960M28a)

187 Malinowski, Bronislaw. The dynamics of culture change. New
     Haven, Yale University Press; London, H. Milford, Oxford
     University Press, 1945. 171p. (AM323M29d)

188 Manning, Charles A. W., ed. Peaceful change. New York, The
     Macmillan company, 1937. 193p. (AM325M31)

189   Maugham, Reginald Charles F. Africa as I have known it. London, John Murray, 1929, 372p. (AM960M44a)

190   Mbeki, G. A. Let's do it together. Cape Town, The African Bookman, 1944. 12p. (AM960M451)

191   Middleton, L. The rape of Africa. New York, H. Smith and R. Haas, 1936. 331p. (AM960M58)

192   Morel, Edmund Dene. Africa and the peace of Europe . . . London, National Labour Press, ltd., 1917. 123p. (M960M81a)

193   Morel, Edmund Dene. The black man's burden . . . New York, B. W. Huebsch, Inc., 1920. 241p. (M960M81b)

194   Padmore, George. Africa and world peace. London, M. Secker and Warburg, ltd., 1937. 285p. (AM960P13)

195   Padmore, George. Africa: Britain's third empire. London, D. Dobson, 1949. 266p. (M960P13a)

196   Padmore, George. Afrika unter dem joch der weissen. Erlenbach-Zurich, Leipzig, Rotapfel Verlag. 458p. (M960P13af)

197   Padmore, George. How Britain rules Africa. New York, Lothrop, Lee and Shepard co., 1936. 402p. (M960P13h)

198   Padmore, George. Pan-Africanism or communism? The coming struggle for Africa. New York, Ray Publishers, 1956. 463p. (M960P13p)

199   Parks, H. B. Africa, The Problem of the new century. New York, Board of Home and Foreign Missionary. Dept. of the A.M.E. Church, 1899. 66p. (AM960P23)

200   Parsons, Ellen C. Christus liberator, an outline study of Africa. New York, London, The Macmillan Co., 1905. 309p. (M960P25)

201   Penn, Peter. Tomorrow's continent. London, Sidgwick and Jackson, 1948. 179p. (M960P38t)

202   Powell, Edward Alexander. The last frontier. New York, C. Scribner's Sons, 1912. 216p. (AM960P87)

203   Ragatz, Lowell Joseph. Africa in the post-war world. New York, Research Bureau for post-war economics, 1944.   16p. (M960R12)

204   Reynolds, Reginald. Cairo to Cape Town; a pilgrimage in search of hope [1st ed.] Garden City, N.Y., Doubleday, 1955. 370p. (M960R33c)

205   Roberts, Charles Clifton. Tangled justice. London, Macmillan Co., 1937. 157p. (AM960R54t)

206   Robeson, Eslanda (Goode). What do the people of Africa want?
        New York, Council on African Affairs, 1945. 23p. (M960-
        R54w)

207   Rowley, Henry. Africa unveiled. London, Society for promoting
        Christian knowledge, 1876. 313p. (M960R79)

208   Sanderson, Edgar. Africa in the nineteenth century. London,
        Seeley and Co., 1898. 335p. (AM960Sa5)

209   Schieffelin, Henry Maunsell. The people of Africa. New York,
        A.D.F. Randolph & Co., 1871. 157p. (M960Sch3)

210   Seligman, Charles Gabriel. Les races de l'Afrique. Paris, Payot,
        1935. 224p. (AM572Se4)

211   Seminar on the development of public libraries in Africa. Develop-
        ment of public libraries in Africa. Paris, 1954. 155p.
        (AMO27Se5)

212   Smith, Edwin William. The golden Stool. London, Holborn Pub-
        lishing House, 1927. 328p. (M960.323Sm5)

213   Smith, Edwin William. Knowing the African. London, United So-
        ciety for Christian Literature, Lutterworth Press, 1946. 194p.
        (M960Sm49)

214   Smith, Edwin William. Plans and people! London, Lutterworth
        press, 1948. 70p. (AM572Sm5p)

215   Smith, Jan Christiaan. Africa and some world problems; including
        the Rhodes memorial lectures delivered in Michaelmas term,
        1929. . . . Oxford, The Clarendon press, 1930. 5p. (M960.-
        323Sm8)

216   Spencer, Herbert. Descriptive sociology . . . African Races. No. 3.
        Edited by David Duncan. London, Williams & Norgate, 1875.
        (AM572Sp3)

217   Stamp, Laurence Dudley. Africa; a study in tropical development.
        New York, Wiley, 1953. 568p. (AM960St2a)

218   Stanley, Henry Morton. Africa, its partition and its future. New
        York, Dodd, Meade & Co., 1898. 263p. (AM916St2a)

219   Stebbing, E. P. Africa and its intermittent rainfall. London, Mac-
        millan, 1938. 32p. (AM960St3)

220   Stillman, Calvin W. (ed.) Africa in the modern world [by] Lord
        Hailey [and others] Chicago, University of Chicago Press
        [1955] 341p. (M960St5a)

221   Swan, C. A. The slavery of today; or, the present position of the
        open sores of Africa. Glasgow, Pickering & Inglish, n.d. 202p.
        (AM916Sw2)

222   That they may live; African women arise ... Berlin, Women's international Democratic Federation, 1954. 22p. (M960T32)

223   Turner, Walter Lee. Under the skin of the Africans. 2nd ed. rev. and enl. Birmingham, Ala., African Musicians, 1948. 337p. (M960T85u)

224   U.S. Dept. of State. Register of Visitors. 1947. 32p. (AM378.-3Un3re)

225   U.S. Dept. of State. Register of students from Africa. 1948. 64p. (AM378.3Un3r)

226   Van der Post, Laurens. The dark eye in Africa. New York, Morrow, 1955. 224p. (M960V28)

227   Varian, H. F. Some African milestones. Wheatley, Oxford, G. Ronald, 1953. 272p. (AM625V42)

228   Verdat, Marguerite. Brèves instructions a l'usage des Bibliothecaires-Archivistes dans les cercles de l'A.O.F. Dakar, IFAN, n.d. 29p.

229   Wells, Carveth. Introducing Africa. New York, G. P. Putnam's sons, 1944. 243p. (M960W59i)

230   Westermann, Diedrich. The African today. London, Oxford, University, 1934. 343p. (M960W52)

231   Westermann, Diedrich. The African today and tomorrow. With a foreword by the Rt. Hon. Lord Lugard. 3d ed. London, New York, Published for the International African Institute by the Oxford University Press, 1949. 174p. (AM572W52a)

232   Westermann, Diedrich. Der Afrikaner heute und morgen. Berlin, Essen, Essener verlagsanstalt, 1937. 362p. (AM960W52a)

233   White, Arthur Silva. The development of Africa. London, Philip & Sons, 1890. 343p. (AM960W58)

234   Wieschhoff, Heinrich Albert. Colonial policies in Africa. Philadelphia, University of Pennsylvania Press, 1944. 138p. (AM-325W63)

235   Willoughby, William Charles. Race problems in the new Africa; A study of the relation of Bantu and Britons in those parts of Bantu Africa which are under British control. Oxford, The Clarendon Press, 1923. 296p. (M960.323W68)

236   Woolbert, W. C. Look at Africa. New York, The Foreign Policy Association, 1943. 96p. (M960W88)

237   Woolf, Leonard. Empire and commerce in Africa. London, George Allen & Unwin, 1927. 374p.

238 Worthington, Edgar Barton. Science in Africa; a review of scientific research relating to tropical and southern Africa, by E. B. Worthington . . . issued by the Committee of the African research survey under the auspices of the Royal Institute of International Affairs. London, New York [etc.] Oxford University Press, 1938. 746p. (AM500W89)

239 Wright, Rose. Fun and festival from Africa. New York, Friendship Press, 1952. 48p. (AM390W93f)

240 Wright, Richard. The color curtain, a report on the Bandung Conference. New York, World Pub. Co., 1956. 221p. (M960-W93c)

241 Yergan, Max. Africa in the War. New York, Council on African Affairs, 1942. 9p. (M960Y4)

242 Yergan, Max. Africa, the west and Christianity [by] Max Yergan. For distribution to the general committee of The World Student Christian Federation, Mysore, India, December 5-16, 1928. 50p. (M910Y4a3)

BIOGRAPHY

243 Abrahams, Peter. Je ne suis pas un homme libre. [Tell Freedom] Paris, Casterman, 1956. 304p.

244 Abrahams, Peter. Tell Freedom; memories of Africa. [1st American ed.] New York, Knopf, 1954. 370p. (MB9Ab8)

245 Ahmed Ibn Fartua. History of the first twelve years of the Reign of Mai Idris Alooma of Bornu 1571-1583, by his Imam, Ahmed ibn Fartua. Lagos, Govt. Printer, 1926. 121p. (M966.98Ah5)

246 The Albert Schweitzer jubilee book, edited by A. A. Roback. Cambridge, Mass., Sci-art, 1945. 508p. (MC9R53)

247 Andrews, Charles Freer. John White of Mashonaland. New York and London, Harper and brothers, 1935. 205p. (MC9W58a)

248 Annamaboe. The Royal African; or, Memoirs of the Young Prince of Annamaboe. London, Printed for W. Reeve, and at the Court of Requests, 1720. 53p. (AM326.99BAn7)

249 Baba of Karo. Baba of Karo, a woman of the Muslim Hausa. [Autobiography recorded], by M. F. Smith. With an introd. and notes by M. G. Smith; pref. by Daryll Forde. London, Faber and Faber [1954.] 299p. (MB9B11)

250 Baker, Ernest. Life and exploration of Frederick Stanley Arnot; the authorized biography of a zealous missionary, intrepid explorer, and self-denying benefactor amongst the natives of

Africa, by Ernest Baker . . . New York, E. P. Dutton and
Co., [1920] 334p. (MC9Ar6b)

251 Bentley, W. Holman. Life on the Kongo. Rev. and enl. Pacific
press pub. co., Oakland, Calif. [c1891] 158p. (M967B44)

252 Besolow, Thomas Edward. From the darkness of Africa to the life
of America; the story of an African prince. 160p. (MB9B46)

253 Bickersteth, E. Memoirs of Simeon Wilhelm, a native of the
Susoo country, West Africa; who dies at the house of the
Church missionary society, London, Aug. 29, 1817; aged 17
years. Together with accounts of the superstitions of the
inhabitants of West Africa. Published for the Yale college
society of enquiry respecting missions. New Haven, printed
by S. Converse, 1819. 108p. (MB9W64b)

254 Blaikie, W. Gordon. The personal life of David Livingstone;
chiefly from his unpublished journals and correspondence in
the possession of his family. New York, Chicago, [etc.]
Fleming H. Revell and Co., [1895?] 508p. (MC9L76b)

255 Breasted, Charles. Pioneer to the past; the story of James Henry
Breasted, archaeologist, told by his son, Charles Breasted.
New York, C. Scribner's sons, 1943. 436p. (MB9B74p)

256 Brice, Arthur John Hallam Montefiore. Henry M. Stanley, The
African exporter. New York, Chicago, Fleming H. Revell,
n.d. 160p. (MC9St2b)

257 Burckhardt, John Lewis. Travels in Nubia. Published by the
Association for promoting the discovery of the interior parts
of Africa. 2nd ed. London, J. Murray, 1822. 498p. (M916.
2B89t)

258 Chalmers, John A. Tiyo Soga; a page of South African mission
work. Edinburgh, Andrew Elliot, 1877. 488p. (MB9So2c)

259 Chamberlin, David. John Mackenzie. London, The Sheldon Press,
1932. 32p. (MC9M19)

260 Chitlangou, of the Khamban Clan. Chitlangou, son of a chief.
Translated by Margaret A. Bryan. With a foreword by Alan
Paton. London, United Society for Christian Literature [1950.]
208p. (MB9C44)

261 Cleaver, Ferrar Reginald Mostyn. A young South African, a memoir of Ferrar Reginald Mostyn Cleaver, advocate and veld-
cornet, edited by his mother. Johannesburg, W. E. Horton
& Co., 1913. 200p. (MC9C58y)

262 Cloete, Stuart. . . . Against these three, a biography of Paul Kruger,
Cecil Rhodes, and Lobengula, last king of the Matabele . . .

illustrated with maps and portraits by Roland Cosimini. Boston Houghton Mifflin Co., 1945. 472p. (MC9C59)

263 Crabitès, P. Gordon, the Sudan and slavery. London, G. Routledge and sons, ltd., 1933. 334p. (MC9G65c)

264 Cushman, Mary Floyd. Missionary doctor, the story of twenty years in Africa, by Mary Floyd Cushman, M.D. New York and London, Harper & brothers, [1944] 279p. (MC9C95)

265 Dawson, F. C. James Hannington, first bishop of Eastern Equatorial Africa. A history of his life and work 1847-1885. New York, Anson D. F. Randolph and Co., 1886. 472p. (AM967D32j)

266 Eaton, Jeanette. David Livingstone, foe of darkness; illus. by Ralph Ray. New York, W. Morrow, 1947. 256p. (MC9L761)

267 Edwards, Margaret (Dulles) Child of the sun, a pharaoh of Egypt. Boston, The Beacon Press, Inc., 1939. 111p. (MC-9Am3e)

268 Fahs, Sophia Blanche (Lyon) Uganda's white man of work; a story of Alexander M. MacKay. New York, Young People's Missionary Movement, [1907] 289p. (MC9M19f)

269 Frame, H. F. Get through or die (David Livingstone). New York, Friendship Press, 1939. 23p. (MC9L76f)

270 Fraser, Donald. The autobiography of an African, retold in biographical form and in the wild African setting. London, Seeley, Service & Co., 1925. 209p. (MB9M87f)

271 Garry, Gerald T. African doctor. London, J. Glifford, Ltd., 1939. 283p. (MC9G19a)

272 Gollock, Georgina Anne. Daughters of Africa. London, New York, Longman's Green and Company, 1932. 175p. (M960G58d)

273 Gollock, Georgina Anne. Lives of eminent Africans . . . With 5 portraits and 2 maps. London, New York, [etc.] Longmans, Green and Co., Ltd., 1928. 152p. (M960G581)

274 Gollock, Georgina Anne. More stories of famous Africans . . . Aggrey: William Koyi: Onoyom Iya Nya: Kanjundu: Jabavu and others. London, Longmans [1937] 61p. (M960G58m)

275 Gollock, Georgina Anne. Sons of Africa . . . decorations by Aaron Douglas. New York, Friendship press. [1928] 241p. (M960-G58)

276 Gollock, Georgina Anne. Stories of famous Africans . . . Moshoeshoe; Khama; Crowther; Livingstone's carriers; Mohammed Abu Bekr, The Askia; Sir Apolo Kagwa. New York, Longmans, [1937] 61p. (M960G58s)

277 Grahame, Nigel B. M. Arnot of Africa, a fearless pioneer, a zealous missionary and a true knight of the cross. New York, George H. Doran Co., 1926. 59p. (MC9Ar8g)

278 Green, George Alfred Lawrence. An editor looks back; South African and other memories, 1883-1946. With an introd. by J. C. Smuts. Cape Town, Juta, 1947. 288p. (MB9G82e)

279 Gurley, Ralph Randolph. Life of Jehudi Ashmun, late colonial agent in Liberia. With an appendix, containing extracts from his journal and other writings; with a brief sketch of the life of the Rev. Lott Cary. Washington, D. C., Printed by J. C. Dunn, 1835. 396p. [160p.] (MC9As3g)

280 Hagedorn, Hermann. Prophet in the wilderness; the story of Albert Schweitzer. New York, Macmillan Co., 1947. 221p. (MC-9Sch9h)

281 Hake, Alfred Egmont. The story of Chinese Gordon. 9th ed. London, Temington and Co., 1884. 407p. (MC9G65)

282 Hancock, Keith. The Smuts papers. London, University of London. The Athlone Press, 1956. 19p. (MB9Sm8)

283 Harris, J. C. Roger Price. [Broadway, Livingstone Bookshop, 1930.] 15p. (MB9P93H)

284 Harrison, Alexina (Mackay) "Mrs. J. W. Harrison". A. M. Mackay, pioneer missionary of the Church missionary society to Uganda. By his sister. With portrait and map. Author's ed. New York, A. C. Armstrong and son, 1890. 488p. (MC-9M19h)

285 Head, Francis B. The life and adventures of Bruce, the African traveller. New York, Harper and brothers, 1842. 32p. (MC9B83h)

286 Henrich, Ruth. They thought he was mad (Albert Schweitzer of Africa). New York, Friendship Press, 1940. 24p. (MC9Sch9h)

287 Hermann von Wissman, Deutschlands grosster. Afrikaner; sein leben und wirken unter Benutzung des nachlasses, dargestellt von Dr. A. Becker . . . G. Richelman . . . C. V. Perbandt . . . Rochus Schmidt . . . Dr. W. Steuver . . . Berlin, Alfred Schall, 1914. 598p. MC9W76h)

288 Holmes, I. M. In Africa's service; the story of Mary Kingsley. London, Saturn Press, [1949] 223p. (MB9K61h)

289 Holt, Basil Fenelon. Joseph Williams and the pioneer mission to the southeastern Bantu [Lovedale, C.P.] Lovedale Press, 1954. 186p. (MC9W67h)

290   Horner, Esther Daniels. Jungles ahead! New York, Friendship Press, 1952. 116p. (AM960H78j)

291   Jennings, A. E. Shomolekae. [Broadway, Livingstone Bookshop, 1930] 15p. (MB9Sh7j)

292   Jones, E. Edwin. The life of Rowland Hill Evans of Cameroun; a narrative of service in the West Africa Mission, Presbyterian Church, U.S.A., 1909-1932. Columbus, Ohio, F. J. Heer printing co., 1932. 29p. (MB9Evlk)

293   Jones, W. M. A. A leader of Africa; stories from the life of James Emman Kwegyir Aggrey, retold and simplified with questions. London, George G. Harrap, 1940. 94p. (MB9Ag81)

294   Kellersberger, Julia Lake. A life for the Congo; the story of Althea Brown Edmiston. New York, Fleming H. Revell company [1947] 171p. MB9Ed5)

295   Kraus, René. Old Master; the life of Jan Christian Smuts [by] René Kraus. New York, E. P. Sutton & co., inc., 1944. 471p. (MB9Sm79k)

296   Kruger, Stephanue Johannes Paulas. The memoirs of Paul Kruger; four times President of the South African Republic, told by himself. London, T. Fisher Unwin, 1952. 543p. (MC9K93)

297   Laye, Camara. The dark child. With an introd. by Phillipe Thoby-Marcellin. Translated by James Kirkup, Ernest Jones [and] Elain Gottlieb. New York, Noonday Press, 1954. 188p. (MB9L45)

298   Laye, Camara. Einer sus kurussa (L'enfant noir). Zurich, Speer, 1954. 237p. (MB9L45ef)

299   Livingstone, David. The last journals of ... in Central Africa. From 1865 to his death, continued by a narrative of his last moments and sufferings, obtained from his faithful servants Chuma and Susi, by Horace Waller ... with portrait, maps, and illustrations. New York, Harper & Brothers, 1875. 541p. (M967L76)

300   Livingstone, David. Some letters from Livingstone, 1840-1872. London, New York, [etc.] Oxford Univ. Press, 1940. 280p. (MC9L76)

301   Livingstone, William Pringle. Mary Slessor of Calabar, pioneer misionary. 6th ed., London, New York, [etc.] Hodder & Stoughton, 1916. 347p. (MC9S121)

302   Livingstone, William Pringle. The story of David Livingstone. New York and London, Harper and brothers, 1930. 161p. (MC9L761)

303 LoBagola, B. K. A. I. LoBagola, an African savage's own story.
New York, A. A. Knopf, 1930. 402p. (AM572.662L78)

304 Loftus, E. A. Baker and Lake Albert. Edinburgh, Thomas Nelson
and Sons, ltd., 1954. 100p. (MB9B171)

305 Loftus, E. A. Speke and the Nile source. Nairobi, East African
Literature Bureau, 1954. 73p. (MB9Sp31)

306 McCord, James Bennet. My patients were Zulus. New York,
Rinehart. [1951] 308p. (MB9M13)

307 McDonald, James Gordon. Rhodes; a heritage. London, Chatto
and Windus, 1943. 166p. (MC9R34ma)

308 Mackenzie, William Douglas. John Mackenzie, South African missionary and statesman. New York, A. C. Armstrong and son,
1902. 564p. (MC9M199m)

309 Mackintosh, Catherine Winkworth. Coillard of the Zambesi, the
lives of Francois and Christina Coillard, of the Parish missionary society, in South and Central Africa (1858-1904). With a
frontispiece, a map, and 77 illustrations. New York, American
tract society [London printed] 1907. 484p. (MCM18c)

310 Mackintosh, Cahtarine Winkworth. Lewanika, paramount chief of
the Barotse and allied tribes, 1875-1916. London and Redhill,
United Society for Christian Literature 1942. 63p. (MB9L58m)

311 Maclachlan, T. Banks. Mungo Park. New York, Scribner's sons,
1898. 160p. (MC9P22m)

312 MacNair, James I. Livingstone, the liberator; a study of dynamic
personality. London, Glasgow, Collins Clear-type Press, 1940.
302p. (MC9L76m)

313 Maguire, James Rochfort. Cecil Rhodes; a biography and appreciation by Imperialist. With personal reminiscences by Dr. Jameson; two portraits of Mr. Rhodes and a map of South Africa.
London, Chapman & Hall, 1897. 413p. (MC9R34mag)

314 Maran, René. Livingstone et l'exploration de l'Afrique. Paris,
Librairie Gallimard, 1938. 276p. (M843.9M321)

315 Mathews, Basil Joseph. Livingstone, the pathfinder. With seventeen
illustrations by Ernest Prater, twenty-four other pictures and
photographes and three maps. New York, Missionary Education Movement of the United States and Canada, 1912. 213p.
(MC9L76m5)

316 Maurice, Albert. Félix Éboué, sa vie et son oeuvre. Bruxelles, Memorial Institute Royal Colonial Belge, 1954. 54p. (MB9Eb7m)

317 Maurice, Albert. Stanley, lettres inédites. Préface de Denzil M.

Stanley. Bruxelles, Office de Publicité, 1955. 219p. (MB9-St2m)

318 Maurois, André. Cecil Rhodes. Translated from the French by Rohan Wadham. London, Collins, 1953. 140p. (MC9R34mau)

319 Millin, Sarah Gertrude (Liebson). Cecil Rhodes. New York and London, Harper and Bros., 1933. 449p. (MC9R34m)

320 Montefiore, A. David Livingstone; his labours and his legacy. New York, Fleming Revell, n.d. 160p. (MC9L76m)

321 Musson, M. Aggrey of Achimota. London and Redhill, United Society for Christian Literature, 1944. 55p. (MB9Ag8m)

322 Naigisiki, Joseph Saverio. Escapade Ruandaise. Journal d'un clerc en sa trentiéme année. Preface de M. J. M. Jadot. Bruxelles, G. A. Deny, Librairie Editeur, 1950. 208p. (MB9N14e)

323 Nkrumah, Kwame. Ghana; the autobiography of Kwame Nkrumah. New York, Nelson, 1957. 302p.

324 Northcott, William Cecil. Hero of the Hottentots (John Vanderkemp). New York, Friendship Press, 1939. 24p. (MB9V28n)

325 Nutter, Cecil. Timothy Kandeke; through the long grass. Broadway, Livingstone Bookshop, 1930. 4p. (MB9K13n)

326 Opwa, Antonio. An East African chief in England. Nairobi, The Eagle Press, 1952. 38p. (MB9Op8)

327 Page, Jesse. Samuel Crowther, the slave boy who became the bishop of the Niger. London, S. W. Partidge, n.d. 160p. (MB9C88p)

328 Park, Mungo. The life and travels of Mungo Park; with the account of his death, from the journal of Isaaco, the substance of later discoveries relative to his lamented fate, and the termination of the Niger, New York, G. Munro, c1866. 165p. (MC9P221)

329 Parsons, Ellen C. A life for Africa; Rev. Adolphus Clemens Good. American Missionary in Equatorial West Africa. 2d ed. New York, Fleming H. Revell, 1900. 316p. (MC9G59p)

330 Percy, Douglas Cecil. Stirrett of Sudan; the beloved physician of the Sudan. [Toronto] Sudan Interior Mission [1948] 87p. (MB9St58p)

331 Perham, Margery Freda. Lugard; the years of adventure 1858-1898; the first part of the life of Frederick Dealtry Lugard, later Lord Lugard of Abinger ... London, Collins, 1956. 750p. (MC9L96)

332 Perham, Margery Freda, ed. Ten Africans. London, Faber and Faber, 1936. 356p. (M960P41)

333 Pringle, Patrick. Lion of Africa; the story of David Livingstone. New York, Roy Publishers [1953] 144p. (MC9L76p)

334 Rankin, Arthur Edward. Livingstone returned; the story of a measureless labor of love. [1st ed.] New York, Exposition Press [1955] 131p. (MB9L76r)

335 Regester, John Dickinson. Albert Schweitzer, the man and his work. New York, Cincinnati [etc.] The Abingdon press, 1931. 145p. (MC9Sch9r)

336 Richards, C. G. Krapf, missionary & explorer. London, Nelson, 1950. 85p. (MB9K86r)

337 Rix, M. Bright. Mary and the black warriors (Mary Slesser of Africa.) New York, Friendship Press, 1938. 23p. (MC9S12r)

338 Sachs, Wulf. Black Hamlet. Boston, Little, Brown, 1947. 324p. (MB9C39b)

339 Sandford, Christine. The lion of Judah hath prevailed, being the biography of His Imperial Majesty Haile Selassie I. London, J. M. Dent, 1955. 192p. (MB9H12s)

340 Seabrook, William Buehler. The White monk of Timbuctoo. New York, Harcourt, Brace and co., [1934] 279p. (MC9D92)

341 Seabury, Ruth Isabel. Daughter of Africa. Boston, Chicago, The Pilgrim Press [1945] 144p. (MB9So2)

342 Sillitoe, Percy. Cloak without dagger. New York, Abelard-Schuman [1955] 206p. (MB9Si3c)

343 Slater, Montagu. The trial of Jomo Kenyatta. London, Secker & Warburg, 1955. 255p. (MB9K42s)

344 Smith, Edwin W. Aggrey of Africa, a study in black and white. New York, Doubleday, Doran and Co., 1929. 292p. (MB-9Ag8s)

345 Smuts, Jan Christian. Jan Christian Smuts; a biography. New York, Morrow, 1952. 496p. (MB9Sm8j)

346 Tabouis, G. R. The private life of Tutankhamen; love, religion, and politics at the court of an Egyptian king. With preface by Théodore Reinach. New York, R. M. McBride & Company, 1929. 322p. (MB9T88t)

347 Thomson, J. B. Joseph Thomson, African explorer, a biography by his brother (Rev. J. B. Thomson, Greenock) with contributions by friends . . . London, Sampson Low, Marston and Company, 1896. 358p. (MC9T37t)

348 Thomson, Joseph. Mungo Park and the Niger. London, G. Philip & Son, 1890. 338p. (MC9P22t)

349 Timothy, Bankole. Kwane Nkrumah; his rise to power. Foreword
      by the Honourable Kojo Botsio. London, George Allen &
      Unwin, Ltd., 1955. 198p. (MB9N65)

350 Vaucaire, M. Paul Du Chaillu, gorilla hunter; being the extraor-
      dinary life and adventures of Paul Du Chaillu, as recounted
      for the house of Harper, his ancient publishers, by his young
      compatriot. New York, and London, Harper and brothers,
      1930. 322p. (MC9D85v)

351 Verhoeven, Joseph Ch. M. Jacques de Dixmunde l'Africain; Con-
      tribution à l'historie de la Société anti esclavagiste belge, 1888-
      1894. Bruxelles, Libraririe Coloniale, R. Weverbergh, [1929.]
      159p. (M967V58)

352 Wallis, John Peter Richard, Fitz, the story of Sir Percy Fitz.
      New York, Macmillan, St. Martins' Press, 1955. 278p. (MB-
      9F58)

353 Westermann, Diedrich. . . . Autobiographies d'Africains; onze auto-
      biographies d'indigènes originaires de diverses régions de l'Afri-
      que et représentant des métiers et des degrés de culture dif-
      férents. Traduction française de L Homburger . . . Paris,
      Payot, 1943. 338p. (MB9W52a)

354 Whily-Tell, A. E. Je suis un civilisé. Paris, Societe d'Impres-
      sions de Lancry, 1953. 253p.

355 Wilder, George Albert. The White African; the story of Magavuke,
      "who dies and lives again," told by himself, at the request of
      his relatives and friends . . . [Bloomfield, N. J., Printed by
      the Morse Press] 1933. 192p. (MC9W645)

356 Williams, C. Kingsley. An address delivered at the service of
      remembrance and thanksgiving for James Emmon Kwegyir Ag-
      grey . . . at Achimota, 7th August, 1927. Accra, Government
      printer, 1927. 5p. (MB9Ag8w)

357 Williams, J. Grenfell. Moshesh; the man on the mountain. London,
      Oxford University Press, Goeffrey Cumberlege, 1950. 150p.
      (MB9M848)

358 Williams, Samuel. Four years in Liberia. A sketch of the life
      of the Rev. Samuel Williams. With remarks on the missions,
      manners and customs of the natives of Western Africa. To-
      gether with an answer to Nesbit's book. Philadelphia, King
      & Baird, printers, 1857. 66p. (MB9W676)

359 Woodson, Carter Godwin. African heroes and heriones. Wash-
      ington, D. C. The Associated Pub., 1939. 249p. (M960W86a)

360 Yates, P. Apolo in Pygmyland. New York, Friendship Press, 1940. 24p. (MB9K65y)

RELIGION

361 The African valley. [lacks title page] 36p. (AM916Af8a)

362 Anderson, J. N. D. . . . Islamic law in Africa. London, H. M. S. O., 1954 409p. (AM297An2)

363 Anderson, Susan. "So this is Africa". Nashville, Tenn., Broadman Press, 943. 138p. (AM266An2)

364 Atterbury, Anson Phelps. Islam in Africa; its effects—religious, ethical and social—upon the people of the country. New York and London, G. P. Putnam's Sons, 1899. 208p. (M297-At8i)

365 Bartlett, S. C. Historical sketch of the missions of the American board in Africa. Boston, published by the board, 1880. 18p. (AM266B28)

366 Bell, William Clark. African Bridge Builders. New York, Friendship Press, 1936. 168p. (AM916B41)

367 Bickersteth, E. Memoirs of Simeon Wilhelm, a native of the Susso country, West Africa; who dies at the house of the Church missionary society, London, Aug. 29, 1817; aged 17 yrs. Together with some accounts of the superstitions of the inhabitants of West Africa. New Haven, S. Converse, 1819. 108p. (MB-9W64b)

368 Blyden, Edward Wilmot. Philip and the eunuch; or the instruments and methods of Africa's evangelization. A discourse delivered in the Park Street Church, Boston, U. S. A., Sunday, Oct. 22, 1882. Cambridge, John Wilson and Son, 1883. (M276B62p)

369 Broomfield, Gerald Webb. The chosen people; or, The Bible, Christianity and race. London, New York, Longmans, Green, [1954.] 91p. (AM323B79)

370 Chapman, Louise Robinson. Africa, O Africa. Kansas City Missouri, Beacon Hill Press, 1945. 221p. (AM266C36a)

371 Chirgwin, A. M. The forward tread; or the L. M. S. in Africa; with an introduction by Rev. Edwin W. Smith. London, The Livingstone Press, 1932. 110p. (AM266C44f)

372 Church conference on African Affairs, Otterbein College, 1942. Christian action in Africa. New York, African committee of the Foreign missions and conference of North America, 1942. 200p. (AM266C47)

373 Congress on Africa, Atlanta, 1895. Africa and the American Negro. Addresses and proceedings of the Congress on Africa, held under the auspices of the Stewart missionary foundation for Africa of Gammon theological seminary, in connection with the Cotton states and international exposition, Dec. 13-15, 1895. Atlanta, Gammon theological seminary, 1896. 242p. (M960C76)

374 Culwick, Arthur Theodore. Good out of Africa. Livingstone, Northern Rhodesia, The Rhodes-Livingstone Institute, 1942. 43p. (AM572C89g)

375 Dean, Christopher. The African traveler; or, prospective missions in central Africa. 2d ed. Boston, Massachusetts Sabbath School Society, 1838. 159p. (AM266D34)

376 Dobbins, Frank Stockton. Error's chains: how forged and broken. A complete graphic, and comparative history of the many strange beliefs, superstitious practices, domestic pecularities, sacred writings, systems of philosophy, legends and traditions, customs and habits of mankind throughout the world, ancient and modern. New York, Standard Publishing House, 1883. 785p. (M291D65)

377 Driberg, Jack Herbert. The secular aspect of ancestor-worship in Africa. Supplement to the "Journal of the Royal African Society," January 1936, Vol. 35. 21p. (M960D83)

378 Dunkleberger, Stella C. Crossing Africa. Germantown, Philadelphia, Penna., The Mission Offices. 105p. (AM266D92)

379 Easton, Mabel. Nyilak and other African sketches. New York, Chicago, Fleming H. Revell Co., 1923. 95p. (AM266Ea7)

380 Entwistle, Mary. The call drum. New York, Friendship Press, 1928. 138p. (AM916En8)

381 Flores, Morales Angel. Africa a través del pensamiento espanol. Madrid, Instituto de Estudios Africanos, 1949. 235p. (AM-320F66)

382 Floyd, Olive Beatrice. Partners in Africa. New York, The National Council, Protestant Episcopal Church, 1946? 80p. (AM960F66p)

383 Fraser, Donald. The new Africa. New York, Missionary education movement of the United States and Canada, [c1928.] 207p. (M960F86)

384 Frazer, James George. The fear of the dead in primitive religion; lectures delivered on the William Wyse foundation at Trinity

college, Cambridge. London, Macmillan and Co., 1933-36. 3v. (M291F86)

385 Gouilly, Alphonse. L'Islam dans L'Afrique Occidentale Française. Paris, Larose, 1925. 318p. (AM297G72)

386 Groves, Charles Pelham. The planting of Christianity in Africa. London, Lutterworth Press, 1948-1955. 3 vols. (AM266G91)

387 Hadfield, Percival. Traits of divine Kingship in Africa. London, Watts, 1949. 134p. (M299.6H11t)

388 Heard, William H. The Missionary fields of West Africa. Philadelphia A.M.E. book concern, Printers, N. D. 28p. (AM-260H35)

389 Helser, Albert David. Africa's Bible; the power of God unto salvation. 1st ed., New York, Sudan Interior Mission, 1951. 159p. (A266H36a)

390 Helser, Albert David. The glory of the impossible. New York City, Toronto, Canada, Evangelical publishers, 1940. 144p. (AM266H36g)

391 Imray, Elizabeth. The message of the Old Testament. [Lovedale, South Africa.] Lovedale Press, [Pref. 1933.] 115p. (M221Im8)

392 Irstam, Tor. The king of Ganda, studies in the institutions of sacral kingship in Africa. Sweden, Hakan Ohlssons Boktryskeri, 1944. 203p. (M9601r7k)

393 James, J. A. The path to the bush. Boston, Mass., Sabbath school society, 1843. 64p. (AM266J23)

394 Johnston, James. Missionary landscapes in the dark continent. New York, A. D. F. Randolph & Co., [1892.] 264p. (AM-916J644)

395 Laing, George E. F. A king for Africa. London, United Society for Christian Literature. [1945.] 63p. (M960L14k)

396 Lawyer, Zelma Wood. I married a missionary. Abilene, Tex., Abilene Christian college Press, 1943. 261p. (AM266L44)

397 Libermann, Francis Mary Paul. Notes et documents, relatifs à la vie et à l'oeuvre. Paris, Maison-Mère, 1936. 707p. (AM-266L61)

398 Mackenzie, Jean Kenyon. African adventurers. West Medford, Mass., The Central committee on the united study of foreign missions, etc., 1917. 119p. (M266M19)

399 Mackenzie, Jean Kenyon. An African trail. West Medford, Mass.,

The Central committee on the united study of foreign missions, etc., 1917. 222p. (AM266M21a)

400 Marie Andre du Sacre Ceour, Sister. La condition humaine en Afrique noire. Paris, Grasset, 1953. 262p. (AM301M33)

401 Meinhof, Carl. Die religiomem der Afrikaner in ihrem zusammenhang mit dem wirtschaftsleben. . . . Oslo, H. Aschehing & Co., (W. Nygaard); Cambridge, Mass., Harvard University Press, 1926. 96p. (Instituttet for sammenlignende kulturforskning. Publicationer. Ser. A VII) (M960.2M47)

402 Muller, Edward. Isiguqub sama Protestanti saciteka kanjani namazwe amaningi. Marianhill Mission Press, 1929. 54p. (AM-280M91i)

403 Nadel, Siegfried Frederick. Nupe religion. London, Routledge & Paul, 1954. 288p. (AM290N12)

404 Nassau, Robert Hamill. Fetichism in West Africa. New York, C. Scribner's Sons, 1904. 389p. (AM291.2..N18)

405 Notice sur la société des missions evangeliques, chez les peuples non chretiens. Paris, Chez J. J. Risler, Librairie, 1839. 36p. (AM266N84)

405a Overs, Walter Henry. Stories of African life. New York, E. S. Gorman, 1924. 146p. (M9160v2)

406 Parrinder, Geoffrey. African traditional religion. London, New York, Hutchinson's University Library, 1954. 160p. (AM-290P24a)

407 Parrinder, Geoffrey. Religion in an African city. London, New York, Oxford University Press, 1953. 211p. (AM290P24r)

408 Parrinder, Geoffrey. West African religion; illustrated from the beliefs and practices of the Yoruba, Ewe, Akan, kindred peoples, London, Epworth Press, 1949. 223p. (M290P24W)

409 Ross, Emory. African heritage. New York, Friendship Press, 1952. 145p. (AM960R73a)

410 Sailor, Thomas H. P. Christian adult education in rural Asia and Africa. New York, Friendship Press, 1943. 214p. (AM-960Sa2)

411 Sayre, Leslie C. Africans on safari. New York, Friendship Press, 1952. 164p. (AM266Sa9a)

412 Smith, Edwin William. African ideas of God, a symposium. London, Edinburgh House Press, 1950. 308p. (M299.6Sm5)

413 Smith, Edwin William. The blessed missionaries. Cape Town, Oxford University Press, 1950. 146p. (AM266Sm5b)

414 Smith, Edwin William. The golden stool: some aspects of the conflict of cultures in Africa. London, Holborn publishing house, 1927. 328p. (M960.323Sm5)

415 Smith, Edwin William. Knowing the African. London, United Society for Christian Literature, Lutterworth Press, 1946. 194p. (M960Sm49)

416 Sourey, J. Ch. Sorciers noirs et sorcier blanc: la magie, la sorcellerie et ses drames en Afrique. Bruxelles, Lib. Encyclopedique, 1952. 261p. (AM133So8)

417 Spinner, S. Der Verwendung von Synonymen im Alten Testament. . . . Vienna, The author, 1936. 39p. (AM913Sp4)

418 Stauffer, Milton Theobald. Thinking with Africa; chapters by a group of nationals interpreting the Christian movement, assembled and edited by M. Stauffer. New York, Missionary education movement for the United States and Canada, c1927. 184p. (M266St29)

419 Stewart, James. Dawn in the dark continent. New York, Chicago, Toronto, Fleming H. Revell Co., 1903. 400p. (AM266St4)

420 Taylor, John. Christianity and politics in Africa. London, Penguin Books, 1957. 127p.

421 Taylor, Stephen Earl. The price of Africa. New York, Eaton & Mains, 1902. 225p.

422 Tegnaeus, Harry. Le héros civilisateur; contribution à l'étude ethnologique de la religion et de la sociologie africaines. [Stockholm] 1950. 224p. (AM572.7T23h)

423 Temple, Merfyn M. African angelus. London, Edinburgh House Press, 1950. 71p. (AM266T24a)

424 Thorp, Ellen. Swelling of Jordan. London, Lutterworth Press, 1950. 281p. (AM266T39s)

425 Wengatz, John Christian. Miracles in black. New York, Fleming H. Revell Co., 1938. 177p. (AM266W48)

426 Westermann, Diedrich. The missionary and anthropological research. London, Oxford University Press, International African Institute, 1948. 31p. (AM276W52m)

427 Wieschhoff, Heinrich Albert. Africa. Philadelphia, University of Penna. Press, 1945. 76p. (AM709W43a)

428 Wilcox, William C. The man from an African jungle. New York, The Macmillan Co., 1925. 248p. (AM266W64)

429 Williams, Joseph John. Africa's god . . . Chestnut Hill, Mass., Boston College Press, 1936-38. (Anthropological series of the

Boston college graduate school. vol. 1, no. 1-4; vol. 2, no. 2-4; vol. 3, no. 1-3. Serial no. 1-4, 6-11. April-Dec., 1936. June, 1937-Oct. 1938. (M290W67)

ECONOMIC ASPECTS

430 Banks, Arthur Leslie, ed. The development of tropical and subtropical countries with particular reference to Africa. London, Arnold [1954] 217p. (M960B22)

431 Cline, Walter Buchanan. Mining and metallurgy in Negro Africa. Menasha, Wis., George Banta publishing Co., 1937. 155p. (AM572C61)

432 Dun Jonchay, Ivan. L'Industrialization de l'Afrique, Paris, Payot, 1953. 344p. (AM338D85)

433 Foucart, George. Introductory questions in African ethnology. Cairo, Printing Office of the French Institute of Oriental Archaeology, 1919, 157p.

434 Frankel, Sally Herbert. Capital investment in Africa; its course and effects. London, New York [etc.] Oxford University Press, 1938. 487p. (M960F85)

435 Furon, Raymond. Les ressources minérales de l'Afrique. Paris, Parot, 1944. 271p. (AM338F98r)

436 Githens, Thomas. The food resources of Africa. Philadelphia, Univ. of Pennsylvania, 1943. 105p. (AM338.1G44)

437 Great Britain British Information Services. From darkness to light; new developments in British Africa. New York [1949] 24p. (AM330G79)

438 Great Britain Colonial Office. Memorandum on colonial mining policy. London, H. M. Stationery off., 1946. 10p. (AM-338.2G79)

439 Great Britain Colonial Office. Colonial Advisory Council of Agriculture, Animal Health and Forestry. Report of a survey of problems in the mechanization of native agriculture in tropical African colonies. London, H. M. Stationery Off., 1950. 121p. (AM631C79r)

440 Guernier, E. L. L'Afrique, champ d'expansion de l'Europe; avec 14 cartes et graphiques. Paris, Librairie Armand Colin, 1933. 283p. (AM325G93)

441 International Labour Conference. Twelfth Session. Geneva, 1929. Forced labour. Report and draft questionnaire. Geneva, International Labour Office, 1929. 320p.

442 Postel, Albert Williams. The mineral resources of Africa. Philadelphia, Univ. of Pennsylvania Press, 1943. 105p. (AM-338.2P84)

443 Le Travail en Afrique noire. [Paris] Seuil, 1952. 427p. (AM-331T69)

444 Noon, John A. Labor problems of Africa. Philadelphia, Univ. of Pennsylvania Press, The University Museum, 1944. 144p. (AM331N73)

445 Newlyn, Walter Tessier. Money and banking in British Colonial Africa; a study of the monetary and banking systems of eight British African territories. Oxford, Clarendon Press, 1954. 301p. (AM332N46m)

446 Orde-Browne, G. The African labourer. London, Pub. for the International institute of African languages and cultures by Oxford University Press, H. Milford, 1933. 240p. (AM331Orl)

447 Organisation for European Economic Co-operation. Investments in overseas territories in Africa, South of the Sahara. Paris, 1951. 105p. (AM334Or2c)

448 Pim, Alan William. The economic development of Africa; an address . . . to the annual meeting of the Anti-slavery and aborigines protection society on 15th June, 1944. London, Anti-slavery and aborigines protection society, 1944. 12p. (M960-P64)

449 Read, Margaret. Native standards of living and African culture change . . . London, Oxford univ. press, 1938. 56p. (AM-960R22n)

450 United Nations. Review of economic activity in Africa 1950-1954. Supplement to World Economic Report, 1953-54. New York, United Nations, Dept. of Economic and Social Affairs, 1955. 146p. (AM330Un3re)

451 United Nations. Scope and structure of money economies in tropical Africa. New York, United Nations, Dept. of Economic and Social Affairs, 1955. 52p. (AM330Un3s)

452 United Nations. Dept. of Economic and Social Affairs. Economic developments in Africa 1954-1955; supplement to World Economic Survey, 1955. New York, United Nations, 1956. 100p. (AM330Un3e)

453 United Nations. Dept. of Economic and Social Affairs. Review of economic conditions in Africa Supplement to World Economic Report. New York, 1951. 119p. (AM330Un3r)

454 U. S. Dept. of State. Office of Intelligence Research. Agriculture

in point 4 countries; Near East and independent Africa. Washington, D. C., 1952. 52p. (AM960Un3a)

EDUCATION

455 African education commission. Education in East Africa a study of East, Central and South Africa by the second African education commission under the auspices of the Phelps-Stokes fund, in cooperation with the International education board. New York, Phelps-Stokes fund, 1925. 416p. (M370.96Af8e)

456 African student conference proceedings. Vol 1.—1953, Vol. 2—1954. (AM378.3Af8)

457 Aggrey House Club. Constitution and by-laws. London, Aggrey House, n.d. 12p. (AM370.4Ag3c)

458 Aggrey House Club. Report and accounts for the year ending 31st December, 1939. London, Aggrey House, 1939. 20p. (AM-370Ag3r)

459 Bull-Oswin Boys. Training Africains for trades; a report on a visit to the United States of America and Canada under the auspices of the Carnegie corporation visitors' grants committee. Pretoria, South Africa, The Carnegie visitors' grants committee, 1935. 72p. (M370B87t)

460 Davis, Jackson. Africa advancing; a study of rural education and agriculture in West Africa and the Belgian Congo. New York, The International committee on Christian literature for Africa, [1945.] 230p. (M966J29)

461 Eells, Walter Crosby. Communism in education in Asia, Africa, and the Far Pacific. Washington, D. C., American Council on Education [1954.] 246p. (AM370Ee5)

462 Fortes, M. Social and psychological aspects of education in Taleland. London, Published for the Oxford Press for the International institute of African languages and cultures, 1938. 64p. (AM370F77)

463 Great Britain. Inter-university council for higher education overseas 1946-54. London, H.M.S.O., 1954. 34p. (AM325.342-G798)

464 Guggisberg, F. The future of the Negro. London, Student Christian movement press, 1929. 152p. (AM370G94)

465 Hambly, Wilfred Dyson. Origins of education among primitive peoples, a comparative study in racial development. London, Macmillan and Co., 1926. 432p. (M572H17o)

466 Hussey, E. R. J. Higher education in East Africa. Report of the Commission appointed by the Secretary of the State for the Colonies. Journal of the Royal African Society, vol. 36, 30th Nov., 1937. 19p. (AM370H96)

467 Jones, Thomas J. Education in Africa. New York, Phelps-Stokes, 1922. 323p. (AM370Af8)

468 Jowitt, Harold. The principles of education for African teachers in training. London, Longmans, Green and Co., 1932. 216p. (AM370J63)

469 Lewis, L. J. Equipping Africa. Educational development in British colonial Africa. London, Edinburgh House Press, 1948. 42p. (M916L58e)

470 Lewis, L. J. Towards a literate Africa; report of the Conference held under the auspices of the International Committee on Christian Literature for Africa and the Colonial Department of the University of London. Institute of Education, December 1947. London, Longmans, Green and Co., 1948. 80p. (M960L58t)

471 Murray, Albert Victor. The school in the bush. London, New York, Longsmans, Green and Co., 1929. 413p. (AM370M96)

472 Oldham, J. H. The remaking of man in Africa. London, Oxford University Press, H. Milford, 1931. 185p. (AM370O11)

473 Phelps-Stokes fund. A survey of African students studying in the United States. New York, Phelps-Stokes fund, October 1949. 78p. (AM378.3P51s)

474 Read, Margaret. Africans and their schools. London, Longmans, Green and Co., 1953. British Commonwealth Affairs, No. 8. 23p. (AM370R22)

475 Stuart, Mary. African pattern; letters to an administrater. London, Edinburgh House Press, 1945. 95p. (AM370.96St4)

476 UNESCO Educational studies and documents. African languages and English education; a report of a meeting of experts on the use in education of African languages in relation to English, where English is the accepted second language, held at Jos, Nigeria, Nov., 1952. [n.p.] Education Clearing House, June 1953. 91p. (M496Un3e)

477 UNESCO Etudes et documents d'éducation. Les langues africaines et l'anglais dans l'enseignement; rapport d'une réunion d'experts sur l'emploi des langues africaines dans l'enseignement lorsque la seconde langue adoptée est la langue anglaise. Réunion tenue à Jos, (Nigeria) en Novembre 1952. [n.p.] Centre

d'enformation du Department de l'education, Novembre 1953. 94p. (M496Un3et)

478 UNESCO. The Commission on Technical Needs. Press, film, radio; following surveys in fourteen countries and territories. Paris, UNESCO, 1949. 295p. (M961Un3)

479 Ward, William E. African education; a study of educational policy and practice in British tropical Africa. London, Crown Agents for the Colonies, 1953. 187p. (AM370W21)

FOLKLORE

480 African folktales and sculpture. New York, Pantheon Books, 1952. 355p. (AM398Af8)

481 Barker, William Henry. West African folk-tales. London, George G. Harrap and Co., 1917. 184p. (AM398.2B24w)

482 Baskerville, Rosetta Gage (Harvey). "Mrs. George Baskerville". The king of the snakes. London, The Sheldon Press, New York and Toronto. The Macmillan Company, 1922. 88p. (AM398B29)

483 Basset, René Marie Joseph. Contes populaires d'Afrique. Paris, Librairie Orientale et Américaine, 1903. 455p. (AM396B294c)

484 Best, Herbert. Garram the hunter, a boy of the hill tribes. Garden City, New York. Doubleday, Doran & Company, Inc., 1930. 332p. (M813.5B469)

485 Bleek, Dorothea. The Mantis and his friends. Cape Town, T. Maskew Miller, n.d. 63p. (AM398B61m)

486 Bleek, Wilhelm H. I. Specimens of Bushman folklore. London, G. Allen and Co., 1911. 468p. (AM398B61b)

487 Bouche, [Pierre Bertrand] Les noirs peints par eux-memes, par M. l'abbe Bouche. Paris, Librairie Poussielgue Freres, 1883. 144p. (AM398.9B66n)

488 Brownlee, Frank. Lion and jackel with other native folktales from South Africa. London, G. Allen and Unwin, [1938] 174p. (AM398B821)

489 Burckhardt, John Lewis. Arabic proverbs; or, The manners and customs of the modern Egyptians, illustrated from their proverbial sayings current at Cairo. London, Quaritch, 1875. 232p. (M962B89)

490 Burlin, Natalie Curtis. Songs and tales from the dark continent. Recorded from the singing and the sayings of C. Kamba

Simango . . . and Madikane Cole. New York, Schirmer, 1920.
170p. (AM398B92)

491 Camphor, Alexander Priestly. Missionary story sketches, folk-lore
from Africa. Cincinnati, Jennings and Graham; New York,
Eaton and Mains, 1909. 346p. (AM398.C15)

492 Cardinall, Allan Wolsey. Tales told in Togoland. London, Oxford University Press, H. Milford, 1931. 290p. (AM398C17)

493 Cendrars, Blaise. The African saga; translated from l'Anthologie
Negre by Margery Bianco. New York, Payson and Clark,
1927. 378p. AM398C33b)

494 Cendrars, Blaise. Anthologie nègre. Nouvelle edition. Paris.
Au Sans Pareil, 1927. (AM398C33a)

495 Cendrars, Blaise. Little black stories for little white children.
New York, Payson and Clarke, ltd., 1929. 138p. (AM398C33)

496 Chatelain, Heli. Folk-tales of Angola; fifty tales with Ki-umbundu
text, literal English translation . . . Boston and New York,
Published for the American Folklore Society by Houghton
Mifflin Co., 1894. 315p. (AM398C39)

497 Cobban, James Maclaren. An African treasure. How the doctor
and Sandy Pebbles outwitted the basha misfiwa in his search
for the meaning of the strange cryptogram and how Jim greath-
ed by the aid of the lovely Susannah, dispelled the mystery of
"Bro'r Sol," together with their adventures in the interior of
Morocco. New York: New Amsterdam Book Co., 1900. 367p.
(M813.4C63)

498 Delafosse, Maurice. L'Ame Negre. Paris, Payot et cie. 1922.
180p. (AM398D37a)

499 Demaison, Andre. . . . Diaeli; le livre de la sagesse noire. Paris,
H. Piazza, 1931. 169p. (AM398D39d)

500 Dennett, Richard Edward. Nigerian studies; or, The religious
and political system of the Yoruba. London, Macmillan and
Co., 1910. 235p. (M966.9D41n)

501 Dennett, Richard Edward. Notes on the folklore of the Fjort
(French Congo). London, Published for the Folk-lore Society
by D. Nutt, 1898. 169p. (AM398D41n)

502 Dinkins, P. E. African folk-tales. Tennessee, Sunday School
Pub. Board, 1933. 21p. (AM398D61)

503 Doke, C. M. Lamba folk-lore. New York, The American Folklore Society, G. E. Stechert and Co., agents, 1927. 570p.
(AM398D68)

504 Dugmore, Arthur Radclyffe. African jungle life. London, Macmillan and Co., 1928. 246p. (AM398D87)

505 Elliott, Geraldine. The hunter's cave. London, Routledge and Kegan, 1951. 174p. (AM398E15h)

506 Elliott, Geraldine. Where the leopard passes. London, Routledge and Kegan Paul, Ltd, 1949. 134p. (AM398.3E57w)

507 Faithlovitch, Jacques. Proverbs abyssins, traduits, expliqués, et annotés. Paris, P. Geuthner, 1907. 86p. (M963F17p)

508 Farrow, Stephen Septimus. Faith, fancies and fetich; or, Yoruba paganism; being some account of the religious beliefs of the West African Negroes, particularly of the Yoruba tribes of Southern Nigeria. London, Society for promoting Christian knowledge; New York and Toronto, The Macmillan Co., [1926.] 180p. (M966.92F24)

509 Fell, J. R. Folk tales of the Batonga and other sayings . . . told in the school at Kachindu . . . London, Holborn Publishing House, n.d. 247p. (AM398F33f)

510 Ferrand, Gabriel. Contes populaires, malgaches, recueillis, traduits et annotés. Paris, Ernest Leroux, 1893. 266p. (AM398.3F41)

511 Frobenius, Leo. . . . African genesis. New York, Stackpole sons, 1937. 236p. (AM398F92)

511a Frobenius, Leo. Atlantis; volksnmärchen und volksdichtungen afrikas. Muenchen, Veroffentlichungen d. Forschungsingsinstituts für kulturmorphologie (1921-28) 12 Vol. (M398-F92a)

512 Graham, Lorenz B. How God fix Jonah. New York, Reynal and Hitchcock, 1946. 171p. (M896.1Gr76)

513 Greenwood, James. Legends of savage life. 1867. (AM398 G85)

514 Haigh, Richmond. An Ethiopian saga. New York, H. Holt and co., 1919. 207p. (AM398 H12)

515 Hambly, Wilfrid Dyson. Talking animals. Washington, Associated Publishers, 1949. 100p. (AM398H17t)

516 Harvey, Isadore Church. Kimolowland stories. New York, London, The Abbey Press, 1903. 131p. (AM398 H26)

517 Helser, Albert David. Education of primitive people; a presentation of the folklore of the Bura animists, with a meaningful experience curriculum. New York, Fleming H. Revell co., [c1934] 316p. (AM370H36)

518 Hertslet, Jessie. Bantu folk tales, seven stories. Cape Town, African Bookman, 1946. 91p. (AM398H44b)

519 Herzog, George. Jabo proverbs from Liberia; maxims in the life of a native tribe ... London, Published for the International Institute of African Languages and Culture by Oxford University Press, H. Milford, 1936. 272p. (AM398H44)

520 Hobley, Charles William. Bantu beliefs and magic, with particular reference to the Kikuyu and Kamba tribes of Kenya Colony; together with some reflections on East Africa after the War. London, H. F. and G. Witherby, 1922. 312p. (M967.6H65)

521 Hobson, G. C. no S. B. U-Adonisi Wasentlango; ixulwe kumabali adumbileyo. Pretoria, originally published in Afrikaans by J. L. Van Schail, Ltd., 1945. (AM398H65a)

522 Hollis, Afred Claud. The Nandi; their language and folklore. Oxford, Clarendon Press, 1909. 328p. (AM496.4H72)

523 Honeij, James Albert. South-African folktales. New York, The Baker and Taylor co., 1910. 151p. (AM398H75)

524 Hurel, Eugene. La poésie chez les primitifs au contes, fables, récits et proverbes du Rwanda (Lac Kivu). Bruxelles, Goemaere, Imprimeur du a Roi, Editeur, 1922. 260p. (AM398H93)

525 Jacottet, Edouard. Litsomo tsa Basotho. Buka ca bobeli. Morija, Sesuto Book Depot, 1941. 148p. (AM398J151)

526 Kayombo, Innocent K. Stories of our Tanganyika forefathers. London, The Sheldon Press, 1952. 29p. (M967.82K185)

527 Koelle, Sigmund Wilhelm. African native literature; or, proverbs, tales, fables and historical fragments in the Kanuri or Bornu language. London, Church Missionary House, 1854. (M496.-4 K81)

528 Lindblom, Gerhard. Kamba folklore III. Kamba riddles, proverbs and songs, text, translations and notes. Uppsala, Appelbergs-Boktrycheriaktiebolag, 1934. 58p. (AM398L64)

529 Lo Bagola, B. K. A. Folk tales of a savage. New York, A. A. Knopf, 1930. 199p. (AM398L78)

530 Lowe, Harry William. African animal stories. Nashville, Southern Publishing Association, 1952. 176p. (AM398L95a)

531 Maris, Faith. African Negro folk tales. Girard, Kansas, Halderman-Julius co., 1925. 64p. (AM398M33)

532 Monteil, Charles Victor. Soudan francais. Contes soudanais. Paris, E. Leroux, 1905. 205p. (AM398M76)

533 Nyabongo, Akiki K. The "Bisoro" Stories. Oxford, Basil Blackwell, 1937. 2 vols. (AM398N98)

534　Nyabongo, Akiki K. Winds and lights. New York, The Voice of Ethiopia, 1939. 45p. (AM398N98)

535　Nyembezi, Cyril Lincoln Sibusiso. Zulu proverbs. Johannesburg, Witwatersrand University Press, 1954. 238p. (M968.3N98)

536　O'Connell, Ruby M. Iintsomi; Bantu folk stories. Lovedale press, 1938. 47p. (English and Khosa in parallel columns) (M398-Oc5i)

536a　Ogumefu, M. I. The staff of Oranyan and other Yoruba tales London, The Sheldon Press, 1930. 32p (M966.90g9s)

536b　Ogumefu, M. I. Tales of tortoise, Yoruba tales. London, The Sheldon Press, n.d. 32p. (M966.90g9t)

536c　Ogumefu, M. I. Yoruba legends. London, The Sheldon Press, 1929. 87p. (M966.90g9y)

537　Price, Pattie. Bantu tales. New York, E. P., Dutton & Co., Inc., 938. 64p. (AM398P93)

538　Ramon Alvarez, Heriberto. Leyendas y mitos de Guinea; prologo por Antonio de la Nuez Caballero. Madrid, Instituto de Estudios Africanos, 1951. 272p. (AM398R14)

539　Rattray, Robert Sutherland. Ashanti proverbs (the primitive ethics of a savage people) translated from the original with grammatical and anthropological notes. Oxford, the Clarendon Press, 1916. 190p. (M966.74R18ap)

540　Roland, Hadelin. Quarante contes: de la region des Basanga (Katanga). Brussells, Imprimerie Typ' Art, 1937. 44p. (AM398-R64Q no. 6)

541　Torrend, J. Specimens of Bantu folk-lore from northern Rhodesia. London, K. Paul, Trench, Trubner and co., ltd., New York, E. P. Dutton and co., 1921. 187p. (M398.3T63)

542　Trautman, Rene. La literature populaire a la côte des esclaves. Contes, proverbs, divinettes. Paris, Institut d'Ethnologie, 1927. 105p. (M398T69)

543　Travélé, Moussa. Proverbs et contes Bambara accompagnés d'une traduction francaise et précédés d'un abrégé de droit coutumier Bambara et Malinke. Paris, Librairie Orientaliste Paul Geuthner, 1923. 240p. (M298T69p)

544　Tremearne, Arthur J. N. Hausa superstitions and customs; an introduction to the folklore and the folk. London, J. Bale, sons & Danielson, ltd., 1913. 548p. (M966.9T72h)

545　Vergiat, Antonin Marius. Moeurs et coutumes des Manjas. Paris, Payot, 1937. 323p. (M967.41V58m)

546 Waters, Mary W. Cameos from the Kraal. Lovedale Institutions Press, n.d. 58p. (AM398W31c)

547 Woodson, Carter G. African myths. Washington, D.C. The associated publishers, Inc., 1928. 184p. (AM398.96W86)

LANGUAGES

548 Abraham, Roy Clive. Dictionary of the Hausa language. London, Crown Agents for the Colonies, 1949. 902p. (M493.5Ab8d)

549 Abraham, Roy Clive. A dictionary of the Tiv language. London, Pub. on behalf of the Government of Nigeria by the Crown agents for the Colonies, 1940. 331p. (AM496.4Ab8d)

550 Abraham, Roy Clive. The principles of Amharic . . . London, The Author, 1942. (M492.8Ab82)

551 Aginsky, Ethel. A grammar of the Mende language. Philadelphia University of Pennsylvania, Linguistic Society of America, 1935. 11p. (AM496Ag4g)

552 Ardant du Picq, Charles Jean Jacques Joseph. La langue Songhay; dialecte Dyerma. Paris, Larose Editeurs, 1933. 170p. (M496-Ar21)

553 Armstrong, Lilias Eveline. The phonetic and tonal structure of Kikuyu. London, Oxford University Press, H. Milford, 1940. 363p. (M496.3Ar5)

554 Ashton, Eric Ormerod. Notes on form and structure in Bantu speech. London, Oxford University Press, International African Institute, 1945. 19p. (AM496.3As3)

555 Atkins, Guy. Suggestions for an amended spelling and word division of Nyanja. London, Oxford University Press, International African Institute, 1950. 19p. (AM496.3A5)

556 Bargery, George Percy. A Hausa-English dictionary and English-Hausa vocabulary, compiled for the government of Nigeria, with some notes on the Hausa people and their language. London, Oxford University Press, H. Milford, 1934. 1226p. (Am493.5B23)

557 Barnouw, Adriaan J. Language and race problems in South Africa. The Hague, M. Nijhoff, 1934. 71p. (M960.32B26)

558 Basset, André. La langue berbère. London, New York, Oxford Univ. Press, 1952. 72p. (AM493.3B29)

559 Bell, Christopher R. V. The Somali language. London, New York, Longsmans, Green, 1953. 185p. (M493.51B41)

560 Bleek, D. F. Comparative vocabularies of Bushman languages. Cam-

bridge, England, The University Press, 1929. 94p. (AM496-B61)

561   Bowen, T. J. Grammar and Dictionary of the Yoruba language. With a description of the country and people of Yoruba .[Washington, D.C.] Smithsonian Institution, 1858. (Smithsonian contributions to knowledge). 136p. (AM496.4B67)

562   Bryan, Margaret Arminel. Distribution of the Nilotic and Nilo-Hamitic languages of Africa. London, New York, Oxford University Press, 1948. (M496.4B84d)

563   Bryant, Alfred T. An abridged English-Zulu word-book. Incwadi yabantu uamazwi esingisi ecasiselwe ngesizulu. Mariannhill, South Africa, Mariannhill mission press, 1940. 471p. (AM496.-3B84a)

564   Bud-M'belle, I. Kafir scholar's companion [Lovedale, Lovedale Missionary Press, 1903.] 181p. (M496B85k)

565   Bulck, G. van. Les recherces linguistiques au Congo Belge; resultats acquis nouvelle enquêtes a entreprendre. Bruxelles, 1948. 767p. (M496B87r)

566   Calloc'h J. Vocabulaire Française-sango et sango-Français. Paris P. Geuthner, 1911. 86p. (AM496C13)

567   Chamberlain, George Digby. A brief account of the Brissa language Accra, Gold Coast, Printed at the Government Printing Office. 1930. 53p. (M496C35)

568   Chesswas, J. D. The essentials of Luganda. Kampala The Eagle Press, 1954. 169p. (M496C42e)

569   Christaller, Johann Gottlieb. A dictionary of the Asante and Fante language called Tshi. Basel, The Evangelical Missionary Society, 1933. 607p. (AM496.5C46)

570   Clercq, August de, bp., Dictionnaire Luba. Luba-Français Français-Luba. Bruxelles, Albert Dewit, 1914. 583p. (M496C59)

571   Cohen, Marcel Samuel Raphael. Études d'éthiopien méridional. Paris, Librairie orientaliste. Paul Geuthner, Librairie de la Société asiatique, 1931. 416p. (AM493.5C66)

572   Cole, Desmond T. An introduction to Tswana grammar. London, New York, Longmans, Green and Co., 1955. 473p.

573   Cordeiro da Matta, J. D. Esaio de diccionario kimbúndu-portuguez, Lisboa, A. M. Pereira, 1893. 174p. (M496C81e)

574   Crawshaw, C. J. A first Kafir course. 5th ed. Capetown, J. C. Juta & co., 1903. 133p. (AM496.3C85f)

575   Crazzolara, J. Pasquale. A study of the Acooli language ... Lon-

don, New York, Published for the International Institute of
African Languages and Cultures by the Oxford University
Press, 1938. (M496.4C85)

576 Crowther, Samuel Adjai. A grammar and vocabulary of the Yoruba
language. London, Seeleye, 1852. 291p. (M496C88g)

577 Crowther, Samuel Adjai. Vocabulary and dictionary of the Yoruba
language. London, W. M. Watts, 1865? 254p. (M966.9C88v)

578 Cust, Robert N., A sketch of the modern languages of Africa,
London, Trubner and Co., Ludgate Hill, 1883. 1 vol. (M496-
C96s)

579 DeGaye, Jule A. Yoruba grammar ... London, K. Paul, Trench,
Trubner & co., ltd. [etc. etc.] 1923. 96p. (AM496.4D34)

580 Delafosse, Maurice. Vocabulaires comparatifs de plus ... Paris, E.
Leroux, 1904. 284p. (AM496D37v)

581 Dictionary of the Yuroba language. 2nd edition. Lagos, Church missionary society bookshop, 1937. 243p. (AM496.4D56)

582 Dictionary of the Yoruba language. London, Oxford University,
1950. 243p. (AM496.5D56)

583 Dillmann, August. Grammatik der athiopischen sprache. Leipzig,
Chr. Herm. Tauchnitz, 1899. 488p. (M492.8D58)

584 Dillman, [Freidrich,] August. Ethiopic grammar. London, Williams
and Norgate, 1907. 581p. (M492.8D58e)

585 Dillmann [Freidrich] August. Grammatik de Athiopischen sprache.
Leipzig, T. O. Weigel, 157. 435p. (M492.8D58)

586 Doke, Clement Martyn. Bantu linguistic terminology. London,
New York [etc.] Longmans, Green and co. [1935] 237p.
(AM496.3D68b)

587 Doke, Clement Martyn. Bantu language pioneers of the nineteenth
century ... Johannesburg, University of Witwatersrand press,
1940. 246p. (AM496.3D68b5)

588 Doke, Clement Martyn. Bantu; modern grammatical, phonetical,
and lexicographical studies since 1860 . . . London, Pub. for
International African institute. Humphries & co., ltd., 1945.
119p. (AM496.3D68)

589 Doke, Clement Martyn. Phonetics of the Zulu language. Johannesburg, University of the Witwatersrand Press, 1926. 310p.
(AM496.3D68p)

590 Doke, Clement Martyn. The southern Bantu languages. London,
New York, Published for the International African Institute
by the Oxford University Press, 1954. 262p. (AM496.3D68s)

591 Doke, Clement Martyn. Zulu-English dictionary. Johannesburg, Witwatersrand Univ. Press, 1953. 918p. (AM496.3D68z)

592 Douglin, Philip Henry. A reading book in the Soso language. London, Society for Promoting Christian Knowledge, 1887. 120p. (M496D74r)

593 East, R. M. A vernacular bibliography for the languages of Nigeria. Zaria, Literature Bureau, 1941. 85p. (M496Ea7v)

594 Edmiston, Althea Brown. Grammar and dictionary of the Bushonga or Bukuba language. Luebo, Congo Belge, J. Leighton Wilson Press, n.d. (M496Ed5)

595 Fligelman, F. Moral vocabulary of an unwritten language. (Fulani). Reprinted from Anthropos, 1932. v.27. (AM496F64m)

596 Fligelman, F. The richness of African languages . . . Reprinted from "Actes du Congrès de l'Institut International des Langues et des civilisations Africaines." Paris, 1931. (M496F64)

597 Foot, Edwin C. A Galla-English, English-Galla dictionary. Cambridge, University Press, 1913. 118p. (AM493.52F73g)

598 Foulkes, H. D. Angass manual, grammar and vocabulary. London, Kegan Paul, Trench, Trubner and co., 1915. 313p.

599 Gachon, Fr. Dictionnaire pongoué-français. Paris, Maisonneuve et cie., 1881. 287p. (AM496G11)

600 Gardiner, Alan Henderson. Egyptian grammar; being an introduction to the study of hieroglyphs. Oxford, The Clarendon Press, 1927. 595p. AM493.1G16)

601 Gecaga, Bethuel Mareka. A short Kikuyu grammar. London, Macmillan and Co., Ltd., 1953. 156p. (AM496G26s)

602 Grammar e nyenyana ea ba ithutang se English. Morija, Sesuto book depot, 1940. 30p. (AM496.3G76)

603 Groff, William N. Oeuvres Egyptologiques de William N. Groff, publiées par sa soeur avec l'aide de G. Maspero. Paris, Ernest Leroux, 1908. 503p. (AM493.1G75)

604 Grout, Lewis. The Isizulu. A grammar of the Zulu language; accompanied with an appendix. London, Trubner and Co., 1859. 432p. (M496G91)

605 Guthrie, Malcolm. The Bantu languages of western Equatorial Africa. London, New York, Oxford Univ. Press, 1953. 94p. (M496.3G8b)

606 Guthrie, Malcolm. Bantu word division; a new study of an old problem. London, Oxford Univ. Press, International African Institute, 1948. 32p. (AM496.3G98ba)

607 Guthrie, Malcolm. The classification of the Bantu languages. London, New York, Pub. for the International African Institute by the Oxford Univ. Press, 1948. 91p. (AM496. 3G98a)

608 Hamlyn, W. T. A short study of the Western Mandinka language. London, Published on behalf of the Government of Gambia by the Crown Agents for the Colonies, 1935. 110p. (AM496H18s)

609 Hinde, Hildegarde Beatrice. Vocabularies of the Kama and Kikuyu languages of East Africa. Cambridge, University Press, 1904. 75p. (M496H58)

610 Hollis, Alfred Claud. The Masai; their language and folklore. Oxford, The Clarendon Press, 1905. 359p. (M493.5H72m)

611 Hollis, Alfred Claud. The Nandi, their language and folklore. 1909. (AM496.4H72)

612 Homburger, Lilias. The Negro-African languages. London, Routledge & Kegan Paul, Ltd., 1949. 275p. (M496.4H75n)

613 Howeidy, A. Concise Hausa grammar. Wheatley George Ronald, 1953. 232p. (M496.5H83c)

614 International Institute of African Languages and Cultures. Practical orthography of African languages. London, Oxford University Press, International Institute of African Languages and Cultures, 1930. 24p. (AM421.1In8p)

615 Inter-territorial language (Swahili) committee to the East African dependencies. A standard English-Swahili dictionary . . . London, Oxford University Press, H. Milford, 1939. 635p. (AM496.3J63)

616 Jabavu, Davidson D. T. Bantu literature. Classification and reviews. . . . South Africa, P. O. Lovedale, 1921. 27p. (AM-496.3J11)

617 Jacottet, Edouard. A practical method to learn Sesuto, with exercises and a short vocabulary. Marija, Sesuto book depot, 1936. 324p. (AM496.3J15p)

618 Johnston, Harry Hamilton. A comparative study of the Bantu and semi-Bantu languages . . . Oxford, The Clarendon Press, 1919. 2v. (M496J64)

619 Jones, Daniel. The tones of Sechuana Nouns. London, International Institute of African Languages and Cultures, 1928. 26p. (AM496.3J71t)

620 Koelle, Sigismund Wilhelm. African native literature, or Proverbs, tales, fables, and historical fragments in the Kanuri or Bornu

language . . . London, Church missionary house, 1854. 434p.
(AM496.4K81)

621 Koelle, Sigismund Wilhelm. Outlines of a grammar of the Vei
language, together with a Vei-English vocabulary and an account of the discovery and nature of the Vei mode of syllabic
writing. London, Kegan Paul, Trench, Trubner, 1851. (M496
K81o)

622 Kolbe, F. W. A language-study based on Bantu; or an inquiry into
the laws of root-formation, the original plural, the sexual dual,
and the principles of word-comparison. 1888. 97p. (AM-
496.3K83)

623 Kriel, T. The new Afrikaans school dictionary; Afrikaans-English
and English Afrikaans. Capetown (South Africa), Dusseau,
1937. 299p. (AM496.3K89)

624 Labouret, Henri. La langue des peuls on Foulbé. Dakar, IFAN,
1952. 286p. (M496L11)

625 Lavergne de Tressan, Georges A. Inventaire linguistique de l'
Afrique Occidentale Française et du Togo. Dakar, IFAN,
1952. 240p. (M496L38)

626 Le Coeur, Charles. Dictionnaire ethnographique Teda. Paris,
Librarie Larose, 1950. (AM572L49d)

627 Le Coeur, Charles. Grammaire et textes Teda-Daza. 394p.
(M496L49) Dakar, IFAN, 1956.

628 Lukas, Johannes. A study of the Kanuri language, grammar and
vocabulary. London, New York, Published for the International Institute of African Languages and Cultures by the
Oxford University Press, 1937. 253p. (AM496.4L96)

629 MacDougald, Duncan. The languages and press of Africa. Philadelphia, University of Pennsylvania University Museum, 1944.
86p. (AM496M14)

630 McLaren, J. A concise English-Kafir dictionary. London, New
York, Longsman Green & Co., 1923. 319p. (AM496.3M22c)

631 McLaren, James, d. 1934. A Xhosa grammar . . . London, New
York, Lonsgman Green and Co., 1939. 248p. (AM496.3M22x)

632 Meinhof, Carl. An introduction to the study of African languages.
London and Toronto, J. M. Dent and sons, Ltd.; New York,
E. P. Dutton and Co., 1915. 169p. (AM496M47)

633 Melzian, Hans Joachim. A concise dictionary of the Bini language
of southern Nigeria. London, K. Paul, Trench, Trubner &
Co., Ltd., 1937. 232p. (AM496.4M49)

634 Migeod, Frederick William. A grammar of the Hausa language. London, K. Paul, Trench, Trubner and Co., 1914. (AM493. 5M58)

635 Migeod, Frederick William. The languages of West Africa. London, K. Paul, Trench Trubner and Co., 1913. 2 vols. (AM496M58s)

636 Migeod, Frederick William H. The Mende Language. London, K. Paul, Trench, Trubner and Co., 1908. (M496.4M58)

637 Mulira, E. M. K. A Luganda-English and English-Luganda dictionary. London, Society for promoting Christian Knowledge, 1952. 233p. (AM496M891)

638 Nhlapo, Jacob M. Bantu Babel. Will the Bantu languages live? Cape Town, The African Bookman, 1944. 15p. (AM496.3N51b)

639 Nhlapo, Jacob M. Nguni and Sotho, a partical plan for the unification of the South African Bantu languages. Cape Town, The African Bookman, 1945. 22p. (M968N49)

640 Nordfeldt, Martin. A Galla Grammar. Uppsala, A. B. Lundequistska Bohandeln, 1941. 232p. (In: Le Monde Oriental, revue des etudes orientales tidskrift for orientaliska studier, pub., by H. S. Nyberg, vol. 33-35, 1939-1941)

641 Odunjo, J. F. Iwe-Kini A B D Alawiye . . . Lagos, The Ife-Olu printing works, 1946. 32p. (AM496.40d8i)

642 Perrott, D. V. Teach yourself Swahili. London, English Universities Press, 1951. 183p. (AM496.3P42t)

643 Plaatje, Solomon Tshekisho. Sechuana proverbs with literal translations and their European equivalents. Diane tsa secoana le maele a sekgooa a a dumalanang naco. London, K. Paul, Trench, Trubner and Co., Ltd., 1916. 98p. (AM496P69)

644 Plaatje, Solomon Tshekisho. A Sechuana reader in international phonetic orthography with English translations. London, The University of London Press, 1916. 45p. (M968P69se)

645 Rattray, Robert Sutherland. An elementary Mole grammar with a vocabulary of over 1000 words for the use of officials in the Northern territories of the Gold Coast. Oxford, The Clarendon Press, 1918. 85p. (AM496.5R18)

646 Roberts, Charles. The Zulu-Kafir language simplified for beginners. London, Kegan Paul, Trench, Trubner and Co., 1899. 177p. (M496R545)

647 Roberts, Charles. A Zulu manual. London, Kegan Paul, Trench, Trubner and Co., 1900. 153p. (M469R546)

648 Robinson, Charles Henry. Dictionary of the Hausa language. 3d

ed. rev. and enl. Cambridge, University Press, 1913-14. 2v. (AM496.5R56d)

649 Robinson, Charles Henry. Hausa grammar with exercises, readings, and vocabularies, and specimens of Hausa script. London, Kegan Paul, Trench, Trubner and Co., 1942. 218p. (AM496R56)

650 Sadler, Wesley. Untangled Loma; a course of study of the Loma language of the western province, liberia, West Africa. [Baltimore] Board of Foreign Missions of the United Lutheran Church in America for the Evangelical Lutheran Church in Liberia, 1951. 465p. (M496Sa1)

651 Savage, G. A. R. A short Acoli-English and English-Acoli vocabulary. Nairobi, The Eagle Press, 1955. 50p. (M967.61Sa9s)

652 Schon, James Frederick. Dictionary of the Hausa language, Part I. Hausa-English, Part II. English Hausa with appendices of Hausa literature. London, Church Missionary House, 1876. 142p. (AM496.5Sc6d)

653 Stuart, P. A. A Zulu grammar for beginners. Pietermaritzburg, Shuter and Shooter, [1940] 159p. (AM496St9)

654 Summer, A. T. A handbook of the Temme language. Freetown, Sierra Leone, West Africa, Government Printing Office, 1922. 157p. (M496C46ht)

655 Sutton, G. W. Quick Swahili. New York, Berlitz School of Languages, 1952. 74p. (AM496.3Su8q)

656 Taylor, Frank William. A Fulani-English dictionary. Oxford The Clarendon Press, 1932. (AM496T21)

657 Taylor, Frank William. A practical Hausa grammar. 1923. London, Oxford University Press, 1923. 141p. (AM496T21p)

658 Tervueren, Belgium. Musée du Congo Belge. Notes analytiques sur les collections ethnographiques du Musée du Congo. Bruxelles, En vente chez Spineux et cie, 1902. (AM572T27n)

659 Tien, Anton. Egyptian, Syrian, and North-African handbook. New York, F. Ungar, [1934] 173p. (M492.7T44)

660 Tisserant, Charles. Dictionnaire Banda-français. Paris, Institut d' éthnologie, 1931. 611p. (M496T52d)

661 Tisserant, Charles. Essai sur la grammaire Banda. Paris, Institut d'éthnologie, 1930. 185p. (M496T52e)

662 Tobias, George W. R. English-Kwanyama dictionary. Johannesburg, Witwatersrand University Press, 1954. 199p. (M496T55)

663 Torrend, J. A comparative grammar of the South Africa Bantu

languages; comprising those of Zanzibar, the Zambesi, Karir-
land, Benguela, the Lake region. London, Kegan, Paul, Trench,
Trubner and Co., 1891. 340p.

664 Travélé, Moussa. Petit dictionnaire Français-Bambara et Bambara-
Français. Paris, Librairie Paul Geuthner, 1913. 281p. (M496-
T69pe)

665 Travélé, Moussa. Petit manuel Francais-Bambara. 2e edition
revue et augmentee. Paris, Librairie orientaliste Paul Geuthner, 1923. 89p. (M496T69p)

666 Tucker, Archibald Norman. The Eastern Sudanic languages. Lon-
don, New York, Published for the International Institute of
African Languages and Cultures by the Oxford University
Press, 1940. (AM495T79)

667 Tucker, Archibald Norman. The non-Bantu languages of North-
Eastern Africa. With a supplement of the non-Bantu languages of Southern Africa. London, Oxford University Press,
1956. 228p. (Handbook of African Languages, Part III)
(M496T79n)

668 Ullendorff, Edward. The Semitic languages of Ethiopia; a comparative phonology. London, Taylor's (foreign) Press, 1955.
273p. (M496U14)

669 UNESCO Etudes et documents d'education. Les langues africaines
et l'anglais dans l'enseignement; rapport d'une reunion d'experts sur l'emploi des langues africaines dans l'enseignement
lorsque la second langu adoptee est la langue anglaise. Reunion tenue a Jos, Nigeria en Novembre 1952. n.p. Centre
d'enformation du Department de l'education, Novembre 1953.
94p. (M496Un3et)

670 UNESCO The use of vernacular languages in education. Paris,
1953. 156p. (M407Un3u)

671 U. S. Army. Special Service Division. A language guide to North
Africa. Washington, D. C. War and Navy Departments,
[1934] 113p. (M961Un31)

672 Van Os, Leonard W. Afrikaans self-taught by the natural method,
with phonetic pronounciation. London, E. Marlborough and
Co., 1930. 246p. (M439.36V34a)

673 Walker, Andre. Essai de grammaire Tsogo. Brazzaville, Institute
do Etudes Centrificanies, n.d. 63p. (M496W15)

674 Ward, Ida Caroline. An introduction to the Yoruba language.
Cambridge, W. Heffer, 1952. 255p. (AM496.4W21)

675 Ward, Ida Caroline. Practical suggestions for the learning of an

African language in the field. London, Milbank House, 1937. 39p. (AM496W21)

676 Warsama, Solomon. The principles of Somali. [n.p.] The author, 1951. 481p. (M496.3W26)

677 Watkins, Mark Hanna. A grammar of Chichewa; a Bantu language of British Central Africa . . . Philadelphia, Linguistic Society of America, University of Pennsylvania, 1937. 158p. (Journal of Linguistic Society of America, Supplement No. 24, April-June, 1937). (M496.3W32g)

678 Werner, Alice. Introductory sketch of the Bantu languages . . . London, K. Paul, Trench, Trubner and Co., Ltd., 1919. 346p. (AM496.3W49)

679 Werner, Alice. The language-families of Africa. London, Society for promoting Christian Knowledge, 1951. 149p. (AM496-W951)

680 Westermann, Diedrich. The Kpelle language in Liberia; grammatical outline, colloquial sentences and vocabulary. Berlin, Reimer, Vohsen, 1930. 85p. (AM496W52k)

681 Westermann, Diedrich. Die Mossi-sprachengrauppe im westlichen Sudan. 1913. 469-504p. (AM496.3W52)

682 Westermann, Diedrich. Practical phonetics for students of African languages. London, Oxford University Press, 1931. (M496-W52p)

683 Westermann, Diedrich. Die Westlichen Sudan-sprachen. Berlin, In Kommission bein Walter de Gruyter u. Co., 1927 (AM496W52)

684 Witte, Anton. Zur trommelsprache bei den Ewe-Leuten. 1910. Pp. 50-53. Reprinted from Anthropos, Revue Internationale d'Ethnologie et de Linguistique. Time V., 1910, fasc. 1. (M496.3W78)

685 Wolf, Franz. Grammatik der Kposo-Sprache (Nord-Togo, West-Afrika). 1909. 142-67p. (AM496.3W83)

686 Yahuda, Abraham S. The language of the Pentateuch in its relation to Egyptian. London, Oxford University Press, H. Milford, 1933. (AM493.1Yal)

687 Young, Edward Joseph. Arabic for beginners. Grand Rapids, Eerdmans Publishing Company, 1949. (M492.7Yo8)

HEALTH AND SOCIAL CONDITIONS

688 Blackie, William Kerr. Malaria, with special reference to the

African forms. Cape Town, Post-Graduate Press, 1947. 101p. (AM616.936B56m)

689 Bolinder, Gustaf. Devilman's jungle. London, Kegan Paul, Trench, Trubner & Co. 1954. 190p. (AM390B63)

690 Carothers, John Colin. The African mind in health and disease; a study in ethnopsychiatry. Geneva. World health organization. 1953. 177p. (AM136C23)

691 Entwistle, Mary. Children of the chief. Illustrations by Erick Berry. New York, Friendship Press, 1928. 67p. (AM136.-7En87c)

692 Fiawoo, Charity (Zomelo) Health and diet of the African child. London, Longmans, Green and Co., 1947. 38p. (AM640F44h)

693 Fraser, Agnes Renton (Robson) The teaching of healthcraft to African women. London, New York, Longmans, Green and Co., 1932. 134p. (AM614.07F86)

694 Gelfand, Michael. The sick African. Cape Town, South Africa, Post Grad. Press in association with the Stewart printing Co., Ltd., 1944. 373p. (AM614G28)

695 Githens, Thomas Stotesbury. Drug plants of Africa. Philadelphia, Univ. of Pennsylvania Press, 1948. 125p. (AM338.1G44d)

696 Harley, George W. Native African medicine. Cambridge, Mass., Harvard Univ. Press, 1941. 294p. (AM610H22)

697 Kayamba, H. Martin Th. African problems. London, United Society for Christian Literature [1948] 93p. (M916K18a)

698 Lagercrantz, Sture. Contribution to the ethnography of Africa. London, K. Paul, Trench, Trubner, 1950. 430p. (AM572.-96L13c)

699 Nicholson, Marjorie. Self-government and the communal problem. London, Fabian Pub., 1948. 45p. (M960N52s)

700 Notcutt, Leslie Alan. The African and the cinema. London, Edinburgh House Press, 1937. 256p. (AM791.4N84)

701 Olivier, Lord. The anatomy of African misery. London, The Hogarth Press, 1927. 233p.

702 Pedrals, Denis Pierre de. La vie sexuelle en Afrique noire. Paris, Payot, 1950. 188p. (AM572P34v)

703 Phillips, Arthur. Survey of African marriage and family life. London, New York, Published for the International African Institute by Oxford University Press, 1953. 462p. (AM392P54)

704 Radcliffe-Brown, Alfred Reginald. African Systems of kinship and

marriage, ed. by A. R. Radcliffe-Brown and Daryll Forde. London, New York, Published for the International African Institute by the Oxford University Press, 1950. 399p. (AM-392R11a)

705 Radcliffe-Brown, Alfred Reginald. Systémes familiaux et matrimoniaux en Afrique. Paris, Presses Universitaires de France, 1953. 521p. (AM392R11a2)

706 Ray, Mary M. Inoculations and medical supplies for research workers in Sub-Saharan Africa. Evanston, Ill., Northwestern University, 1955. 11p. (AM614.47R21)

707 Ritchie, J. F. . . . The African as suckling and as adult (a psychological study) Livingstone, Northern Rhodesia, The Rhodes-Livingstone Institute, 1943. 61p. (AM136R51)

708 Sharp, Evelyn. The African child; an account of the International conference on African children. London, New York, [etc.] Longmans, Green and Co., [etc., etc.] 1931. 125p. (AM362.-7Sh2)

709 Souroy, J. Ch. Sorciers noirs et sorcier blanc, la magie, la sorcellerie et ses drames en Afrique. Bruxelles, Librairie Encyclopedique, 1952. 261p.

710 Vivian, S. Africa attacks poverty; a guide to clear thinking for Africans on a vital subject. London, Longmans, Green and Co., 1947. 85p. (AM339.1V83a)

ANIMAL LIFE

711 Akeley, Carl Ethan. In brightest Africa. Garden City, N. Y., Doubleday, Page & Company, 1923. 276p. (M960Ak3)

712 Akeley, Carl and Mary L. Jobe. Lions, gorillas and their neighbors. New York, Dodd, Meade & Company, 1933. 260p. (AM799.2Ak3)

713 Arbuthnot, Thomas S. African Hunt. New York, Norton, 1954. (AM799.2Arl)

714 Bannerman, David Armitage. The birds of West and Equatorial Africa, Edinburgh, Oliver and Boyd, 1953. 2v. (AM598B22)

715 Berg, Bengt M. K. To Africa with migratory birds. N. Y., London, G. P. Putnam's Sons, 1930. 274p. (A598.2B45)

716 Bigland, Mrs. Eileen. The lake of the royal crocodiles. [London] Hodder and Stoughton, [1939] 299p. (AM966.23B48L)

718 Blixen Finecke, Broy, baron. . . . African hunter, translated from

the Swedish by F. H. Lyon. New York, A. A. Knopf, 1938.
284p. (M916.7B61)

719 Conseil Scientifique pour l'Afrique au Sud du Sahara. Record of
symposium on African hydrobiology and inland fisheries, held
October, 1952, at Entebbe, Uganda. Bukavu, Published under
the sponsorship of the Commission of Technical Co-operation
in Africa South of the Sahara, 1954. 153p. (AM597C76)

720 Copley, Hugh. The game fishes of Africa. London, H. F. & G.
Witherby, 1952. 276p. (AM597C79)

721 Daly, Marcus. Big game hunting and adventure, 1897-1926. London, Macmillan & Co., Limited, 1937. 322p. (AM799.2D17)

722 Dollman, Guy. African antelopes. Supplement to the "Journal
of the Royal African Society," October, 1936, Vol. XXXV,
No. CXLI. 28p. (AM636.2938D69)

723 Hemingway, Ernest. Green hills of Africa. New York, C. Scribner's Sons, 1935. 294p. (AM799.2H37)

724 Hunter, John A. Hunter. London, H. Hamilton, 1952. 242p.
(AM799.2H91)

725 Jearey, Bertram Frederick. Pride of lions. London, New York,
Longmans, Green & Co., 1936. 159p. (AM799.28J34)

726 Koffler, Camilla. Animals in Africa. New York, Harper, 1953.
144p. (AM591K82)

727 Lagercrantz, S. . . . Fish-hooks in Africa and their distribution
Stockholm [Printed by Broderna Lagerstrom] 1933. 38p
(AM639.2L13)

728 McCutcheon, John Tinney. In Africa; hunting adventures in the
big game country. Indianapolis, The Bobbs-Merill Co., 1910.
402p. (AM916M13)

729 Mochi, U. African shadows. New York, R. O. Ballou, 1933.
208p. (AM591M71)

730 Paulian, Renaud. Les Corylophidae d'Afrique (Coleoptera) [Dakar,
IFAN] 1950. (AM595P28)

731 Ramecourt, Gabriel de. Grandes chasses et petites choses d'Afrique.
Paris, Firmin-Didot, 1936. 383p. (AM799.2R14)

732 Riddell, James. In the forests of the night. New York, A. S.
Barnes & Co., 1946. 228p. (AM591R43i)

733 Swaife, Sydney Harold. African insect life. London, New York,
Longmans Green [1953?] 387p. (AM595.7Sk1)

733a Stockley, Charles Hugh. African camera hunts. London, Country

Life, 1948. 182p. (AM960St6a)

733b Streeter, Daniel Willard Camels! New York, London, Putnam's
Sons, 1926. 277p. (AM799.2St8c)

733c Streeter, Daniel Willard. Denatured Africa. New York, London,
Putnam's Sons, 1926. 338p. (AM799.2St8)

733d Taylor, John. Pondoro: last of the ivory hunters. New York
Simon and Schuster, 1955. 354p. (AM799T21)

733e Tjader, Richard. The big game of Africa . . . with many illustrations from photographs by the author. New York and London,
D. Appleton and Co., 1910. 363p. (M960T54)

ART

734 Abbott, Nabia. The monasteries of the Fayyum. Chicago, University of Chicago Press, 1937. 66p. (AM913.32Ab2)

735 Adam, Leonard. Primitive art. New York, Allen, Penguin Books,
1949. 158p.

736. Aldred, Cyril. Middle Kingdom art in ancient Egypt, 2300-1590
B. C. London, A. Tiranti, 1950. 56p. (AM709.32A12m)

737 Aldred, Cyril. Old Kingdom art in ancient Egypt. London, A.
Tiranti, 1949. 40p. (AM932AL20)

738 L'art Nègre. Paris, Seuil, 1951. 254p. (AM700Ar7)

739 Artes Africanae. Publication de la Commission pour la Protection
des Arts et Metiers Indigenes. Bruxelles, Imprimerie Typ'art,
1936-37. (various pagings).

740 Baltimore Museum of Art. An exhibition of African art. Baltimore,
1946. 44p.

741 Baumann, Herman. Völkerkunde von Afrika, by H. Baumann,
Richard Thuenwald, and Diedrich Westermann. Essener, Verlagsanstalt, 1940. 665p. (AM572B32)

742 Benoit, Fernand. . . . L'Afrique méditerranéene; Algérie-Tunisie-
Maroc. Paris, Lex Beaux-arts, édition d'études et de documents, 1931. 106p. (AM709B44)

743 Bernatzik, Hugo Adolf. Zwischen weissen nil und Belgisch-Kongo.
Wien, L. W. Seidel & Sohn, 1929. 138p. 204 plates.

744 Bleek, Dorothea. Cave artists of South Africa, 48 unpublished
reproductions of rock paintings collected by the late Dorothea
Bleek. Cape Town, A. A. Balkema, 1953. 80p. (AM750B61)

745 Blondian-Theatre Arts Collection of Primitive African Art. New
York, The Art Circle, 1927. 30p.

746. Boas, Franz. . . . Primitive art. Oslo, H. Aschehoug & Co.;

Cambridge, Mass., Harvard University Press, 1927. 376p.
(M572B63p)

747 Bouche, Pierre Bertrand. Les noirs peints par eux-mêmes. Paris,
Librairie Poussielgue Freres, 1883. 144p. (AM398.9B66n)

748 British Museum. Dept. of British and mediaeval antiquities and
ethnography. Antiquities from the city of Benin and from
other parts of West Africa in the British museum. London,
British museum, sold by Longsman & Co., 1899. 61p. (M913.-
6B77)

749 British Museum. Handbook to the ethnographical collections, with
15 plates. 275 illustrations and 3 maps. Oxford University
Press, 1910. 304p.

750 Bronzes and Ivories from the Old Kingdom of Benin. Exhibitions
from Nov. 25 to Dec. 14, 1935 at the Galleries of M. Knoedler
and Co., 1935. 36p.

751 Brooklyn Museum. Department of Ethnology. (Catalog of)
Primtive Negro art chiefly from the Belgian Congo with illus-
strations and notes by Stewart Culin. Brooklyn Museum, 1923.
(M700B79)

752 Buraud, Georges. Les masques; essai. Paris, Éditions du Seuil,
1948. 238p. (AM371.75B89)

753 Burkitt, Miles Crawford. Our forerunners; a study of Palaelithic
(!) man's civilizations in western Europe and the Mediterranean basin. New York, H. Holt and Company, 1924. 256p.
(M571B82)

754 Burkitt, Miles Crawford. South Africa's past in stone and paint.
Cambridge, England, The University Press, 1928. 183p.
(AM572.68B91)

755 Capart, J. Lectures on Egyptian art. Chapel Hill, University of
North Carolina Press, 1928. 290p. (AM700C17)

756 Christensen, Erwin Ottomar. Primitive art. New York, Crowell,
1955. 384p. (M709C46)

757 Christol, Frédéric. . . . L'art dans l'Afrique australe; impressions
et souvenirs de mission, avec 220 dessins de l'auteur, dont 12
planches en couleur, 1 planche en noir et 207 illustrations dans
le texte. Paris, Berger-Levrault, 1911. 144p. (M700C46)

758 Clouzot, Henri. Sculptures Africaines et Océaniennes; colonies
françaises et Congo Belge. Paris, Librairie de France, 1920.
24p. (AM730C62)

759 Collections of André Breton and Paul Eluard. Sculptures d'Afri-

que, d'Amérique, d'Oceanie.   Paris, Exposition, Chez M. Rat-
ton, 1931.   50p.   23 plates.

760   Collection of G. de Miré. Sculptures anciennes d'Afrique et d'Amérique.   Paris, 1931.   28p.   16 plates.

761   Cory, Hans.   Wall-paintings by snake charmers in Tanganyika.
London, Faber & Faber, 1953.   99p.   (AM750C81)

762   Craig, Barbara June. . . . Rock paintings and petroglyphs of South
and Central Africa.   Bibliography of prehistoric art.   Cape
Town, University of Cape Town, School of librarianship, 1947.
v. 58p.   (mimeographed)   (AM01C84r)

763   Daye, Pierre, Crockaert, Jacques, and others.   Le miroir du Congo
Belge.   Bruxelles, Aux Editions N.E.A., 1929.   284p.

764   Decorations Egyptienne.   Paris, Ernst Henri, ed., (n.d.) 36 col.
plates.   (M932D35)

765   De Young Memorial Museum, San Francisco.   African Negro sculpture by Paul S. Wingert.   A loan exhibition.   Sept. 24-Nov. 19,
1948.   San Francisco, 1948.   26p.   (AM730.96 D53a)

766   Diop, Cheikh Anta.   Nations Nègres et culture.   Paris, Éditions
Africaines, 1955.   390p.   (M960D62n)

767   Dronsfield, John.   Non-Europeans only, thirty-six drawings.   Cape
Town, Cape Times for Denis Bullough, 1942.   36 drawings.

768   Edwards, Amelia Ann Blandford.   Pharaohs, fellahs and explorers.
New York, Harper & brothers, 1891.   325p.   (M962 Ed9)

769   Einstein, Carl.   Afrikanische plastik.   Berlin, Ernst Wasmuth.
(n.d.)   32p.   48 plates.

770   Einstein, Carl. Negerplastik.   Munchen, Kurt Wolff, 1920.   27p.
108 plates.

771   Exposition bronzes et ivoires du Benin au Musée d'etnnographie
Palais du Trocadero.   Cahiers d'art.   Numéro special.   Paris,
1932.

772   Fagg, William.   The Webster Plass collection of African art.   The
catalogue of a memorial exhibition held in the King Edward VII
Galleries of the British Museum 1953.   London, The Trustees
of the British Museum, 1953.   45p.   (AM700 F13)

773   Fechheimer, Hedwig.   Kleinplastik der Agypter.   Berlin, Bruno
Cassirer Verlag, 1921.   40p.   158 plates.

774   Fleming, Daniel Johnson.   Each with his own brush; contemporary
Christian art in Asia and Africa.   New York, Friendship Press,
1938.   85p.   (AM755 F62)

775 Francis, René. Egyptian aesthetics. Chicago, Open court publishing company, 1912. 276p. (M916.2 F84)

776 Frobenus, Leo. Die Atlantische Götterlebre. Jena. Verlegt bei Eugen Diederichs, 1926. 318p. (M966.92 F92)

777 Frobenius, Leo. Dokumente zur Kulturphysiognomik von Kulturreich des Festlandes. Berlin, Volksverband der Bucherfreunde, 1923. 344p.

778 Frobenius, Leo. Hádschra máktuba urzeitliche felsbilder Klein-Afrikas. München, K. Wolff, 1925. 160p. (M913.3 F92)

779 Frobenius, Leo. Der Kopfals schicksal. München, Kurt Wolff Verlag, 1924. 185p. (AM573.7 F92)

780 Frobenius, Leo. Kulturgeschichte Afrikas; prolegomena zu einer historischen gestaltlehre. Zurich, Erschienen in Phaidon, 1922. 652p. (AM916 F921k)

781 Frobenius, Leo. Prehistoric rock pictures in Europe and Africa, from material in the archives of the Research Institute for the Morphology of Civilization. New York, Museum of Modern Art, 1937. 79p. AM709 F92p)

782 Frobenius, Leo. Das unbekannte Afrika, Aufhellung der Schicksale eines Erdteils. München, Beck, 1923. 184p. (M960 F92u)

783 Fuhrmann, Ernst. Afrika, sakralkulte Vorgeschichte der hieroglyphen. Folkwang Verlag G.M.G.H. Hagen i. W. und Darmstadt, 1922. 59p. 121 plates.

784 Gordon-Brown, Alfred. Pictorial art in South Africa during three centuries to 1875. With notes on over 400 artists and 59 plates. London, C. J. Sawyer, 1952. 172p. (AM709 G65)

785 Griaule, Marcel. Arts de l'Afrique noire. Paris, Des Editions du Chêne, 1947. 126p. (AM700 G87a)

786 Griaule, Marcel. Folk art of black Africa. Paris, Editions du Chêne New York, Tudor Publishing Co., 1950. 126p. (AM709.-6 G87f)

787 Guillaume, Paul and Monro, T. Primitive Negro sculpture. New York, Harcourt, Brace and Co., 1926. 134p. (M730 G93)

788 Guillaume, Paul. La sculpture Nègre primitive. France, Cres et Cie. 1929. 43p. (AM730 G931)

789 Hambly, Wilfrid Dyson. Clever hands of the African Negro. Washington, D.C. The Associated Publishers, 1945. 192p. (AM700 H17)

790 Hardy, George. L'art Nègre, l'art animiste des noirs d'Afrique. Paris, Henri Laurens, 1927. 168p. (AM700 H21)

791 Harley, George W. Masks as agents of social control in Northeast Liberia. Cambridge, Mass., Published by the Museum, 1950. 44p. (AM572.966 H22)

792 Hausenstein, Wilhelm. Barbaren and klassiker. Munchen, R. Piper and Co., 1922. 101p. (AM709 H29)

793 Herskovits, Melville J. The backgrounds of African art. Denver, Denver Art Museum, 1945. 63p. (AM700 H43)

794 Himmelheber, Hans. Negerkünstler. Stuttgart, Strecker und Schröder, 1935. 80p. (AM572 H57)

795 Honey, James Albert. South African folk-tales. New York, The Baher and Taylor Co., 1910. 151p. (AM398 H75)

796 Hooper, James T. The art of primitive peoples, by J. T. Hooper and C. A. Burland. With 116 photos of specimens from the Hooper collection. New York, Philosophical Library, 1954. 168p.

797 Howard University Gallery of Art. Exhibition of African Negro art, assembled by James V. Herring, May 6-May 31, 1953. Washington, D.C., 1953. 20p. (AM700 H83)

798 Iakovlev, Aleksandr E. Dessins et peintures d'Afrique. Paris, Jules Meynial, 1927.

799 Impey, Samuel Patton. Origin of the bushmen and the rock paintings of South Africa. Cape Town and Johannesburg, Juta & co., ltd., 1926. 102p. (AM700 Im7)

800 Jahrbuch des Stadtischen Museums fur Völkerkunde zu Leipzig. Leipzig, R. Voigtlander, 1911-12. 174p. v.5 1912.

801 Kjersmeier, Carl. Afrikanske negerskulturer. New York, Wittenborn, Schultz, 1948. 86p. (AM730 K65)

802 Kjersmeier, Carl. Centres de style de la sculpture négre Africaine. Paris, A. Morance, 1935. (AM730 K65)

803 Kochnitzky, Leon. Negro art in Belgian Congo. New York, Belgian Government Center, 1952. 83p. (AM700 K81n)

804 Langlois, Pierre. Art Soudanais, tribus dogons; texte et notices de Pierre Langlois. Bruxelles, Editions de la Connaissance, 1954. 62p. (AM736 L26)

805 Lips, Julius E. The savage hits back. New Haven, Yale University Press, 1937. 254p. (AM573 L66)

806 Maes, Joseph. L'art nègre à l'exposition du Palais des beaux-arts du 15 novembre au 31 décembre 1930. Bruxelles-Paris, Librairie Nationale d'art et d'histoire, 1930. 31p. (AM709.6 M26)

807 Maes, Joseph. Aniota-Kifwebe. Les masques des populations du Congo Belge et le materiel des rites de circoncision. Antwerp, Editions de Sikkel, 1924. 63p. (M967.5 M26a)

808 Maes, Joseph. Guide ethnographique, du Musée du Congo Belge. Premiere Partie-L'Alimentation Indigene. Bruxelles, Goemaere, Imprimeur du Roi, 1921. 72p.

809 Marquart, Joseph. Die benin-Sammlung des reichsumseums fur völkerkunde in Leiden. Leiden, Buchhandlung und Druckerai, 1913. 129p. (AM572 M34b)

810 Meier-Graefe, Julius, Pyramid and temple. New York, The Macaulay company, 1930. 361p. (M916.2 M47)

811 Miers, Henry Alexander. A report on the museums and art galleries of British Africa. Edinburgh, T. and A. Constable, ltd., 1932. 90p. (AMO69 M65)

812 Minotuare. Revue artistique et litteraire. Mission Dakar-Djibouti, 1931-33. Paris, Albert Skira, 1933. 88p. (AM700 M66)

813 Moszeik, Otto. Die Malereien de Buschmänner in Südafrika. Berlin Dietrich Reimer, 1910. 100p. (AM700 M85)

814 Murray, K. C. Our art treasures. Lagos, Nigeria, Published by the Public Relations Department (n.d.) 16p. (AM700 M96)

815 Musée du Congo Belge (Tervueren). Notes analytiques sur les collections du Musée du Congo. Vol. 1, no. 1: Les instruments de Musique; no. 2, La réligion. Vol. II, no. 1: La céramique. Annales du Musée du Congo Belge, 1902; 1906.

816 Museum für Völkerkunde. Fuhrer durch das Museum für Völkerkunde, zu Leipzig. Leipzig. Im Gelbstverlage des Museum für Völkerkunde, 1922. 155p.

817 New York Museum of Modern Art. African Negro art. New York, The Museum of Modern Art, 1945. 58p. (AM700 N42)

818 Nuoffer, Oskar. Afrikanische plastik. Dresden, Carl Reissner, 1926. 80p. 45 plates.

819 Pechuel-Loesche, E. Volkskunde von Loango. Stuttgart, verflag von Strecker and Schroder, 1907. 482p. (AM967.25 P33)

820 Periér, Gaston Denys. Les arts populaires du Congo Belge. Bruxelles, Office de Publicite, J. Lebegue & cie., editeurs, 1948. 77p. (AM967.5 P41a)

821 Periér, Gaston Denys. Le blanc et le noir, curiosités congolaises. Anvers, Éditions de l'Essor Colonial. 45p.

822 Perier, Gaston Denys. Nêgreries et curiosités congolaises. Illustrations d'après des croquis de Dulonge, des aquarelles de

peintre bakongo Lubaki et des photographies. Bruxelles, L'Eglantine, 1930. 122p. (M967.2 P41n)

823   Perrot, Georges. A history of art in ancient Egypt, from the French of Georges Perrot and Charles Chipiez. Illustrated with five hundred and ninety-eight engravings in the text, and fourteen steel and coloured plates. London, Chapman and Hall, limited, 1883. 2 vols. (AM709 P43)

824   Perry, Walter Scott. Egypt, the land of the temple builders. One hundred and twenty-seven illustrations. Boston, New York, The Prang educational company, 1898. 249p. (AM962 P42)

825   Petrie, William Matthew Flinders. Egyptian decorative art. New York, Putnam's Sons, 1895. 128p. (AM700 P44)

826   Playne, Beatrice. St. George for Ethiopia. London, Constable, 1954. 200p. (AM726.5 P69)

827   Porter, James Amos. The appreciation of African Negro art. Howard University, Washington, D.C., Gallery of Art, 1953. (AM-700 H83)

828   Portier, André. Les arts sauvages: Afrique. Paris, Editions Albert Morancé, 1930. 14p. (AM700P83)

829   Rasmussen, Rene. Art Negre. Presses du Livre Français, 1951. 23p. (AM730 R18a)

830   Ratzel, Friedrich. Die naturvölker Afrikas. Leipzig, Bibliographischen, 1887. 660p. (AM960 R18n)

831   Rivers, Pitt. Antique works of art from Benin. London, Harrison and Sons, 1900. 100p. (AM913.3 R52)

832   Ross, Sir Edward Denison. The art of Egypt through the ages. London, The Studio, ltd., 1931. 354p. (AM913.32 R73)

833   Roth, Henry Ling. Great Benin; its customs, art and horrors. Halifax, Eng., F. King & Sons, ltd., 1903. 234p. (M966.93 R74)

834   Sadler, Michael E. Arts of West Africa (excluding music). London, Oxford University Press, 1935. 101p. (AM700 Sal)

835   Schmalenbach, Werner. L'art Nègre. Paris, Charles Massin, 1953. 175p. (AM730 Sch4)

836   Sculptures d'Afrique d'Amérique et d'Oceanie. Vente a l'Hotel Drouot. May 7, 1931. Paris, 1931. 30p. 8 plates.

837   Segy, Ladislas. African sculpture speaks. New York, A. A. Wyn, 1952. 254p. (AM730 Sc3a)

838   Smith, Helen Ainslie. The great cities of the ancient world. New York, G. Routledge and sons, 1885. 256p. pp. 371-77.

839 Smith, William Stevenson. A history of Egyptian sculpture and painting in the Old Kingdom. London, Oxford University Press, 1949. 422p. (AM732 Sm5)

840 Spain. Consejo Superior de Investigaciones Cientificas. Instituto de Estudios Africanos. Exposicion de pintores de Africa. Madrid, 1951. 3 v. (AM750 Sp1)

841 Stedelijk Museum Amsterdam Tentoonstelling van oude Negerplastieken. Collectie Kunstzaal van Lier Laren, N. H., Jan., 1927. 22p.

842 Sweeney, James Johnson. African Negro art. New York, The Museum of Modern Art, 1935. (AM709.68 N48)

843 Sydow, Eckart von. Exotische Kunst, Afrika und Ozeanien. Leipzig, Verlag von Klinkhardt & Biermann, 1921. 38p.

844 Sydow, Eckart von. Handbuch der Westafricanischen plastik. Berlin, Reimer, 1930. (AM730 Sy2)

845 Sydow, Eckart von. Kunst der naturvölker Afkira, ozeanien, Indonesien. Berlin, Verlag Bruno Cassirer, 1932. 215p. (AM730-Sy2k)

847 Tongue, M. Helen. Bushman paintings. Oxford, Clarendon press, 1909. 47p. (AM700 T61)

848 Traditional sculpture from the colonies. London, H.M. Stationery Office, 1951. 38p. (AM730 T67)

849 Trowell, Margaret. Classical African sculpture. London, Faber and Faber, 1954. 103p. (AM732 T75)

850 Trowell, Margaret. Tribal crafts of Uganda, by Margaret Trowell and K. P. Wachsmann, with a foreword by H. J. Braunholtz. London, Oxford University Press, 1953. 422p. (M967.61T75t)

851 Ucell, Jeanne d'. . . . Berber art; an introduction. Norman, University of Oklahoma press, 1932. 227p. (M709 Uc3)

852 Underwood, Leon. Figures in wood of West Africa. London, J. Tiranti, 1947. (AM731 Un2)

853 Université de Paris. Les Bas-reliefs de batiments royaux d'Abomey (Dahomey). Paris, Institute d'Ethnologie, 1926. 10p. (AM-709.668Un3)

854 Utzinger, Rudolf, Masken. Berlin, Ernest Wasmuth, (n.d.) 26p. 48 plates.

855 Vail, Memorial Library. The Lincoln University, Chester County, Pennsylvania. The Susan Reynolds Underhill African Collection. Chester County, Pa., Vail Memorial Library, Lincoln University, (n.d.) 16p. (AM708.96 V19)

856 Wieschhoff, Heinrich Albert. Africa. Philadelphia, Published for
the University Museum by the University of Pennsylvania
press, 1945. 76p. (AM709 W43a)

857 Wingert, Paul Stover. The sculpture of Negro Africa. New York,
Columbia University Press, 1950. 96p. (AM730 W72s)

MUSIC AND DANCE

858 Carrington, John F. Talking drums of Africa. London, Carey
Kingsgate Press, 1949. 96p. (AM789.1C23t)

859 Chauvet, Stéphen. Musique négre. Paris, Société d'Éditions Geog-
graphiques, Maritimes et Coloniales, 1929. 242p. (AM780-
C39m)

860 Danseurs du Ruanda. Dix planches en couleurs par Marthe Molitor. Préface de Gaston-Denys Périer. Commentaires par Albert Gille. Éditions des Artistes [1957]

861 Forney, Evelyna. African dances. Cincinnati, The Author, 1948.
14p. (AM793F76a)

862 Gorer, Geoffrey. Africa dances; a book about West African Negroes. London, Faber and Faber, 1935. 363p. (M916G66)

863 Gorer, Geoffrey. Africa dances; a book about West African Negroes. London, J. Lehmann, 1949. 254p. (M916G661949)

864 Hambly, Wilfrid Dyson. Tribal dancing and social development,
by W. D. Hambly ... with a preface by Charles Hose ... photographs, sketches and a map. London, H. F. & G. Witherby,
1926. 296p. (AM572H17t)

865 Jones, A. M. African music. Livingstone, Northern Rhodesia, The
Rhodes-Livingstone Institute, 1943. 33p. (AM781J71a)

866 Kirby, Percival Robson. The musical instruments of the native
races of South Africa. London, Oxford university press, H.
Milford, 1934. 285p. (AM781.91K63)

867 Kyagambiddwa, Joseph. African music from the source of the Nile.
New York, Praeger, 1955. 255p. (M967.61K98)

868 Mseleku, William J. Zulu solfa music. Dunban, Natal, The Orient
Music Saloon. Printed at Mariannhill Mission Press, 1936.
31p. (M784M87z)

869 Ogumefu, Ebun. Yoruba melodies. London, Society for Promoting Christian Knowledge, [1929.] 16p. (M784Og9y)

870 Patterson, John Robert. Kanuri songs. Lagos, Printed by the
Government Printer, 1926. 31p. (AM784P27)

871 Schaeffner, André. Les Kissi; un société noire et ses instruments
    de musique. Paris, Hermann, 1951. 85p. (AM780Sclk)

872 Tracey, Hugh. Chopi musicians, their music, poetry and instru-
    ments. New York, International African Institute, 1948. 180p.
    (AM780T67c)

873 Tracey, Hugh. "Lalela Zulu;" 100 Zulu lyrics. Johannesburg,
    African Music Society, n.d. 121p. (AM784T67a)

874 Tremearne, Arthur J. N. The ban of the bore; demons and demon-
    dancing in West and North Africa. London, Heath, Cran-
    ton and Ouseley, 1914. 504p. (AM796.13T72b)

875 Tucker, Archibald Norman. Children's games and songs in the
    Southern Sudan. London, Royal Anthropological Institute of
    Great Britain and Ireland. n.d. pp. 165-187. (Reprinted from
    the Journal of the Royal Anthropological Institute, vol. 63, Jan.-
    June, 1933) (AM796.13T79)

876 Tucker, Archibald Norman. Tribal music and dancing in the
    Southern Sudan (Africa), at social and ceremonial of the
    music, rhythm, etc., from personal observation. London, Wil-
    liam Reeves, 1933. 57p. (AM781.71T79)

877 Varley, Douglas Harold. African native music, an annotated
    bibliography, compiled by Douglas H. Varley . . . London,
    The Royal empire society, 1936. 116p. (AM01V42a)

LITERATURE

Collections, History and Criticism

878 Bennie, William Govan. Imbengo ["Titbits"] an anthology of
    Xhosa prose and poetry. Lovedale Press, 1949. 276p. (M-
    896.8B43i)

879 Duprey, Pierre. Le coupeur de bois; recits africains. Preface de
    Georges Pillement. Paris, Nouvelles Éditions Latines, 1946.
    251p. (M843.9D92c)

880 Franz, G. H. The literature of Lesotho (Basutoland) Johannes-
    burg. The University of Witwatersrand Press, 1930. 38p.
    (M968.61F851)

881 Jabavu, Davidson Don Tengo. Bantu literature, classification and
    review. [n.d.] South Africa, P. O. Lovedale, 1921. 27p.
    (AM469.3511)

882 Jabavu, Davidson Don Tengo. The influence of English on Bantu
    literature. Lovedale, Lovedale Press 1943. 26p. (M968J11i)

883 Kagame, Alexis. La poésie dynastique au Rwanda. Bruxelles, In-

stitut Royal Colonial Belge, 1951. 240p. (M967.5K10p)

884 Lebel, Roland. L'Afrique Occidentale dans la littérature Français
depuis, 1870. 277p. (M966.1L49)

885 Lebel, Roland. Etudes de littérature coloniale. Paris, J. Peyronnet
et cie, 1928. 221p.

886 Lebel, Roland. Historie de la littérature coloniale en France.
Librairie Larose, 1931. 236p. (M840L11)

887 Lebel, Roland. Le livre du pays noir (anthologie de littérature
Africaine.) Paris, Les Éditions du Monde Moderne, 1928.
248p. (M896.08L49)

888 Leslau, Wolf. Falasha anthology, translated from Ethiopic
sources. New Haven, Yale University Press, 1951. 222p.
(M896.8L56f)

889 Présence Africaine. Le 1er Congrès International des Écrivains
et Artistes Noirs. Paris, Sorbonne, 1956. 408p.

890 Présence Africaine. Le monde noir. Paris, Présence Africaine,
1950. 443p. (M960P92 No. 8-9)

891 Robinson, Charles Henry. Specimens of Hausa literature. Cambridge [Eng.] University Press, 1896. 112p. (AM493.5R56)

892 Sehoza, Samuel. St. Augustine, translated from the Swahili. London, Society for Promoting Christian Knowledge, [1927] 47p.
(M896Se4s)

893 Shepherd, Robert Henry Wishart. Bantu literature and life. Lovedale, The Lovedale Press, 1955. 198p. (M496Sh4)

894 Shepherd, Robert Henry Wishart. Literature for the South African
Bantu. A comparative study of Negro achievement. Pretoria,
S. Africa, The Carnegie Corporation, 1936. 81p. (M968Sh4)

895 Shepherd, Robert Henry Wishart. Lovedale and literature for
the Bantu; a brief history and a forecast. [Lovedale] The
Lovedale Press, 1945. 11p. (M896Sh4)

896 Trautman, René. La littérature populaire à la côte des esclaves.
Contes, proverbs, devinettes. Paris, Institut D'Ethnologie,
1927. 105p. (AM398T69)

897 Trois ecrivains noirs. Paris, Présence Africaine [1955] 426p.
(M896.3T74)

POETRY

898 Abedi, K. Amri. Sheria za kutunga mashairi na diwani ya Amri.
[The poems of Amri with an essay on Swahili poetry and the

rules of versification] Kampala, The Eagle Press, 1954. 148p.
(M967.82Ab3)

899 Anang, Dei. Wayward lines from Africa, a collection of poems.
London, United Society for Christian Literature, 1946. 47p.
(AM896.1An1w)

900 Armattoe, Raphael Ernest Gail. Between the forest and the sea
[poems] London-berry, Lomshire Research, 1950. 78p. (AM-
896.1Ar5b)

901 Awoonor-Renner, Bankole. This Africa. Biographical note by
J. B. Danquah. London, Central Books, 1943. 72p. (M896.
1Aw6t)

902 Bereng, David Crammer Theko. Lithothokiso tsa moshoeshoe le
tse ling. Morija, Sesuto Book Depot, 1931. 114p. (M896.
1B451)

903 Bolamba, Antoine Roger. Esanzo; chants pour mom pays. Poèms.
Préface de Léopold Sédar Senghor. Paris, Présence Africaine, 1955. 42p. (M967.5B63e)

904 Darlow, D. J. African heroes—Ntsikana, Tshaka, Khama, Moshoeshoe; Poems. Lovedale, Lovedale Press, n.d. 75p. (M896.
1D24a)

905 Dhlomo, H. I. E. Valley of a thousand hills; a poem. Durban,
The Knox Publishing Co., 1941. 42p. (M896D53v)

906 Fodeba, Keita. Poems Africains. Paris, Pierre Seghers, 1950.
47p. (M966.52F68p)

907 Jankie, H. E. Lithoko tsa makoloane. Morija, Sesuto Book Depot,
1939. 42p. (M896.1J25)

908 Jolobe, James J. R. Lovedale Xhosa rhymes (IziCengcelezo zase-
Dikeni) Ezilungele la Mabanga: Sub A, Sub B, Std 1, Std 11.
Lovedale, The Lovedale Press, 1952. 44p. (M896J68L)

909 Jolobe, James J. R. Poems of an African. Lovedale, Lovedale
Press, 1946. 34p. (AM896.1J86p)

910 Jolobe, James J. R. Umyezo [Xhosa poems] okugabula izigcawu
enziwe ngu W. G. Bennie. Johannesburg, The University of
the Witwatersrand Press, 1944. 71p. (M896J68u)

911 Kagame, Alexis. La divine pastorale, traduction français, par
l'auteur, de la première Veillée d'une épopée écrite en langue
Ruandaise. Bruxelles, Editions du Marais, 1952. 108p.
(M967.5K10d)

912 Kagame, Alexis. La naissance de l'univers. Bruxelles, Editions
du Marais, 1955. 85p. (M967.5K10n)

913 Kagame, Alexis. La poésie dynastique au Rwanda. Bruxelles, Institut Royal Colonial Belge, 9151. 240p. (M967.5K10p)

914 Komai, Felicia. Cry, the beloved country, a verse drama; adapted from Alan Paton's novel. New York, Friendship Press, 1948. 79p. (M896.2K83)

915 Mangoaela, Zekea D. Lithoko tsa Marena a Basotho, tse bokeletsoeng ke Z. D. Mangoaela. Morija, Sesuto Book Depot, 1928. 246p. (M896M311)

916 Mqhayi, Samuel Edward Krune. Imihobe nemibongo, Yokufundwa ezikolweni. Yenziwe. London, The Sheldon Press, [1927.] 116p. (M896M87i)

917 Mqhayi, Samuel Edward Krune. I-nzuzo. Johannesburg, The University of Witwatersrand Press, 1942. 96p. (M896M87in)

918 Muraz, Gaston. Sous le grand soleil chez les primitifs images d'Afrique Equatoriale. France, Coulemmiers, 1923. 197p. (AM960M93s)

919 Muyaka bin Haji al-Ghassaniy. Diwani ya Muyaka bin Haji al-Ghassaniy; pamoja na khabari za maisha yake ambazo zimehadithiwa ni W. Hichens. Johannesburg, University of Witwatersrand Press, 1940. 115p. (M896.1M98d)

920 Ntsane, K. E. 'Musa-pelo. Morija, Sesuto Book Depot, 1946. 76p. (M896.1N88mu)

921 Osadebay, Dennis Chukude. Africa sings. Ilfrancombe, Arthur H. Stockwell, 1952. 104p. (M896.10s1)

922 Pienaar, E. C. Dichters uit Zuid-Afrika. Bloemlezing voor groot-Nederland. Pretoria, J. H. DuBussey, 1917. 126p. (M896.1D59d)

923 Senghor, Léopold Sédar. Anthologie de la nouvelle poesie nègre et malgache de langue française, par Léopold Sédar Senghor précedeé de Orphée noir, par Jean-Paul Sartre. (1 éd) Paris, Presses universitaires de France, 1948. 227p. (M896.1Se5a)

924 Senghor, Léopold Sédar. Chants d'ombre. Paris, Editions du Seuil, 1945. (M896.1Se5c)

925 Senghor, Léopold Sédar. Chants pour naett. Paris, Pierre Seghers, Editeur, 1949. 48p. (M896.1Se5ch)

926 Senghor, Léopold Sédar. Éthiopiques; poèms. Paris, Éditions du Seuil, 1956. 125p. (M896.1Se5e)

927 Senghor, Léopold Sédar. Hosties noires. Paris, Seuil [1948] 86p. (M896.1Sc5h)

928 Sinda, Marital. Premier chant du départ. Paris, Pierre Seghers, 1955. 60p. (M967.2Si6p)

929 Tshaka, R. M. Iintsika zentlambo ye-tyhume. Lovedale, Lovedale Press, 1953. 95p. (M896.1T78i)

930 Vilakazi, Benedict Wallet. Amal'ezulu. Johannesburg, The University of Witwatersrand Press, 1945. 46p. (M896V71a)

FICTION

931 Abrahams, Peter. Dark testament. London, G. Allen and Unwin, Ltd., 1942. 160p. (M896.3Ab8d)

932 Abrahams, Peter. Mine boy. New York, Knopf, 1955. 252p. (M896.3Ab8m)

933 Abrahams, Peter. Nork horisont. Oslo, Norsk Forlag, 1954. 323p. (MB9Ab83)

934 Abrahams, Peter. The path of thunder. New York and London, Harper and Bros., Co., 1948. 278p. (M896.3Ab8p)

935 Abrahams, Peter. Return to Goli. London, Faber and Faber, 1953. 224p. (M896.3Ab8r)

936 Abrahams, Peter. Sig det til de frie. Paa Dansk ved Jens Kruuse. Kbenhavn, Det Schnberhske forlag, 1956. 200p. (M896.3Ab8si)

937 Abrahams Peter. Song of the city. London, Published by Dorothy Crist and Co., Ltd., 1943. 179p. (M896.3Ab8s)

938 Abrahams, Peter. Wild conquest. New York, Harper, 1950. 309p. (M896.3Ab8w)

939 Abrahams, Peter. Wild conquest. London, Faber and Faber, 1951. 382p. (M896.3Ab8w)

940 Abrahams, Peter. Wilder Weg; ein roman (Wild conquest). Zurich, Im verlag der Arche, 1952. 332p. (M896.3Ab8wi)

941 Abrahams, Peter. A wreath for Udomo. New York, Knopf, 1956. 356p. (M896.3Ab8)

942 Adam, Paul Auguste Marie. La ville inconnue. Paris, P. Ollendorf, 1911. 446p. (M843.91Ad1)

943 The African slaves; a missionary tale. London, Haughton and Co., (ca. 1870) 58p. (AM896.Af8)

944 Anciaux, Leon. Ekondja; ou, lavie d'une tribu négre du centre de l'Afrique. Anvers, L. Bruyninex-De Block, n.d. 124p. (AM896A21e)

945 Armandy, André. La voie sans disque, roman. Paris, A. Lemerre, 1931. 241p. (M843.91Ar5)

946 Bancel, Marthe. La Faye sur le Niger, roman. Paris, Aux Editions de Belleslettres, 1923. 251p. (M843.91B22)

947 Baptist, R. Hernekin, (pseud.) A cargo of parrots. Boston, Little, Brown and Co., 1937. 181p. (AM896B22c)

948 Barnard, Winifred E. Kembo, A little girl of Africa. New York, Friendship Press, 1928. 60p. (AM896.3B25k)

949 Barnes, Annie Marie. Children of the Kalahari. A story of Africa. Philadelphia, Presbyterian board of publication and Sabbath school work, 1890. 352p. (AM896B26)

950 Barton, Elizabeth. Our little Ethiopian cousin. Boston, L. C. Page and Co., 1935. 134p. (AM896B640)

951 Bateman, George W. Zanzibar tales, told by natives of the East Coast of Africa. Chicago, A. C. McClurg and Co., 1901. 224p. (AM896B31)

952 Bertrand, Louis. Le sang des races. Paris, P. Ollendorf, 1920. 343p. (M896.3B46s)

953 Best, Allena (Champlin). Juma of the hills, a story of West Africa by Erick Berry (Pseud.) New York, Harcourt, 1932. 260p. (M896B46j)

954 Best, Allena (Champlin). Girls of Africa. New York, The Macmillan Co., 1928. 128p. (AM896B46g)

955 Best, Herbert. Tale of the Four Tribes. New York, Doubleday, Doran and Co., 1938. 295p. (M896B46)

956 Blackburn, Douglas. Leaven: a black and white story. London, Alston Rivers, Ltd., 1908. (M896.3B561)

957 Bloom, Harry. Episode in the Transvaal, a novel. Garden City, New York, Doubleday, 1955. 295p. (M896.3B62)

958 Booth, Esma (Rideout). Chama's choice. New York, Friendship Press, 1952. 136p. (AM896.3B64c)

959 Booth, Esma (Rideout). Nyanga's two villages. New York, Friendship Press, [1945.] 126p. (M896.3B64n)

960 Barton, Elizabeth. Our little Ethiopian cousin. Boston, L. C. Page and Co., [c1935.] 134p. (M896B64o)

961 Bosman, Herman Charles. Mafeking road. Johannesburg, Dassie books, 1949. 173p. (AM896.3B65m)

962 Boto, Eza. Ville cruelle. Paris, Editions Africaines, 1955. 219p. (M967.11B65v)

963 Breton, Claude. Bilali ou la vengeance du lion; roman soudanais. Paris, E. Fammarion, 1927. 248p. (M843.91B75)

964 Burman, Ben Lucien. Rooster crows for day. New York, Dutton and Co., 1945. 308p. (AM896.3B92r)

965 Canaday, John Edwin. The Congo Venus. New York, Simon and Schuster, 1950. 207p. (AM896H34c)

966 Cary, Joyce. The African witch. New York, W. Morrow and Co., 1936. 416p. (M896C25a)

967 Cary, Joyce. Mister Johnson. New York, Harpers, 1948. 261p. (AM896C25m)

968 Charbonneau, Louis. Mambu et son amour, roman. Paris, J. Ferenczi et fils, 1924. 261p. (M843.91C37m)

969 Chaumel, Alfred. Aminata, Femme noire. Paris, les presses Françaises, 1923. 123p. (M843.91C39)

970 Cleeve, Brian Talbor. The night winds. Boston, Houghton Mifflin, 1954. 244p. (AM896.3C58)

971 Cloete, Stuart. Congo song. Boston, Houghton Mifflin Co., 1943. 399p. (M813.5C62c)

972 Cloete, Stuart. The curve and the tusk; a novel of change among elephants and men. Boston, Houghton Mifflin, 1952. 272p. (M896.3C62c)

973 Cloete, Stuart. Mamba. Boston, Houghton, Mifflin, 1956. 232p. (M896.3C62)

974 Cloete, Stuart. The turning wheels. Boston, Houghton Mifflin co., 1937. 434p. (M813C62)

975 Cloete, Stuart. Watch for the dawn. Boston, Houghton Mifflin, 1939. 498p. (M813.5C62w)

976 Collodon, Augustus C. Congo Jake, the story of an adventurous life. With an introduction by Edwin C. Hill. New York, C. Kendall, 1933. 278p. (M960C69)

977 Courlander, Harold. The cow-tail switch, and other West African stories. New York, H. Holt and co., 1947. 143p. (AM896C83c)

978 Craig, Denys. Man in ebony, a novel. London, Victor Gollancz, 1950. 159p.

979 Dadié, Bernard B. Le pagne noir, contes africains. Paris, Présence africaine, 1955. 156p. (M966.68 D12p)

980 Daniel Roland. The Kenya tragedy. London, Wright and Brown, ltd., 1948. 223p. (AM896D22k)

981 Davidson, Basil. The rapids; a novel. London, Jonathan Cape, [1956] 288p. (M896.3D28r)

982 Davis, Norman. Picken's treasure hunt. New York, Oxford University Press, 1955. 64p. (M896D29p)

983 Davis, Robert. Pepperfoot of Thursday market. New York, Holiday House, 1941. 187p. (AM896D29)

984 Demaison, André. The new Noah's Ark. New York, Macmillan co., 1940. 294p. (AM896D39)

985 Demaison, André. Les oiseaux d'ébène, roman. Paris, Editions du Monde Moderne, 1925. 271p. (M843.91B390)

986 Demaison, André. La reine de l'ombre. Paris, Les éditions de France, 1925. 252p.

987 Dhlomo, Rolfes Robert Reginald. An African tragedy, Lovedale, Lovedale institution press, (n.d.) 40p. (M896 D531a)

988 Driberg, Jack Herbert. People of the small arrow. New York, Payson and Clarke, ltd., 1930. 338p. (AM896D83p)

989 Ebers, Georg Moritz. An Egyptian princess. New York, A. L. Burt, n.d., 518p. (M893.1Eb3e)

990 Ebers, Georg Moritz. Uarda; a romance of ancient Egypt. New York, A. L. Burt, 1901. 485p. (M893.1Eb3u)

991 Elliot, Geraldine. The hunter's cave; a book of stories based on African folk-tales. Cambridge, Robert Bentley, inc., 1953. 174p. (M896.3E15h)

992 Enright, Elizabeth. Kintu. New York, Farrar and Rinehart, inc., 1935. 54p. (AM896En7k)

993 Eschevannes, Carlos, Comte d'. La sirène des ravageurs, roman. Bois gravé par Auger-Stève. Paris, Marcelle Lesage, Editeur, 1928. 253p. (M896.3)

994 Fazakerley, George Raymond. Kongoni, a novel. London, Thames and Hudson, 1955. 239p. (M896.3F29)

995 Fula, Arthur Nuthall. Johannie giet die beeld. Johannesburg, Afrikaanse Pier Bockhandel, 1954. 162p. (M896.3F95j)

996 Futshane, Zora Z. T. 1-Jujuju. Lovedale, The Lovedale Press, 1943. 48p. (M896.3F98u)

997 Gatti, Attilio. Adventure in black and white. New York, C. Scribner's sons, 1943. 172p. (AM896G22)

998 Garnier, Christine. Fetish. New York, Putnam, 1952. 250p. AM896.3G18f)

999 Gilligan, Edmund. One lives to tell the tale. New York, J. Cape and H. Smith, 1931. 356p. (AM896G41)

1000 Gillon, Philip. Frail barrier. New York, Vanguard Press, 1952. 249p. (AM896.3G41f)

1001 Gordimer, Nadine. The lying days, a novel. New York, Simon and Schuster, 1953. 340p. AM896.3G651)

1002 Gordimer, Nadine. Six feet of the country, short stories. London, Gollancz, 1956. 223p. (M896.3G65s9)

1003 Gordimer, Nadine. The soft voice of the serpent. New York, Simon and Schuster, 1952. 244p. (AM896.3G65s)

1004 Gordon, Gerald. Let the day perish. London, Methuen, 1952. 263 p. (AM896.3G6531)

1005 Graham, Lorenz B. Tales of Momolu. New York, Reynal and Hitchcock, 1946. 169p. (AM896G76)

1006 Guary-César-Lainé, G. Les batards du soleil, (amours et pensées africaines) Paris, Edition de la Novelle égalité, 1922. (AM-896.3G93h)

1007 Guebhard, Paul Pierre. Mireille entre les négresses, roman, Paris, Les èditions du Monde Moderne, 1925. 220p. (M843.91G928m)

1008 Guillot, René. Contes et légendes d'Afrique noire. Paris, Societe d'Éditions Geographiques, Maritimes et Coloniales, 1946. 42p. (M896.3G94)

1009 Guma, Enoch S. U Nomalizo okanye izinto zalomhlaba ngamajing-iqiwu. London, Society for Promoting Christian Knowledge, 1927. 47p. (M896.3g95u)

1010 Guma, Enoch S. Nomalizo; or, "The things of this life are sheer vanity." London, The Sheldon Press, 1928. 64p. (M896.3095n)

1011 Gyford, C. Barrington. N'Gaga, king of the gorillas. London, I. Pitman, 1937. 251p. (AM896G95)

1012 Haggard, Sir Henry Rider. King Solomon's mines. London, Pan Books, 1951. 190p. (AM896.3H12k)

1013 Hahn, Emily. With naked foot. Indianapolis, The Bobbs-Merrill co., 1934. 302p.

1014 Hall, Leland. Salah and his American. New York, A. A. Knopf, 1933. 198p. (M916.4H14)

1015 Hambly, Wilfred Dyson. Jamba. Chicago, Pellegrini and Cudahay, 1947. 246p. (AM896H17j)

1016 Hanley, Gerald. Drinkers of darkness. New York, Macmillan co., 1955. 256p. (M896.3H19)

1017 Hastings, Archibald Charles Gardiner. Gone native. New York, The Macaulay co., 1929. 319p. (AM896H27)

1018 Hazoumé, Paul. Doguicimi. Paris, Larose, 1938. 510p. (M896.-3H33d)

1019 Hichens, Robert. The pyramid, a novel. Garden City, New York, The Sun Dial Press, 1936. 466p. (AM896H52)

1020 Hoüel, Drasta. Cruautés et tendresses, vieilles moeurs coloniales francaises. Paris, Payot, 1925. 25p. (M8435.91H81)

1021 Hulme, Kathryn. Desert night. New York, The Macaulay co., 1932. 251p. (AM896H98)

1022 Huxley, Elspeth. Red Strangers. New York and London, Harper and Bros., 1939. 405p. (AM896H98)

1023 Huxtable, Grace. African boy. London, Methuen, 1950. 254p. (AM896H983a)

1024 Jacobson, Dan. The trap, a novel. New York, Harcourt, Brace, [1955] 122p. (M896.3J15)

1025 Jacoby, Jean. Abimbolu. London, University of London Press, ltd., 1955. 112p. (M896.3J17)

1026 Jervis, Vera Murdock Stuart. The peach orchard. London, G. Bles, 1937. 313p. (AM896J48)

1027 Jones, Denys. Look not upon me, a novel. New York Criterion Books, 1954. 286p. (M896.3J711)

1028 Jordan, A. C. Ingqumbo yeminyanya. Lovedale, The Lovedale Press, 1946. 250p. (M896.3J76i)

1029 Joseph, Alfred Ward. Sondo, a Liberian boy. Chicago, A. Whitman and co., 1936. 32p. (AM896J77)

1030 Joseph, Gaston. Koffi, the romance of a Negro. London, John Bale, Sons and Danielson, 1923. 147p. (AM896.3J77k)

1031 Kalibala, Ernest Balintuma. Wakaima and the clay man. New York, Toronto, Longmans, Green and co., 1946. 145p. (AM896K12)

1032 Kalipa, the story of a Kafir boy by three missionaries. Westminister, the Society for the Propagation of the Gospel in Foreign Parts, 1916. 97p. (AM896.3K12)

1033 Karani, Palan. Heiden vor Afrika. Leipzig, Das Zelt, 1930. 69p.

1034 Kayombo, Innocent K. Stories of our Tanganyika forefathers. London, Sheldon Press, 1952. 29p. (M967.82K18s)

1035 Keable, R. The mother of all living. New York, E. P. Dutton and co., 1922. 359p. (AM896K19)

1036 Kelsey, Alice Geer. Tales from Africa. New York, Friendship Press, 1945. 80p. (AM896K29)

1037 Knittel, John. Dr. Ibrahim. New York, Frederick A. Stokes, co., 1935. 386p. (AM896K74d)

1038 Larsen, Jens Peter Mounitz. 10,000 tom-toms. Philadelphia, Muhlenberg Press, 1952. 268p. (AM896.3L32t)

1039 Laye, Camara. The dark child. New York, Noonday Press, 1954. 188p. (MB9L45d)

1040 Laye, Camara. L'enfant noir, roman. Paris, Plon, 1953. 256p. (M896.3L45e)

1041 Laye, Camara. The radiance of the King. London, Collins, 1956. 319p. (M96.3L45)

1042 Laye, Camara. le regard du roi. Paris, Librairie Plon, 1954. 254p. (M966.52)

1043 Le Quimener. Hommes d'Afrique; les batisseurs. Roman. Paris, SEGEP, 1952. 224p. (AM896.3L55h)

1044 Leigh, Michael. Cross of fire. London, W. Laurie, 1949. 224p. (AM896.3L53c)

1045 Léonard, Louis. La simple vie de Kamata Yé. Bruxelles, Les Editions de l'Expansion Belge, 1931. 160p. (M843.9155s)

1046 LoCascio, Alfred. Bloods of the equator. Boston, Meador Publishing co., 1939. 202p. (AM896L78)

1047 LoCascio, Alfred. The tom-toms speak. Boston, Meador Publishing co., 1940. 163p. (AM896L78t)

1048 Lomami-Tshibamba, Paul. Ngando (Le crocodile). Bruxelles, G. A. Deny, 1949. (M896.3L83n)

1049 Lorimer, Norma Octovia. By the waters of Carthage. New York, J. Pott and co., 1906. 368p. (AM916.11L81)

1050 MacOrlan, Pierre. Rues secretes. Paris, Librairie Gallimard, 1934. 252p. (M896.3M23r)

1051 Malonga, Jean. La légende de M'Pfoumou ma Mazono. Paris Editions Africaines, 1954. 153p. (M896.3M291)

1052 Mangoaela, Zekea D. Har'a libatana le linyamat'sane. Morija, Sesuto Book Depit, 1913. 205p.

1053. Manners-Sutton, Doris. Black god; a story of the Congo. London, Longman's, Green and co., 1934. 299p. (AM896.3M31)

1054 Maran, René. Afrique équatoriale française, terres et races d'avenir. Paris, Imprimerie de Vaugirard, 1937. 82p. (M843.9M32a)

1055 Maran, René. Bacouya, le cynocéphale, roman. Paris, A. Michel, 1953. 241p. (M843.9M32b)

1056 Maran, René. Batouala; véritable roman, nègre. Paris, A. Michel, 1921. 189p. (M843.9M32b)

1057 Maran, René. Batouala; véritable roman nègre. Edition definitive. Paris, Editions Albin Michel, 1938. 250p. (M843.9M32ba)

1058 Maran, René. Batouala. New York, Thomas Seltzer, 1922. 207p. (M843.9M32ba)

1059 Maran, René. Batouala. Paris Mornay, 1928. 169p.

1060 Maran, René. Batouala; a novel. New York, The Limited Editions Club, 1932. 117p.

1061 Maran, René. Betes de la brousse. Paris, A. Michel, 1941. 253p. (M843.9M32be)

1062 Maran René. La coeur serré; roman. Paris, A. Michel, 1931. 252p. (M843.9M32c)

1063 Maran, René. Deux amis, nouvelle inédité. In les Oeuvres libres. Paris, Fayard, 1931. pp. 85-128. (M843.9M32de)

1064 Maran, René. Djouma, chien de brousse, roman. Paris, A. Michel, Editeur, 1927. 253p. (M843.9M32dj)

1065 Maran, René. Dschuma; ein negerhund. Basel, Im Rhein-Verlag, n.d. 279p.

1066 Maran, René. Un homme pareil aux autres; roman. Paris Editions Arc-en-Ciel, 1947. 248p. (M843.9M32h)

1067 Maran, René. L'homme qui attend; roman inédit et complet. In: Les Oeuvres libres, v. 176. Paris, Fayard, 1936. pp. 37-130. (M843.9M32ho)

1068 Maran, René. Journal sans date. In: Les Oeuvres libres, v. 73. Paris, Fayard, 1927. pp. 104-236. (M843.9M32j)

1069 Maran, René. Le libre de la brousse; roman. Paris, A. Michel, Editeur, 1934. 287p. (M843.91M32Li)

1070 Maran, René. Mbala, l'elephant. Paris, Editions Arc-en-Ciel, 1943. 143p. (M843.9M32mb)

1071 Maran, René. Mbala; l'elephant. Paris, Editions Arc-en-Ciel, 1947. 186p. (M843.8M32m)

1072 Maran, René. Le petit roi de chimérie; conte. Paris, A. Michel, Editeur, 1924. 237p. (M843.9M32pc)

1073 Maran, René. Les pioniers de l'empire. Paris, A. Michel, 1943-46. 2 vols. (M843.9M32pi)

1074 Maran, René. Youmba, la mangouste. In: Les Oeuvres libres, v. 159. Paris, Fayard, 1934. pp. 5-48. (M843.9M32y)

1075 Marchman, Margaret R. Fentola, a little girl of Africa. Nashville, Tennessee, Broadman Press, 1950. 43p. (AM896.3M33f)

1076 Mayo, William Starbuck. The Berber; or the mountaineer of the Atlas. A tale of Morocco. New York, G. P. Putnam's sons, 1873. 442p. (M896M456)

1077 McGavran, G. W. Mpengo of the Congo. New York, Friendship Press, 1945. 127p. (AM896N98a)

1078 McKinley, Frances Burke. Death sails the Nile. Boston, Mass. The Stratford co., 1933. 222p. (AM896M21d)

1079 Mercer, Charles E. Rachel Cade. New York, Putnam, 1956. 320p. (M896.3M53)

1080 Mikhelson, Andre Lwoff. Kings and knaves in the Cameroons. London, Putnam, 1938. 335p. (AM896M58)

1081 Millin, Sarah Gertrude Liebson. Adam's rest. New York, H. Liveright, 1930. 315p. (AM896M62a)

1082 Millin, Sarah Gertrude. An artist in the family. New York, Boni and Liveright, 1928. 281p. (M813.5M62a)

1083 Millin, Sarah Gertrude. The burning man, a novel. New York, Putnam, [1952]. 310p. (M813.5M62d)

1084 Millin, Sarah Gertrude. The coming of the Lord. New York, H. Liveright, [1928]. 284p. (M813.5M62c)

1085 Millin, Sarah Gertrude. The dark gods, a novel. New York and London, Harper & brothers, [c1941]. 296p. (M813.5M62d)

1086 Millin, Sarah Gertrude. God's stepchildren. New York, Boni and Liveright [c1924]. 319p. (M813.5M62g)

1087 Millin, Sarah Gertrude. King of the Bastards, a novel. New York, Harper, [1949]. 304p. (M813.5M62k)

1088 Mofolo, Thomas. Chaka. Morija, Sesuto Book Depot, 1925. 288p. (Written in Sotho) (M896.3M72)

1089 Mofolo, Thomas. Chaka der Zulu: roman. Zurich, Manesse verlag, 1953. 268p. (M896.3M72c3)

1090 Mofolo, Thomas. Chaka, an historical romance. London, Published for the International Institute of African languages and cultures by Oxford University Press, H. Milford, 1931. 19p. (M896.3M72)

1091 Monfried, Henry de. Evasion sur mer. Paris, Editions Bernard Grasset. n.d. 102p. (AM896M74)

1092 Monmarson, Raoul. Iroko, Samba and cie., roman de la Cote d'Ivoire. Paris, Baudiniere, 1930. 254p. (M896.3M75i)

1093 Moorish literature; comprising romantic ballads. New York, The
Colonial Press, 1901. 281p. (M893.3M78)

1094 Moosdorf, Johanna. Flight to Africa. New York, Harcourt, Brace,
1954. 256p. (M833.91 M78)

1095 Mopeli-Paulus, Attwell Sidwell. Blanket boy, by Peter Lanham
(pseud.) and A. S. Mopeli-Paulus. New York, Crowell, 1953.
309p. (M896.3 M79b)

1096 Mopeli-Paulus, Attwell Sidwell. Blanket boys' moon, by Peter Lanham (pseud.) and A. S. Mopeli-Paulus. London, Collins, 1953.
320p. (M896.3 M79bl)

1097 Mopeli-Paulus, Attwell Sidwell. Blut hat nur eine farbe, roman
(Blanket boy's moon) by Peter Lanham, nach einem Tatsachen-
bericht von A. S. Moepli-Paulus. Munchen, R. Piper, 1953.
398p. (M896.3 M79blu)

1098 Mopeli-Paulus, Attwell Sidwell. Turn to the dark. London, Jonathan Cape, 1956. 287p. (M896.3M79)

1099 Motsatse, Ratsebe L. Khopotso ea bongaana. Morija, Sesuto Book
Depot, 1938. 11p. (M896.3M858)

1100 Mphalele, Ezekial L. Man must live and other stories. Cape Town,
The African Bookman, 1946. 46p. (M896.3M87m)

1101 Mqhayi, Samuel Edward Krune. Ityala lama-Wele. Ngama swem-
bezwembe akwa Gxuluwe. Lovedale, Uschicilelo Lwesi-tandatu,
1914. 136p. (M896 M87it 1914)

1102 Mqhayi, Samuel Edward Krune. Ityala lama-wele. NgamaZwembezwembe akwagxuluwe. Lovedale, The Lovedale press, 1931.
167p. (M896 M87it 1931)

1103 Nyabongo, Akiki K. Africa answers back. London, George Routledge and sons, 1936. 277p. (AM896N98a)

1104 Nyabongo, Akiki K. Lebensgeschichte einés negerhäupglings. Leipzig, Paul List verlag, 1937. 278p. (AM896N981)

1105 Nyabongo, Akiki K. The story of an African chief. New York, C.
Scribner's sons, 1935. 312p. (M896N98)

1106 Oyono, Ferinand. Une vie de boy; roman. Paris, Rene Julliard,
1956. 183p. (M896.30y6)

1107 Paton, Alan. Cry, the beloved country. New York, Scribner's sons,
1948. 278p. (M896.3P27c)

1108 Paton, Alan. For sent; Oversatt av Nils Lie. Oslo, Gyldendal
Norsk Forlag, 1953. 253p. (M896.3P27ti)

1109 Paton, Alan. Itke rakastettu maa. Romaani. Helsinki, Kustannusosakeyhtio Tammi, 1952. 280p. (M896.3P27cl)

1110 Paton, Alan. Liian myohaan vesipaaky. Suomentanut Jouko Lin-
turi. Helsinki, Kutannusosakeyhtio Tammi, 1954. 286p.
(M896.3P27t2)

1111 Paton, Alan. Too late the phalarope. New York, Scribner, 1953.
276p. (M986.3P27t)

1112 Percy, Douglas Cecil. Hidden valley. Grand Rapids, Zondervan
Publishing House, 1951. 155p. (AM896P41h)

1113 Pilotaz, Paul. Man alone. London, Longmans, Green and Co.,
1952. 149p. (AM896.3P64m)

1114 Prévaudeau, [Marie-Madeleine.] Narhi, femme de blanc; roman
de moeurs dahoméennes. Bruxelles, La Renaissance du Livre,
1928. 213p. (M896.3P92n)

1115 Rattray, R. S. The leopard priestess. New York, Appleton-Century Co., 1935. 223p. (AM896R18)

1116 Régnier, Marie Louise Antoinette (de Heredia). Esclave amoureuse,
by Gérard d'Houville. Paris, Artheme Fayard et cie., Editeurs, n.d. 157p. (M896.3R26e)

1117 Reid, Mayne. The bush-boys. Boston, Ticknor and Fields, 1856.
356p. (AM896R27)

1118 Reid, Mayne. The young yägers, or a narrative of hunting adventures in Southern Africa. New York, T. R. Knox, 1884.
328p. (AM896R27y)

1119 Rickert, Edith. The bojabi tree. Garden City. New York, Page
and Co., 1923. 47p. (AM896R42b)

1120 Rooke, Daphne. A grove of fever trees. Boston, Houghton Mifflin,
1950. 246p. (AM896.3R67g)

1121 Rooke, Daphne. Mittee. Boston, Houghton Mifflin, 1952. 312p.
(AM896R67m)

1122 Rooke, Daphne. Ratoons. Boston, Houghton Mifflin, 1953. 248p.
(AM896.3R67r)

1123 Ruark, Robert Chester. Something of value. Garden City, New
York, Doubleday, 1955. 566p. (M896.3R8es)

1124 Sachs, Wulf. Black anger. Boston, Little, Brown and Co., 1947.
324p. (AM896Sal)

1125 Schreiner, Olive. From man to man; or, Perhaps only. London,
T. F. Unwin, Ltd., [1926.] 483p. (M896.3Sch7)

1126 Schreiner, Olive. The story of an African farm. A novel. New
York, J. S. Ogilvie, n.d. 258p. (M813.5Sch7)

1127   Schreiner, Olive. The story of an African farm. Boston, Little, Brown, and Co., c1924. 375p. (M813.5Sch7)

1128   Scully, William C. Kafir stories. New York, Henry Holt and Co., 1895. 194p. (M896.3Sc4)

1129   Segal, Albert. Johannesburg Friday. New York, McGraw-Hill, 1954. 320p. (M896.3Se3)

1130   Sherwood, Mrs. The re-captured Negro. Boston, S. T. Armstrong, 1821. 72p. (AM896Sh5)

1131   Simpson, Alyse. Red dust of Africa. London, Cassell, 1952. 200p. (AM896.3Si5r)

1132   Simpson, Charles. A Yankee's adventures in South Africa. Chicago, Rhodes and McClure Publishing Co., 1905. 234p. (AM896Si5)

1133   Singer, Caroline. Boomba lives in Africa. New York, Holiday House, 1935. 64p. (AM896Si6)

1134   Smith, F. Cadwallader. Kongo, the elephant. New York, A. A. Knopf, 1939. 78p. (AM896Sm3)

1135   Socé, Ousame. Karim; roman Sénégalais. Paris, Imprimerie Marcel Puyfourcat, 1935. 125p. (M896.3 Solk)

1136   Southon, Arthur F. A yellow Napoleon. a romance of West Africa. New York, Fleming H. Revell Co., 1928. 253p. (AM896So8)

1137   Sowande, J. S. Awon Arofo-orin ti Sobo A-Ro-bi-Odun 1930. Ake, Abeokuta, 1931. 47p. (AM896.1So9a)

1138   St. John, John R. A trick of the sun. A tragicomedy. London, Heinemann, 1956. 234p. (M896.3Sa2)

1139   Stanley, Sir Henry Morton. My Kalulu, prince, king and slave; a story of Central Africa. New York, Scribner's Sons, 1889. 432p. (AM896.3St25k)

1140   Stevens, Alden Gifford. Lion boy. New York, Frederick A. Stokes Co., 1938. 233p. (AM896St41)

1141   Stevens, Alden Gifford. Lion boy's white brother. Philadelphia, Lippincott, 1951. 241p. (AM896St41i)

1142   Stinetorf, Louis A. White witch doctor. Philadelphia, Westminster Press, 1950. 276p. (AM896.3St5w)

1143   Stockley, Cynthia. Poppy; the story of a South African girl. New York, A. L. Burt, 1912. 452p. (AM896St6)

1144   Stoll, Dennis Gray. Man in ebony; a novel. London, Gollancz, 1950. 159p. (M896.3C84)

1145   Suède, William Guillaume de. Contes noirs. Traduit du Suédois par Karin Dubois-Heyman et Félix Frapereau. Paris, J. Ferenczi & Fils, éditeurs, 1927. 284p. (M896.3Su2)

1146 Swaartbooi, V. N. M. U-Mandisa. Lovedale, Lovedale Press, 1946. 47p. (M896.3Sw1)

1147 Tharaud, Jerome. The long walk of Samba Diouf. New York, Duffield and Co., 1924. 201p. (AM896.3T331)

1148 Tharaud, Jerome. La randonnee de Samba Diouf. Paris, Librairie Plon, 1922. 313p. (M896.3T331r)

1149 Tsotsi, Liziwe L. U-Ntabaziya-duma. Lovedale Press, 1952. 89p. (M896.3T88m)

1150 Tutuola, Amos. My life in the Bush of Ghosts. London, Faber and Faber, 1954. 174p. (AM896.3T88m)

1151 Tutuola, Amos. The palm-wine drunkard. London, Faber and Faber, 1952. 125p. (AM896.3T88s)

1152 Tutuola, Amos. Simbi and the satyr of the dark jungle. London Faber and Faber. 1956. 136p. (M896.3T88s)

1153 Ulenge, Yussuf. Nguzo ya maji; na hadithi nyingine; (The pillar of water, and other stories.) Nairobi, The Eagle Press, 1951. 22p. (M967.82U12)

1154 Vandercook, John Womack. The fool's parade. New York and London, Harper and Bros., 1930. 270p. (AM896.3V28)

1155 Vandercook, John Womack. Forty stay in. London and New York, Harper and Bros., 1931. 323p. (AM896.3V28f)

1156 Van der Post, Laurens. Flamingo feather. London, The Hogarth Press, 1955. (M896.3V28)

1157 Van der Post, Laurens. In a province. London, Hogarth Press, 1934. 350p. AM896V285)

1158 Viaud, Julien. Le roman d'un spahi, par Pierre lote, pseud. Paris Calmann-Levy, 1893. 360p. (M843.91V65)

1159 Viertel, Peter. White hunter, black heart. 1st ed. Garden City, New York, Doubleday, 1953. 344p. (M896.3V67)

1160 Waltari, Milka Toimi. The Egyptian. New York, G. P. Putnam's Sons, 1949. 503p. (AM896W17e)

1161 Werner, Alice. African stories. London, Watts and Co., 1932. 151p. (AM896W49)

1162 Wheeler, Post. The golden legend of Ethiopia; the love story of Mâqedâ virgin queen of Axum and Shêba, and Solomon the great king. New York, London, D. Appleton-Century Co., 1936. 184p. (M896.3W57g)

1163   Williams, J. Grenfell.   I am black, the story of Shabala.   London, Cassell, 1936.   239p.   (AM896W67i)

1164   Williamson, Thames Ross.   Talking drums, a boys story of the African Gold Coast.   Garden City, New York, Doubleday, Doran and Co., 1936.   307p.   (M896.3W67t)

1165   Wilson, Dorothy Clarke.   Prince of Egypt.   Philadelphia, Westminster Press, 1949.   423p.   (AM896W69p)

1166   Young, T. Cullen, ed.   African new writing; short stories.   London, Lutterworth Press, 1947.   126p.   (M896.3Yo8a)

1167   Zeltner, Frantz de.   Contes du Senegal et du Niger, recueillis.   Paris, Ernest Leroux, 1913.   252p.   (M843.91Z3)

DESCRIPTION AND TRAVEL

1168   Abu Abd Allah Muhammad Al-Idrisi, Edrisii Africa.   Curavit Joannes Melchoir Hartman.   Gottingae, Sumitbus Jo Christ Dieterich, 1796.   530p.   (M916H25)

1169   Adams, C. C.   Report of highlights of the third trip to Africa.   April 7-June 4, 1949.   Philadelphia National Baptist Convention, Foreign Mission Board, 1949.   42p.   (M916Ad17)

1170   Adams, John.   Sketches taken during ten voyages to Africa.   London, Edinburgh, Hurst, Robinson and Co., 1822.   119p.   (AM960Ad1s)

1171   Adanson, Michel.   A voyage to Senegal, the Isle of Goree and the river Gambia.   Translated from the French.   With notes by an English gentlemen, who resided some time in that country.   London, Printed for J. Nourse and W. Johnston in Ludgate Street, 1759.   337p.   (M916Ad1)

1172   Akeley, Delia J.   Jungle portraits.   New York, The Macmillan Co., 1930.   251p.   (AM916Ak3)

1173   Akeley, Mary L. (Jobe).   Rumble of a distant drum.   New York, Dodd, Mead and Co., 1946.   364p.   (AM960Ak3r)

1174   Allen, Nellie B.   Africa, Australia and the islands of the Pacific.   Boston, Ginn & Co., 1935.   448p.   (AM916A15)

1175   Allen, Van Nes.   I found Africa.   Indianapolis, New York, The Bobbs-Merril Co., [c1939.]   306p.   (AM916.66AL5)

1176   Anderson, Mrs. Isabel Weld (Perkins).   Circling Africa.   Boston, Marshall Jones Co., 1929.   270p.   (AM916An2)

1177   Appel, Joseph Herbert.   Africa's white magic.   N. Y. & London, Harper & Bros., 1928.   166p.   (AM960Ap4)

1178 Barth, H. Travels and discoveries in North and Central Africa. New York, Harper Bros., 1857. 3v. (AM916B28)

1179 Beaver, Stanley H. A regional geography for higher certificate and intermediate courses. London, New York, Longmans, Green and Co., 1934. 271p. (AM960B386a)

1180 Bernatzik, Hugo Adolf. The dark continent; Africa, the landscape and the people. London, "The Studio," limited, 1931. 256p. (AM916B47d)

1181 Bosman, Willem. A new and accurate description of the coast of Guinea, divided into the Gold, the Slave, and the Ivory coasts. Containing a geographical, political and natural history of the kingdoms and countries: with a particular account of the rise, progress and present condition of all the European settlements upon that coast; and the just measures for improving the several branches of the Guinea trade. Illus. with several cuts. Written originally in Dutch by William Bosman. . . And now faithfully done into English. To which is prefix'd, an exact map of the whole coast of Guinea, that was not in the original. London, J. Knapton, etc., 1705. 493p. (M916.6B65)

1182 Bosman, Willem. A new and accurate description of the coast of Guinea; divided into the Gold, the Slave, and the Ivory coasts. Containing a geographical, political and natural history of the kingdoms and countries: with a particular account of the rise, progress and present condition of all the European settlements upon that coast; and the just measures for improving the several branches of the Guinea trade. Illustrated with seven curious cuts, and a correct map of Guinea. Written originally in Dutch by Willem Bosman . . . and now faithfully done into English. The third edition. London, Printed for J. Wren, at the Bible and Crown, in Salisbury-court, Fleet Street, 1754. 456p. (M916.6B65)

1183 Boteler, Thomas. Narrative of a voyage of discovery to Africa and Arabia performed in His Majestie's ships, Leven and Barracouta, from 1821 to 1826, under the command of Capt. F. W. Owen, R. N. London, R. Bentley, 1835. 2v. (M916B65)

1184 Boyce, William Dickson. Illustrated Africa, North, Tropical, South. Chicago, N. Y., Rand, McNally & Co., 1925. 686p. (M960-B69i)

1185 Bruce, James. An interesting narrative of the travels of James Bruce, esq., into Abyssinia, to discover the source of the Nile: abridged from the original work. To which are added notes and extracts, from the travels of Dr. Shaw, M. Savary, and the memoirs of Baron de Tott. 2d American ed.; being a literal copy of the English. Boston, Printed by Samuel Etheridge, for Alexander Thomas and George Merriam, 1798. 388p. (M963B83)

1186 Bruce, James. Travels to discover the source of the Nile, in the years 1768, 1769, 1770, 1771, 1772, 1773. 3rd ed. enl. To which is prefixed a life of the author. Edinburgh, Printed by George Ramsay and Co., for Archibald Constable and Co., 1813. 2v. (M916B83t)

1187 Buel, James William. Conquering the dark continent. New York, Official publishing Co., 1899. 492p. (M916B86)

1188 Buel, James William. Heroes of the dark continent. Philadelphia, H. W. Kelley, 1890. 576p. (AM960B86)

1189. Busoni, Rafaello. Stanley's Africa. New York, The Viking press, 1944. 288p. (AM916.7B96)

1190 Carney, Mable. African letters. N. P., Privately printed, 1926. 28p. (M916C21)

1191 Carpenter, Frank George. Carpenter's geographical reader. New York, Cincinnati, American book Co., 1905. 336p. (M916C22)

1192 Chapman, Frederick Spencer. Lightest Africa. London, Chatto & Windus, 1955. 288p. (M960C36L)

1193 Childers, James Saxon. Mumbo Jumbo, esquire. New York, London, D. Appleton-Century Co., Inc., 1941. 421p. (M916C43m)

1194 Cloete, Stuart. The African giant, the story of a journey. Boston, Houghton Mifflin, 1955. 400p. (M960C62)

1195 Clough, Ethlyn T. ed. Africa. Detroit, Bay View reading club, 1911. 237p. (M916C62)

1196 Considine, John Joseph. Africa, world of new men. New York, Dodd, Mead, 1954. 398p. (M960C76a)

1197 Court Treatt, Chaplin. Out of the beaten track. London, Hutchinson Co., Ltd., 1930. 288p. (M916C83)

1198 Crowell, Katherine R. Africa for juniors. New York, Domestic and Foreign Missionary Society of the P.E. Church, 1905. 94p. (M916C88a)

1199 Davies, Edward. An illustrated handbook on Africa. Reading, Mass. Holiness Book Concern, 1886. 91p. (M916D28)

1200 Deakin, Ralph. The tour of the Prince of Wales to Africa. Philadelphia, J. B. Lippincott Co., 1926. 302p. (M916D34)

1201 Deherain, Henri. Quid Schems Eddin el Dimashqui geographus de

Africa cognitum habuerit. Thesim, Parisiis, Georges Carre et C. Naud, 1897. 131p. (M960D36q)

1202 Du Chaillu, Paul. The country of the dwarfs . . . New York and London, Harper & Bros., 1871. 261p. (M966D85c)

1203 Denham, Dixon. Narrative of travels and discoveries in Northern and Central Africa, in the years 1822, 1823 and 1824. Boston, Cummings, Hilliard & Co., Philadelphia, Carey and Lea, 1826. 255p. iv, 104, 112. (M916D41)

1204 Denham, Dixon. Narrative of travels and discoveries in Northern and Central Africa, in the years 1822, 1823, and 1824. London, J. Murray, 1826. 335p. 269. (M916D41a)

1205 DuChaillu, Paul Belloni. Explorations and adventures in equatorial Africa; with accounts of the manners and customs of the people, and of the chase of the gorilla, the crocodile, leopard, elephant, hippotamus, and other animals. New York, Harper & bros. 1861. 531p. (M916D86)

1206 DuChaillu, Paul Belloni. King Mombo. New York, C. Scribner's sons, 1902. 225p. (AM916D85k)

1207 DuChaillu, Paul Belloni. Lost in the jungle. New York, Harper and bros., 1872. 260p. (AM916.62D85)

1208 DuChaillu, Paul. My Apingi kingdom. New York, Harper, 1871. 254p. (AM916.62D85m)

1209 DuChaillu, Paul Belloni. Wild life under the equator. New York, Harper & bros. 240p. (AM916D85w)

1210 Ellis, Alfred Burdon. The land of fetish. London, Chapman and Hall, 1883. 316p. (AM916EL51)

1211 Farson, Negley. Behind God's back. London, V. Gollancz ltd., 1940. 448p. (AM916F25b)

1212 Fitzgerald, Walter. Africa, a social, economic and political geography of its major regions. New York, E. P. Dutton and co., inc. [1939?] 499p. (M916F57)

1213 Frobenius, Leo. The voice of Africa, being an account of the travels of the German inner African exploration expedition in the years 1910-1912. London, Hutchinson and co., 1913. 2v. (M916F921b)

1214 Frost, John. Book of travels in Africa, from the earliest ages to the present time. N.Y., D. Appleton, 1848. 252p. (M916F92)

1215 Fyfe, H. Hamilton. Aux pays de l'or et des diaments. Cap. Natal, Orange, Transvaal, Rhodesie. Paris, Pierre Roger et Cie. n.d. 268p. (AM960F99a)

1216 Gatti, Attilio. Killers all! New York, R. M. McBride & co., 1943. 245p. (AM916G22k)

1217 Gatti, Attilio. Tom-Toms in the night. London, Hutchinson & co., ltd., 1932. 285p. (AM916G22)

1218 Gatti, Ellen Morgan (Waddill). Here is Africa. New York Scribner's sons, 1943. 166p. (AM916G22h)

1219 Geda, Gustav Adolf. Wunderwege durch ein wunderland. Stuttgart, Verlag von J. F. Steinkopf, 1939. 183p. (AM960G26w)

1220 Goodrich, S. G. The tales of Peter Parley about Africa. Boston, Carter, Hendes & co., 1835. 128p. (AM916G62)

1221 Green, Lawrence George. Strange Africa. London, S. Paul & Co., ltd., 1938. 287p. (M916G82)

1222 Harris, Sir John Hobbis. Africa: slave or free? New York, E. P. Dutton & co., 1920. 261p. (AM916H24a)

1223 Harris, Sir W. C. Adventures in Africa. Philadelphia, Peterson, 1843. 392p. (AM916H24)

1224 Hatch, John. New from Africa. London, Dennis Dobson, 1956. 123p. (M967.6H28)

1225 Holmes, Prescott. The story of exploration and adventure in Africa. Philadelphia, Henry Altemus, 1898. 264p. (M916H73)

1226 Horn, Alfred Aloysius, pseud. Harold the webbed. New York, Simon and Schuster, 1928. 275p. (M916H78 v.2)

1227 Horn, Alfred Aloysius. Trader horn; Being the life and works of Aloysius Horn, New York, Simon and Schuster, 1927. 302p. (M916H78)

1228 Horn, Alfred Aloysius, pseud. The waters of Africa. New York, Simon and Schuster, inc., 1929. 279p. (AM916H78 v.3)

1229 Hornemann, Friedrich Konrad. The journal of Frederick Horneman's travels. London, G. & and W. Nicol, 1802. 196p. (AM916H78j)

1230 Howe, Edgar Watson. Travel letters from New Zealand, Australia and Africa. Topeka, Kansas, Crane & co., 1913. 476p. (AM-916H83)

1231 Hoyingen-Huene, Georg. African mirage, the record of a journey. London, B. T. Batsford, ltd., 1938. 114p. (AM916H85)

1232 Hutton, Catherine. The tour of Africa. London, Baldwin, Cradock & Joy, 1819-21. 3v. (AM916H97)

1233 Isaaco. [The] journal of Isaaco, Mungo Park's guide. (In: Park, Mungo. The journal of a mission to the interior of Africa, in

year 1805 ... London, John Murray, 1815. v.2 289-335p.)
(M966.3Is1)

1234 Jameson, [Robert] Narrative of discovery and adventure in Africa.
New York, J & J. Harper, 1833. 359p. (AM916J23n)

1235 Johnson, William Percival. My African reminiscences, 1875-1895.
London, Universities' mission to Central Africa, n.d. 236p.
(AM916J62m)

1236 Jones, Charles H. Africa; the history of exploration and adventure
as given in the leading authorities from Herodotus to Livingstone. New York, H. Holt and Co., 1875. 496p. (M916J73)

1237 Jones, Charles H. Negroland; or, Light thrown upon the Dark
continent. New York, Hurst & co., 1881. 496p. (AM916J73n)

1238 Justel, Henri. Recueil de divers voyages faits en Afrique et en
l'Amerique qui n'ont point este' encore publiez. Paris, Chez
Louis Billaine, 1674. 34p. (M916J98)

1239 Kingston, William H. G. Great African travellers. London, George
Routledge, 1874. 509p. (AM916K61)

1240 Krippner, Monica. African way; a seven month's journey from
Cape Town to Algiers. London, Bles, 1952. 224p. (AM960K-
89a)

1241 Landor, Arnold Henry Savage. Across widest Africa. New York,
C. Scribner's sons, 1907. 2v. (AM916L236)

1242 Lander, Richard. Journal of an expedition to explore the course
& termination of the Niger. London, J. Murray, 1892. 3v.
(M916L23)

1243 Lang, Mrs. Sarah McCune (Rice). Critters in Africa. Del Monte,
California, Priv. Print. 1931. 109p. (M916L26)

1244 Lavauden, Louis. The equatorial forest of Africa. Supplement to
the Journal of the Royal African Soc., Apr., 1937. 25p. (AM-
960L38)

1245 Lee, Robert [Sarah W. Bowditch.] The African wanderers; or The
adventures of Carlos and Antonio, embracing interesting des-
criptions of the manners and customs of the tribes and the natural production of the country. New York, Griffith and Far-
ran. n.d., 358p. (M916L51)

1246 Legendre, Sidney J. Okovango; desert river. New York, J. Messner, inc., 1939. 300p. (AM916.88L52)

1247 Leo Africanus, Joannes. Ioannis Leonis Africani Africae descriptio
ix. lib. absoluta. Lugd. Batav., apud Elzevir, a., 1632. 800p.
(AM960L55i)

1248   [Leyden, John.] A historical and philosophical sketch of the dis-
       coveries and settlements of the Europeans in northern and
       western Africa, at the close of the eighteenth century. Edin-
       burgh, Printed by J. Moir, Paterson's Court for F. Brown and
       J. Symington, 1799. 442p. (M960L59h)

1249   Livingston, David. Dr. David Livingston's discoveries in Africa.
       Philadelphia, Barclay and co., 1873. 127p. (AM916.67L76d)

1250   Lobo, Jeronymo. A short relation of the river Nile, of its source
       and current; of its overflowing the campagnia of Egypt, till it
       runs into the Mediterranean; and of other curiosities: written
       by an eye-witness, who lived many years in the Chief King-
       dom's of the Abyssine empire. London, J. Martyn, 1673.
       105p. (AM960L61s)

1251   Lyell, Denis D. African adventure. Letters from famous big-game
       hunters. New York, E. P. Dutton & Co., 1935. 270p. (M916-
       D42)

1252   Mcdonald, Duff. Africana; or, The heart of heathen Africa. Lon-
       don, Simpkin, Marshall & co., 1882. 2v. (AM916M14a)

1253   Makin, William J. Swinging the equator. New York, E. P. Dutton
       & co., inc., 1936. 320p. (AM916M28)

1254   Marcosson, Issac F. An African adventure. New York, John Love
       co., 1921. 288p. (AM916.7M33)

1255   Marten, Otto, ed. The African handbook, a guide to west, south
       and east Africa, edited by Otto Martens and Dr. O. Karstedt
       for the German African lines. 2d ed. London, G. Allen & Un-
       win, ltd., 1938. 726p. (M916M36)

1256   Maurette, F. ... Afrique equatoriale, orientale et australe. Paris,
       Librairie Armand Colin, 1938. 398p. (AM960M44)

1257   Mayo, Willam Starbuck, Kaloolah. The adventures of Jonathan
       Romer ... The Framazudas ed., illustrated by Fredericks. New
       York and London, G. P. Putnam's sons, 1887. 389p. (M916-
       M45)

1258   Meeker, Oden. Report on Africa. London, Chatto & Windus, 1955.
       333p. (M960M47)

1259   Mollien, Gaspard Theodore, comte de. Travels in Africa. London,
       Printed for Sir Richard Phillips and Co., 1820. 128p. (AM-
       916M73)

1260   Morse, I. H. Yankee in Africa. Boston, Mass., The Stratford
       Co., 1936. 297p. (AM916M83)

1261   Muhammad ibn 'Abd Allah, called Ibn Batutah. Travels in Asia and Africa, 1325-1354. London, G. Routledge & Sons, Ltd., 1929. 398p. (AM916M89)

1262 Ogrizek, Doré. South and Central Africa. [Translation by Paddy O'Hanlon] New York, McGraw-Hill [c1954] 431p. (M9600-g7s)

1263 Packer, Joy (Petersen). Apes and ivory. London, Eyre & Spottis-woode [1953] 400p. (M960P12)

1264 Park, Mungo. Travels in the interior districts of Africa. Phila-delphia, James Humphreys, 1800. 94p. (AM916P22)

1265 Pivert. Mes chasses en Afrique et en extreme Orient. Paris, Agence Mondiale de Libairie, 1925. 172p. (AM916P68)

1266 Quinn, Vernon. Picture map geography of Africa. Philadelphia, Lippincott, 1952. 119p. (AM916Q45p)

1267 Rainier, Peter W. My vanished Africa. New Haven, Yale Uni-versity Press, 1940. 307p. (AM916R13)

1268 Reade, Winwood. Savage Africa; being the narrative of a tour in equatorial, southwestern, and northwestern Africa; with notes on the habits of the gorilla; on the existence of unicorns and tailed man; on the slave-trade; on the origin, character, and capabilities of the Negro, and on the future civilization of Western Africa. New York, Harper, 1864. 425p. (M960R22)

1269 Recueil de divers voyages faits en Afrique et en l'Amerique, qui n'ont point esté encore publiez . . . Le tout enrichi de figures, & de cartes geographiques . . . Paris, L. Billaine, 1674 262p. (M916J98)

1270 Reeve, Alan. Africa, I presume? New York, Macmillan Co., 1948. 232p. (AM916R25a)

1271 Reid, C. Lestock. An amateur in Africa. London, T. F. Unwin, Ltd., 1925. 217p. (AM916R27)

1272 Richter, Hans. Buntes Afrika. Berlin, Scherl, 1939. 124p. (AM-916R41b)

1273 Ritter, Paul. Unvergessenes deutsches land. Berlin, Verlag und Vertriebs, n.d. 95p. (AM916.1R51)

1274 Robeson, Eslanda (Goode) African journey. New York, The John Day Co., 1945. 154p. (AM916R54a)

1275 Robinson, Florence. Charles H. Robinson. A record of travel and work. Westminster, S.W.I. The Society for the Propaga-tion of the Gospel in Foreign Parts, 1928. 143p. (AM916R56)

1276 Roome, William J. W. Tramping through Africa. London, A.&C.

Black, Ltd., 1930. 330p. (M916R67)

1277　Scheel, W.　Deutschlands Kolonien in achtzig farbenphotographis-
chen.　Berlin, Verlagsanstalt für Farbenphotographie, Weller
und Nüttich, 1912. 159p. (AM916Sch2)

1278　Schweinfurth, George August.　The heart of Africa.　Three years'
travels and adventures in the unexplored regions of Central
Africa, from 1868-1871.　New York, Harper & Bros., 1874.
2v. (M960Sch9)

1279　Smith, Cicely Fox.　All the round.　London, Michael Joseph, Ltd.,
1938. 284p. (AM916Sm5)

1280　Solem, Elizabeth D.　Kana, prince of darkest Africa . . . Chicago,
Encyclopedia Britannica Press, c1947. 40p. (M960Sa3k)

1281　Suggate, Leonard Sydney.　Africa.　London, G. G. Harrap & Co.,
Ltd., 1929. 377p. (AM916Su3)

1282　Sykes, Sir Percy.　A history of exploration from the earliest times
to the present day.　London, Routledge & Kegan Paul, 1950.
425p. (M960Sy4h)

1283　Taurinius, Zacharias, pseud.　Travels through the interior of Africa.
Boston, S. Etheridge, 1801. 523p. (AM916T194a)

1284　Temple, Richard Carnac.　The itinerary of Ludovico di Varthema
of Bologna from 1502 to 1508 . . . London, The Argonaut
Press, 1928. 121p. (AM960T24i)

1285　Thomas, Charles W.　Adventures and observations on the west
coast of Africa, and its islands.　New York, Derby & Jackson,
1860. 479p. (AM916T36)

1286　Thompson, Era Bell.　Africa, land of my fathers. [1st ed.] Garden
City, N. Y., Doubleday, 1954. 281p. (M960T37)

1287　Thompson, George.　"Let there be light."　Oberlin, the author,
1881. 56p. (AM916T37)

1288　Thurnwald, Richard.　Koloniale gesaltung.　Hamburg, Hoffman
& Campe, 1939. 492p. (AM916T42)

1289　Turner, Walter James.　A pictorial guide to many lands.　New
York, Hastings house, 1944. 311p. (AM960T85p)

1290　Vaillant, Auguste Nicolas.　Voyage de monsieur la Vaillant dans
L'intérieur de l'Afrique, par le Cape de Bonne-Espérance.
Dans les annés 1780, 81, 82, 83, 84 and 85.　Nouvelle edition.
O Lausanne, Chez Mourer, 1790. 2 vols. (M966V24v)

1291　Vellani-Marchi, Mario.　Africa.　Prefazione di Silvio Negro.　Milano, Casa editrice Ceschina, 1938. unp. (AM916V54)

1292 Villegagnon, Nicolas Durand de. Caroli V. Impe-|ratoris ex-
peditio in| Africam ad Argieram: Per Ni-|colaum Villagagnon-
em|Equitem Rhodium| Gallum.|Ad D. G. Bellaium Langaeum
Subal|pinarumgentium Proregem, & pri-|miordinis Equitem
apud Christi|anissimum Francorum|Regem|. Argentorati per|
Vuendelimum Ribelium|1542. 20 leaves. (M960V71c)

1293 Wadstrom, Carl Bernhard. Observations on the slave trade, and
a description of some part of the coast of Guinea, during a
voyage made in 1787, and 1788, in company with Doctor A.
Sparrman and Captain Arrehenius i.e. Arrhenius by C. B.
Wadstrom . . . London, Printed by J. Phillips, 1789. 67p.
(M326.9AW11o)

1294 Walckenaer, Charles Athanese. Collection des relations de voyages
par mer et par terre, en differentes parties de l'Afrique depuis
1400 jusqus' a nos jours. Paris, Chez l'editeur, 1842. 20 vols.
(M916W14)

1295 Watson, S. G. Impressions of travel. London, United society for
Christian literature, 1948. 64p. (AM916W33i)

1296 Weulersse, Jacques. L'Afrique noire. Paris, A Fayard, 1934.
484p. (AM916W54)

1297 Weulersse, Jacques. Noirs et blancs; a travers l'Afrique nouvelle.
Paris, A. Colin, 1931. 242p. (AM960W54n)

HISTORY

1298 Alimen, Henriette. Préhistoire de l'Afrique. Paris, N. Boubee, 1955.
578p. (M913.32A14)

1299 Delafosse, Maurice. The Negroes of Africa, history and culture.
Translated from the French by F. Fligelman. Washington,
D. C., The Associated Publishers, 1931. 313p. (M960D37)

1300 Diop, Cheikh Anta. Nations Nègres et culture. Paris. Éditions
Africaines, 1955. 390p. (M960.3D62n)

1301 Frankel, Sally Herbert. Some reflections on civilization in Africa.
Johannesburg, South African Institute of Race Relations, 1952.
27p. (M960F85)

1302 Goodrich, Samuel Griswold. Lights and shadows of African history.
Boston, Bradbury, Soden and Co., 1844. 336p. (AM960G625)

1303 Hardy, Georges. Vue générale de l'historie d'Afrique. Paris, A.
Colin, 1922. 200p. (M960H21v)

1304 Julien, Charles Andre. Historie de l'Afrique. Paris, Presses universitaries de France, 1946. 125p. (AM960J94h)

1305 Labouret, Henri. Historie des Noirs d'Afrique. Paris, Presses universitaries de France, 1946. 127p. (M960L11L)

1306 Meynier, Octave Frederic Francois. L'Afrique noire. Paris, E. Flammarion, 1911. 335p. (AN960M57a)

1307 Meynier, Octave Frederic Francois. L'Afrique noir, avec 5 croquis dans le texte. Paris, Ernest Flammarion, 1921. 337p. (M960-M57a1921)

1308 Michelet, Raymond. African empires and civilization. [Manchester, England.] Panaf Service [1945?] 39p. (M960M58a)

1309 Pedrals, Denis Pierre de. Manuel scientifique de l'Afrique noire. Paris, Payot, 1949. 202p. (AM572.96P34m)

1310 Pedrals, Denis Pierre de. Archeologie de l'Afrique noire, Nubie, Ethiopie, Niger Sakelien, l'Aire Tchadienne, Niger Ingerieru, Zimbabwe, Senegambie, Congo Belge. Paris, Payot, 1950. 233p. (AM571P34a)

1311 Smith, Edwin, Edwin William. Events in African history; a supplement to The Atlantic charter and Africa from an American standpoint. New York. The Committee on Africa, the war, and peace aims, 942. 67p. (M960C73)

1312 Turner, Walter Lee. Under the skin of the African; an outline of Negro history and the study of the dominant traits in Negro life. 2nd ed. rev. and enl. Birmingham, Ala., African Musicians, 1948. 337p. (AM960T85u)

1313 Woodson, Carter G. African background outlined; or, Handbook for the study of the Negro. Washington, Association for the Study of Negro Life and History, 1936. 478p. (M960W86)

NORTHERN AFRICA

GENERAL

1314 Albertini, Eugène. . . .L'Afrique du Nord française dans l'histoire. Lyon, Paris, Éditions Archat, [1937] 334p. (AM961A11)

1315 Almagro Basch, Martin. Prehistoria del norte de Africa y del Sáhara Español. Barcelona, Consejo Superior de Investigaciones Científicas, Instituto de Estudos Africanos, 1946. 302p. (AM961A16)

1316 Almásy, László Ede. . . . Unbekannte Sahara; mit flugzeug und auto in der Libyschen wüste, bearbeitet von Hansjoachim von der Esch. Leipzig, F. A. Brockhaus, 1939. 214p. (M916A16u)

1317 Atwater tourist agency. North Africa. Automobile tours in Algeria, Tunisia and Morocco. Algiers, 1929. 92p. (AM910.2At9)

1318 [Badia y Leblish, Domingo] Travels of Ali Bey [pseud.] in Morocco,
Tripoli, Cyprus, Egypt, Arabia, Syria, and Turkey, between
the years 1803 and 1807. Philadelphia, James Maxwell,
printer, 1816. 2v. (M916B14)

1319 Baratier, Albert Ernest Augustin. . . . A travers l'Afrique; édition
definitive ornée de huit portraits et ed six cartes. Ouvrage
couronné par Académie française (Prix vitet). Paris, Perrin
et Cie, 1912. 345p. (M966B231912)

1320 Beato González, Vicente. Capacidad mental del negro. Los méthods
de Binet-Bobertag y de Yerkes, para determinar la edad y
coeficiente mental, aplicados al negro. Madrid, Consejo Superior de Investigaciones Científicas, Instituto de Estudios Africanos, 1935. 116p. (AM966B37)

1321 Benoit, Fernand. L'Afrique méditeranéene; Algérie-Tunisie-Maroc.
Paris, Les Beaux-arts, édition d'études et de documents,
[c1931] 321p. (AM709B44)

1322 Bilder aus Afrika, (32 farbfotografien von Dr. Werner Wrage.)
Ravensburg, German, W. Fikentscher Verlag, n.d. 32 plates.
(M961B49)

1323 Boissier, Gaston. Roman Africa; archaeological walks in Algeria
and Tunis. New York and London, G. P. Putnam's Sons,
1899. 344p. (AM961B63)

1324 Brodrick, Alan Houghton. Mirage of Africa. London, Hutchinson, [1953.] 212p. (M961B78)

1325 Brodrick, Alan Houghton. North Africa. London, New York,
Oxford University Press, 1934. 98p. (M916.1B78)

1326 Broughton, Thomas Robert Shannon. The romanization of Africa
Proconsularis. Baltimore, The Johns Hopkins Press; London,
H. Milford, Oxford University Press, 1929. 233p. (M960B79)

1327 Calder, Ritchie. Men against the Desert. London, G. Allen and
Unwin, 1951. 186p. (AM961C12)

1328 Clifton, George. The happy hunted. London, Cassell, 1952. 392p.
(AM961C61h)

1329 Les Colonies Françaises. Paris, Flamrions, 1931. 271p. (M961C71)

1330 Denti di Pirajno, Alberto. A cure for serpents; a doctor in Africa.
[London] A. Deutsch, [1955.] 263p. (M961.2D43)

1331 Epton, Nina Consuelo. Journey under the cresent moon. London,
V. Gollancz, 1949. 286p. (AM961Ep8j)

1332 Erskine, Beatrice. Vanished Cities of Northern Africa. London,
Hutchinson & Co., Ltd., 1927. 284p.

1333 Evans-Pritchard, Edward Evan. The Sanusi of Cyrenaica. Oxford, Clarendon Press, 1949. 240p. (M961.4Ev1)

1334 Field, Henry Martyn. The Barbary Coast . . . New York, C. Scribner's Sons, 1893. 258p. (M916.1F45)

1335 Fletcher-Allen, Edgar. A wayfarer in North Africa; Tunisia and Algeria. Boston, Houghton Mifflin, 1931. 243p. (M916.11F63)

1336 Forbes, Rosita. The secret of Sahara; Kufara. New York, George H. Doran Company, 1921. 356p. (M961.9F74)

1337 Foster, Harry L. A vagabond in Barbary. New York, Dodd, Mead & Co., 1930. 308p. (AM916.1F81)

1338 France. État-major de l'armée. . . . L'Afrique française du nord. Bibliographie militaire des ouvrages français ou traduits en français et des articles des principales revues françaises relatifs à l'Algerie, à la Tunisie et au Maroc de 1830 à 1926. Paris, Imprimerie nationale, 1930- 2v. (MO16.961F84)

1339 Frobenius, Lèo. Hádschra máktuba, urzeitliche felsbilder Klein-afrikas; mit 55 mehrfarbigen. München, K. Wolff, 1925. 5p. (M913.3F92)

1340 Fuchs, Peter. The land of veiled men. London, Weidenfeld and Nicolson, 1955. 168p. (M916F95)

1341 Gaffarel, Paul Louis Jacques. Les colonies françaises. Paris, F. Alcan, 1899. 552p. (AM916G12)

1342 García-Ontiveros y Herrera, Eduardo. La política norteafricana de Carlos I; Madrid, Consejo Superior de Investigaciones. Cien-tíficas, Instituto de Estudios Africanos, 1950. 112p. (AM-961G16)

1343 Gasser, Jules. Rôle social de la France dans l'Afrique du Nord. Paris, G. Crès et cie., 1924. 270p. (AM961G21)

1344 Gil Torres, Rodolfo. Panorama del mundo árabe [por] Rodolfo Gil Benumeya [pseud.] Madrid, Consejo Superior de Investi-gaciones Científicas, Instituto de Estudios Africanos, 1952. 202p. (M953G37)

1345 Girault, Arthur. Principes de colonisation . . . Paris, Librairie du Recueil Sirey, Société Anonyme, 1936. 637p. (AM961G44)

1346 Grant, Cyril Fletcher. African shores of the Mediterranean. New York, McBride, Nast and Co., 1912. 504p. (AM961G76)

1347 Grant, Cyril Fletcher. 'Twixt sand and sea. London, S. Low, Marston & Co., Ltd., 1911. 504p. (AM960G76t)

1348 Great Britain. Treaties, etc. Agreement between the Governments

of the United Kingdom and the French Republic. London, H.
M. Stationery Office, 1951. 7p. (AM961.9G79a)

1349 Gsell, Stephane. Historie ancienne de l'Afrique du nord. Paris,
Hachette et cie., 1913. 8v. (AM961G93)

1350 Hassan, Hassan Ibrahim. Relations between the Fatimids in North
Africa and Egypt and the Umayyads in Spain during the 4th
Century A. H. (10th Century A. D.) Cairo, Fouad I University
Press 1948. 45p. (M962H27re)

1351 Ingold, Francois Joseph Jean. L'appel de l'Afrique primitive,
Juin-Août 1940 and Tchad. Paris, Librairie Grund, 1945.
75p. (AM961In4a)

1352 International Travel Department of the American Automobile Association. Travel Manual. Africa. Vol. 4, New York, International Travel Department, 1949. (M961In8)

1353 Julien, Charles André. . . . Historie de l'Afrique du Nord: Tunisie -
Algérie - Maroc. Paris, Payot, 1931. 886p. (M961J94)

1354 Khun de Prorok, Byron. Digging for lost African gods; the record
of five years archaeological excavation in North Africa. New
York and London, G. P. Putnam's Sons, 1926. 369p. (AM-
916.1K53d)

1355 Lane-Poole, Stanley. The Barbary Corsairs. New York, G. P.
Putnam's Sons, 1890. 316p. (AM961L24)

1356 Liebesny, Herbert. The government of French North Africa. Philadelphia, University of Pennsylvania, University Museum, 1943.
130p. (AM354.61L62)

1357 Lyautey, Pierre. L'empire colonial français. Paris, Les Éditions
de France, 1931. 540p. (M966.1L98)

1358 Lyon, George Francis. A narrative of travels in Northern Africa.
London, J. Murray, 1821. 383p. (AM961.2L99)

1359 Mangin, Charles Marie Emmanuel. Regards sur la France d'Afrique
Paris, Librairie Plon, 1924. 308p. (M966M31r)

1360 Martineau, Alfred Albert. Tableau de l'expansion européenne à
travers le monde de la fin du XIIe au début du XIXe siècle,
par Alfred Martineau . . . et L. Ph. May . . . Paris, Société
de l'histoire des colonies françaises et Librairie Leroux, 1935.
368p. (M961H36t)

1361 Maugham, Hon. Robert Cecil Romer. North African notebook.
London, Chapman & Hall, 1948. 146p.

1362 Mayne, Peter. The alleys of Marrakesh. Boston, Little, Brown,
[1953.] 247p. (AM964.6M45a)

1363 Le Monde Economique. North Africa; a world in fusion. Anglo-American ed., [Tunisia, 1952.] 226p. (M966M74)

1364 Monroe, Elizabeth. The Mediterranean in politics. London, Oxford University Press, H. Milford, 1938. 259p. (AM961M75)

1365 Montague, Robert. . . . Les Berberes et le Makhzen dans le sud de Marco essai sur la transformation politique des Berberes sedentaires (groupe chleuh) . . . Paris, Felix Alcan, 1930. 426p. M961M76)

1366 Ogrizek, Doré. North Africa. New York, McGraw Hill, [1955.] 447p. (M9600g7n)

1367 Paillard, Jean. La fin des Français en Afrique Noire. Paris, Les Oeuvres Françaises, 1935. 188p.

1368 Paris, Ecolé libre des Sciences Politiques. Société des anciens élèves et élèves. . . . L'Afrique du Nord; Conférence organisées par la Société des Anceins Élèves et Élèves de l'Ecolé Libre des Sciences Politiques et Présidées. Paris, F. Alcan, 1913. 275p. (AM961P21)

1369 Piquet, Victor. Les civilisations de l'Afrique du Nord; Berbères-Arabes-Turcs. Paris, Al Colin, 1917. 398p. (AM961P66c)

1370 Prioleau, John. The open road abroad. With 25 decorations by G. E. Chambers and numerous maps. New York, W. Morrow & Company [1932] 206p. (M914P93)

1371 Rosa, Guido. North Africa speaks. New York, John Day, 1946. 247p. (M916.4R7)

1372 Russell, Michael. History and present condition of the Barbary States; comprehending a view of their civil institutions, antiquities, arts, religion, literature, commerce, agriculture, and natural productions. New York, Harper & Bros., 1835. 339p. (M961R91)

1373 Schaefer, René. Drame et chances de l'Afrique du Nord. Paris, Éditions internationales, 1953. 222p. (AM961Sch13)

1374 Stinetorf, Louise A. Children of North Africa. Philadelphia, New York, J. B. Lippincott Co., [1943.] 189p. (M916St5)

1375 U. S. Army. Special Service Division. A language guide to North Africa. Washington, D. C. War and Navy Depts., 1943. 113p. (AM961Un31)

1376 Utting, Mattie Johns. North of Sahara; Madeira-Morocco-Algeria-Tunisia-Egypt. Boston, Christopher Publishing House, 1940. 133p. (M916.1Ut8)

1377 Wagner, Gunther. The changing family among the Bantu Kavirondo. London, Oxford University Press, 1939. 52p. Supplement to Africa, v. 12, No. 1. (M960W12)

1378 Welch, Galbraith. North African Prelude, the first seven thousand years. New York, William Morrow, 1949. 650p. (M961W44)

ALGERIA

1379 Azan, Paul Jean Louis. Les grands soldats de l'Algérie. Paris, Imp. A Pigelet & cie. Orleans, Publications du Comité National Métropolitain du Centenaire de I'Algérie. 124p. (M-965az1)

1380 Bertrand, Louis. Africa. Paris, Albin Michel, 1933. 316p. (M-965B46)

1381 Blottière, Jean. Les productions Algériennes. Algeria, Publications du Comité National Métropolitain du Centenaire de L'Algérie, 19—, 95p. (M965B62p)

1382 Bonneval, de. L'Algérie touristique. Paris, Imp. A. Pigelet et cie. Orleans, Publications du Comité National Métropolitain du Centenaire de l'Algérie, 1930. 62p. (M956B64)

1383 Bourget, Jean Marie. L'Algérie jusqu'à la pénétration Saharienne. Paris, Imp. A. Pigelet & cie. Orleans, Publications du Comité National Métropolitain du Centenaire de l'Agérie. 95p. (M-965B66a)

1384 Charbonneau, Jean and Kouriba Nabhan. Des Africains s'interrogent. Paris, La Colombe, 1955. 175p. (M965C37)

1385 Edwards, Matilda Barbara Betham. In French-Africa, scenes and memories. London, Chapman and Hall, 1913. 324p. (AM-965Ed9i)

1386 Fletcher-Allen, Edgar. A wayfarer in North Africa; Tunisia and Algeria. Boston, Houghton Mifflin, 1931. 243p. (M916.11F63)

1387 France (Republic) Deuxième plan de modernisation et d'équipment. Algérie. Rapport général de la commission d'étude et de coordination des plans de modernisation et d'équipment de L'Algérie, de la Tunisie et du Maroc. France, Commission, 1954. 137p. (M965F84a)

1388 Gautier, Émile, Félix. L'évolution de l'Algérie de 1830 à 1930. Paris, Imp. A. Pigelet & cie. Orleans, Publications du Comité National Métropolitain du Centenaire de l'Algérie. 95p. (M965G23)

1389 Hilton-Simpson, Melville William. Among the hill-folk of Algeria. New York, Dodd, Mead, and Co., 1921. 248p. (AM916.5H56)

1390 Liebesny, Herbert. The government of French North Africa. Philadelphia, University of Pennsylvania Press, the University museum, 1943. 130p. (AM354.61L62)

1391 Lyautey, Pierre. L'empire colonial français. Paris, Les éditions
de France, 1931. 540p. (M966.1L98)

1392 Mangin, Charles Marie Emmanuel. Regards sur la France d'Afrique. Paris, Librairie Plon, 1924. 308p. (M966M31r)

1393 Milliot, Louis. Le gouvernement de l'Algérie. Paris, Imp. A.
Pigelet & cie Orleans, Publications du Comité National Métropolitain du Centenaire de l'Algérie. n.d. 48p. (M965M62)

1394 Mirante, Jean. La France et les oeuvres indigènes en Algérie.
Algeria, Publications du Comité National Métropolitain du
Centenaire de l'Algérie, 19—. 111p. (M965M67f)

1395 Morell, John Reynell. Algeria: the topography and history, political, social, and natural, of French Africa. London, N. Cooke,
1854. 490p. (M916.5M83)

1396 Morgan, J. A complete history of Algiers. To which is prefixed
an epitone of the general history of Barbary, from the earliest
times: interspersed with many curious remarks and passages,
not touched on by any writer whatever. London, J. Betten-
ham, 1728-29. 2v. (M965M82c)

1397 Paillard, Jean. Faut-il faire de l'Algérie un Dominion? Paris,
Fernand Sorlot, 1938. 111p. (AM916.5P15)

1398 Piquet, Victor. L'Algerie française; une siecle de colonisation
(1830-1930). Paris, A. Colin, 1930. 413p. (M965P66)

1399 Rosa, Guido. North Africa speaks. New York, The John Day
Co., [1946.] 247p. (M916.4R7)

1400 Schiaffino, L. L'Algérie, Province Française. Alger, 1952. 68p.
M965Sc3)

1401 Sommerville, Maxwell. Sands of Sahara. Philadelphia, J. B. Lippincott Co., 1901. 162p. (AM916.611So5)

1402 Wagner, Moritez. The tricolor on the Atlas; Algeria and the
French Conquest. New York, T. Nelson and Sons, 1885. 402p.
(M965W12)

1403 Wilkin, Anthony. Among the Berbers of Algeria. London, T. F.
Unwin, 1900. 263p. (M916.5W65)

MOROCCO

1404 Ashmead-Bartlett, Ellis. The passing of the Shereefian empire . . .
New York, Dodd, Mead and Co.; Edinburgh, W. Blackwood

and Sons, 1910. 532p. (AM964As3p)

1405 Barrows, David Prescott. Berbers and blacks; impressions of Morocco, Timbuktu and the western Sudan. New York and London, The Century Co., [c1927] 251p. (M966.2B27b)

1406 Delafosse, Maurice. Les relations du Maroc avec le Soudan a travers les ages. In: Hesperis Archives Berberes et Bulletin de l'Institut des Hautes-Etudes Marocaines, 1924. Pt. 2. (AM964W37)

1407 Felze, Jacques. Au Maroc inconnu; dans le Haut-Atlas et le Sud Marocain. Grenoble, B. Arthaud, [c1935.] 183p. (M916. 44F34)

1408 France (Republic) Dèuxieme plan de modernisation et d'équipment. Maroc. Rapport général de la commission d'étude et de co-ordination des plans de moderisation et d'équipment de l'Algérie de la Tunisie et du Maroc. France, Commission, 1954. 357p. (M964F84m)

1409 France. Prime Minister. Office of Technical Publications. Facts and figures about French North Africa. Paris, 1952. 51p. (AM964F84)

1410 García Bariuso, Patrocinio. Derecho matrimonial Islamico y matri-monios de Musulmanes en Marruecos ... Madrid, 1952. 466p. (M964G16d)

1411 García Figueras, Tomás. Espana en Marruecos (la obra social). Madrid, Consejo Superior de Investigaciones Científicas, In-stituto de Estudios Africanos, 1947. 173p. (AM964.2G16)

1412 García Figueras, Tomás. Economia Social de Marruecos (Tomo II). Madrid, Instituto de Estudios Africanos, 1952. (AM-964G158e)

1413 Gardiner, Wrey. Barbary holiday. London, F. Muller, 1952. 190p. (AM964G16)

1414 Girault, Arthur. Principes de colonisation et de legislation col-oniale. La Tunisie et le Maroc. Paris, Librairie du Recueil Sirey, société anonyme, 1936. 637p. (M961G44)

1415 Guide Maroc. Paris, Services de turisme Michelin, 1950. v. (M-964G94)

1416 Hall, Leland. Salah and his American. New York, A. A. Knopf, 1933. 198p. (M916.4H14)

1417 Hargrave, Carrie Guerphan. Jean and Tom in Casablanca. New York, Exposition Press, 1953. 103p. (AM964H22)

1418 Hoefer, Ferdinand. Afrique Australe; Afrique Orientale; Afrique

Centrale; Empire de Maroc. Paris, Firmin Didot Freres, Editeurs, 1948. 498p. (M967H67)

1419 Jackson, James Grey. An account of the empire of Morocco, and the district of Suse . . . London, W. Bulmer and Co. Sold by G. and W. Nicol, 1809. 287p. (AM964J14a)

1420 Knight, Melvin M. Morocco as a French economic venture; a study of open door imperialism. New York, London, D. Appleton-Century Company, Inc., 1937. 244p. (AM964K74)

1421 Landau, Rom. Moroccan Journal. London, Hale, 1952. 247p. (AM964L23m)

1422 Liebesny, Herbert. The government of French North Africa. Philadelphia, University of Pennsylvania Press, the University museum, 1943. 130p. (AM354.61L62)

1423 Lyautey, Pierre. L'empire colonial français. Paris, Les éditions de France, 1931. 540p. (M966.1L98)

1424 Mangin, Charles Marie Emmanuel. Regards sur la France d'Afrique. Paris, Librairie Plon, 1924. 308p. (M966M31r)

1425 Meakin Budgett, i.e., James Edward Budgett. The Moors, a comprehensive description. New York, The Macmillan Co., 1902. 503p. (AM964M46)

1426 Miege, Jean Louis. Morocco. Paris, B. Arthaud, 1953. 231p. M964M58m)

1427 Montagne, Robert. Les Berbères et le makhzen dans le sud du Maroc; essai sur la transformation politique des Berbères sédentaires. Paris, F. Alcan, 1930. 426p. (M961M76)

1428 Montbard, Georges. Among the Moors. London, S. Low, Marston and Co., 1894. 281p. (AM916.4M76)

1429 Morocco. L'activité coloniale; l'effort français en A.E.F., les travaux publics au Maroc. No. 232, Mars, 1933. 926p. (M964M34a)

1430 Morocco. Encyclopedie mensuelle d'outremer. Special issue. Morocco, 1954. 224p. (M964En1)

1431 Morocco. Housing and town-planning in Morocco . . . Rabat, Editions Africaines Perceval. (M964M82)

1432 Morocco. Service des statistiques. La conjoncture économique marocaine, 1955. (M964M82c)

1433 Morocco, 1950. Editions Africaines, 1950. 162p. (M964M82)

1434 Ossendowski, Ferdynand Antoni. The fire of desert folk; the account of a journey through Morocco. New York, E. P.

Dutton & Co., [c1926.]   354p.   (M964Os2f)

1435   Parent, Pierre.   The truth about Morocco.   Flushing, New York, Moroccan Office of Information and Documentation [1953.] 78p.   (M964P21)

1436   Pick, Frederick Walter.   Searchlight on German Africa.   London, F. Allen and Unwin, Ltd., 1939.   177p.   (AM325P58)

1437   Poiret, Jean Louis Marie.   Voyage en Barbarie, ou Lettres écrites de l'ancienne Numidie pendant les années 1785 et 1786, sur la religion, les coutumes, et les moeurs des Maures et des Arabes-Bédouins; avec un essai sur l'histoire naturalle de ce pays. Paris, Chez J. B. F. Nee de la Rochelle, 1789.   2v.   (M964P75)

1438   Rohlfs, Gerhard.   Adventures in Morocco.   London, S. Low, Marston, Low and Searle, 1874.   371p.   (AM916.4R63)

1439   Settle, Martha A.   Morocco in Diplomacy, 1900-1905.   Washington, D. C., Howard University, 1940.   129p.   (typed thesis). (M378.242HSe7)

1440   Spain.   Dirección General de Marruecos y Colonias.   Biblioteca. Catálogo de materias.   Madrid, Impr. de Sucesores de Rivadeneyra, 1949.   (AM016Sp1)

1441   Spain.   Dirección General de Marruecos y Colonias.   Espana en Africa.   Madrid, 1949.   43p.   (AM964.2Spl)

1442   Terrier, Auguste.   Le Maroc.   Paris, Larousse, 1931.   224p.   (AM-916.4T27)

1443   Torres, Diego de.   Relation de l'origine et succes de cherifs, et de l'estat des royaumes de Maroc, Fez, et Tarudant, et autres provinces qu'ils usurperent.   Paris, Jean Camusat, 1636.   426p. (AM964T63r)

1444   Viaud, Julien.   Into Morocco.   Chicago and New York, Rand McNally & Co., 1892.   343p.

TUNISIA

1445   Fletcher-Allen, Edgar.   A wayfarer in North Africa; Tunisia and Algeria.   Boston, Houghton Mifflin [1931] 243p.   (M916. 11F63)

1446   France (Republic).   Deuxième Plan de modernisation et d'équipment. Tunisie.   Rapport général de la commission d'étude et de coordination des plans de moderisation et d'équipment de l'Algérie, de la Tunisie et du Maroc.   France, Commission, 1954. 125p.   (M961.1F84t)

1447   Girault, Arthur.   Principes de colonisation et de législation coloniale

... La Tunisie et le Maroc. 6. éd., revisée. Paris, Librairie du Recueil Sirey, société anonyme, 1936. 637p. (M961G44)

1448   Hesse-Wartegg, Ernstrow. Tunis, the land of the people. London, Chatto and Windus, 1882. 292p. (M916.11H46)

1449   Laitman, Leon. Tunisia today; crisis in North Africa. New York, Citadel Press, 1954. 216p. (M961.1L14t)

1450   Lorimer, Norma Octavia. By the waters of Carthage ... with coloured frontispiece by Benton Fletcher and 32 illustrations from photographs by Garrigues ... New York, J. Pott & Co.; [etc., etc.] 1906. 368p. (M916.11L81)

1451   Martin, Dahris Butterworth. I Know Tunisia. New York, I. Washburn, Inc., 1943. 270p. (M916.11M36)

1452   Mélia, Jean. En Tunis; Carthage Chrètienne d'aujourd'hui. Paris, Fasquelle editeurs, 1939. 138p. (AM916.11M48)

1453   Paul-Margueritte, Lucie. Tunisiennes. Paris, Les Editions Denoel, 1937. 185p. (AM916.11P28)

1454   Pellegrin, Arthur. Histoire de la Tunisie depuis les origines jusqu'à nos jours. Paris, J. Peyronnet, 1938. 253p. (M961.1P36)

1455   Stephens, E. En Tunisie; cent quatre-vingt-dix photographies. Paris, Hartman, 1939. (AM916.11St4)

1456   Tunisia 54. 72 years of Franco-Tunisian collaboration. Paris, Encyclopédie Mensuelle do'outre mer, 1954. 180p. (English Text) (M961.1T83)

1457   Utting, Mattie Johns. North of Sahara; Madeira-Morocco-Algeria-Tunisia-Egypt. Boston, The Christopher publishing house [c1940] 133p. (M916.1Ut8)

1458   Zanuck, Darrly Francis. Tunis, expedition. New York, Random House, 1943. 159p. (AM916Z17)

LIBYA

1459   Aghion, Raoul. War in the desert; the battle for Africa. New York, H. Holt and Co., [c1941.] 300p. (M962Ag3)

1460   Burneau de Laborie, Emile Louis Bruno. Du Cameroun au Caire par le désert de Libye, chasses au Tchad; avec vingt-quarte gravures hors texte et deux cartes. Paris, E. Flammarion [c1924.] 406p. (M967.11B83)

1461   Depois, Jean. La colonisation italienne en Libye; problèmes et méthodes. Paris, Larose, 1935. 146p. (AM961.2D46)

1462   Falls, J. C. Ewald. Three years in the Libyan Desert ... London, T. F. Unwin, 1913. 356p. (AM961.9F19t)

1463 Forbes, Rosita. The secret of Sahara: Kufara. New York, George
H. Doran Co., [c1921] 356p. (AM961.9F74)

1464 Great Britian. Agreement between the Governments of the United
Kingdom and the French Republic of the one part and the
Government of the United States of America of the other part
on technical assistance for Libya. London, 1951. London,
H. M. Stationery Office, 1951. 7p. (M961.9G79a)

1465 Hill, Russell. Desert war. New York, A. A. Knopf, 1942. 310p.
(M940.542H55d)

1466 Hornemann, Friedrich Konrad. The journal of Frederick Horneman's travels, from Cairo to Mourzouk, the capital of the
kingdom of Fezzan, in Africa. In the years 1797-8. London,
G. and W. Nicol, 1802. 195p. (M916H78j)

1467 Jarvis, Claude Scudamore. Three deserts. New York, E. P.
Dutton and Co., 1937. 313p. (M916.2J29)

1468 McBurney, C. B. M. and Hey, R. W. Prehistory and Pleistocene
geology in Cyrenaican Libya. London, Cambridge University
Press, 1955. (M961.4M12)

1469 Villard, Henry Serrano. Libya, the new Arab kingdom of North
Africa. Ithaca, New York, Cornell University Press, 1956.
169p. (M961.2V71)

NORTH-EASTERN AFRICA

EGYPT

1470 'Abd al-Nasir, Jamal. Egypt's liberation; the philosophy of the
revolution. Washington, Public Affairs Press [1955] 119p.
(M962Ab3)

1471 'Abd al-Ralimàn ibn Abi Baker (Jala al-Din) al-Suyuti. The
Mutawakkili of as-Suyuti, a translation of the Arabic text.
Cairo, Printed at Nile Mission Press, 1924. 71p. (M297B41)

1472 Aghion, Raoul. War in the desert; the battle for Africa. New
York. H. Holt & Co., 1941. 300p. (M962Ag3)

1473 Aldred, Cyril. Middle Kingdom art in ancient Egypt, 2300-1590
B. C. London, A. Tiranti, 1950. 56p. (M709.32A12m)

1474 Aldred, Cyril. New Kingdom art in ancient Egypt, during the
eighteenth dynasty, 1590-1315 B.C. London, A. Tiranti,
1951. 98p. (M709.32A12n)

1475 Aldred, Cyril. Old Kingdom art in ancient Egypt. London, A.
Tiranti, 1949. 40p. (M932A120)

1476 Alford, Henry Stamford Lewis. The Egyptian Soudan, its loss and its recovery. London, New York, Macmillan and Co., 1898. 336p. (M962.4A1e)

1477 Anderson, William Ashley. South of Suez. New York, R. M. McBride and Co., 1920. 240p. (M962An2)

1478 Arkell, Anthony John. Early Khartoum. London, New York, Oxford University Press, 1949. 145p. (M913.32Ar4)

1479 Atteridge, Andrew Hilliard. Towards Khartoum; the story of the Soudan war of 1896. London, A. D. Innes and Co., 1897. 357p. (M962.4At8t)

1480 Ayrton, Edward Russell. Pre-dynastic cemetery at El-Mahasna. London, Published by order of the Committee, Sold at the offices of the Egypt Exploration Fund, [1911.] 39p. (M913-32Ay7)

1481 Badaoui, Zaki. La legislation du Travail en Egypte. Cairo, C. D. Beneducci, n.d.

1482 Baikie, James. A century of excavation in the land of the Pharaohs. New York, Fleming H. Revell Co., [1924.] 252p. (M932B14c)

1483 Baikie, James. Egyptian antiquities in the Nile valley; a descriptive handbook. London, Methuen and Co., 1932. 874p. (M932.32B14)

1484 Baikie, James. The glamour of Near East excavation; an account of the treasure-hunt for the buried art, wisdom and history of the ancient East, from the Nile to Babylon, the adventures, disappointments and triumphs of the hunters, and the knowledge thus acquired of the ancient world. London, Seeley, Service and Co., 1927. 348p. (M932B14g)

1485 Baikie, James. A history of Egypt from the earliest times to the end of the XVIIIth dynasty. London, A. and C. Black, Ltd., 1929. 2v. (M932B14)

1486 Baikie, James. The life of the ancient East, being some chapters of the romance of modern excavation. New York, MacMillan Co., 1923. 463p. (M913.3B14)

1487 Baikie, James. The story of the Pharaohs. London, A. and C. Black, 1926. 415p. (M913.32B14s)

1488 Baker, Samuel White. The Albert N'yanza, great basin of the Nile, and explorations of the Nile sources. London, MacMillan and Co., 1866. 2v. (M962B17)

1489 Bartlett, William Henry. The Nile boat; or, glimpses of the land of Egypt. A. Hall, Virtue and Co., 1852. 218p. (AM916B28n)

1490 Beadnell, Hugh John Llewellyn. An Egyptian oasis . . . London,

J. Murray, 1909. 248p. (AM916.19B35)

1491 Bell, Archie. The spell of Egypt. Boston, The Page Co., 1916. 366p. (M932B41s)

1492 Bell, C. F. Moberly. From Pharaoh to Fellah. London, Wells Gardner, 1888. 187p. (AM916.2B41)

1493 Bell, Edward. The architecture of ancient Egypt; a historical outline. London, G. Bell and Sons, Ltd., 1915. 255p. (M932-B41a)

1494 Bell, Harold Idris. Egypt, from Alexander the Great to the Arab conquest ... Oxford, Clarendon Press, 1948. 168p. (M932-B41e)

1495 Belzoni, Giovanni Battista. Narrative of the operations and recent discoveries within the pyramids, temples, tombes, and excavations, in Egypt and Nubia: and of a journey to the coast of the Red Sea, in search of the ancient Berenice; and another to the oasis of Jupiter Ammon. 3d. ed., London, J. Murray, 1822 2 vols. (M913.32B41)

1496 Beni Hasan. London, Sold by K. Paul Trench, Trubner & co., 1893. 4 vols (M913.32B43)

1497 Bevan, Edwyn Robert. A history of Egypt under the Ptolemaic dynasty with 62 illustrations and a map. London, Methuen & co., [1927] 409p. (M932B44)

1498 Bible. N. T. John. Coptic. The Gospel of St. John according to the earliest Coptic manuscript. London, British school of archaeology in Egypt, 1924. 70p. (M913.32B47)

1499 The Book of the dead. The Egyptian book of the dead. London, The Society of biblical archaeology, 1904. 376p. (M932B64)

1500 Breasted, James Henry. Ancient records of Egypt, historical documents from the earliest times to the Persian Conquest. Chicago, The University of Chicago Press, 1906-7. 5 vols. (M932B47a)

1501 Breasted, James Henry. Egyptian servant statues. [New York] Pantheon Books, [1948] 113p. (M932B74e)

1502 British museum. Department of Egyptian and Assyrian antiquities. A guide to the Egyptian galleries (sculpture). London, Printed by order of the Trustees, 1909. 351p. (M709.32B77g)

1503 British School of Archaeology in Egypt. Historical studies by E. B. Knobel, W. W. Midgley, J. G. Milne, M. A. Murray, and W. M. F. Petrie. London, School of Archaeology in Egypt, 1911. 50p. (M913.32B77)

1504 Brodrick, Mary & A. Anderson Morton. A concise dictionary of

Egyptian archaeology, a handbook for students and travellers, with 80 illustrations and many cartouches. London, Methuen & co., 1902. 198p. (M913.32B78)

1505 Bruce, James. Travels to discover the source of the Nile, in the years 1768, 1769, 1770, 1771, 1772 and 1773. Edinburgh, G. G. J. and J. Robinson, 1790. 5 vols. (M916B83t)

1506 Brugsch, Henrich Karl. A history of Egypt under the Pharaohs ... London, J. Murray, 1879. 2 vols (M932B83)

1507 Brunton, Guy & Gertrude Caton-Thompson. The Badarian civilisation and predynastic remains near Badari. London, British School of Archaeology in Egypt, 1928. (M913.32B83b)

1508 Brunton, Guy. Gurob, by Guy Brunton, O.B.E., and Reginald Engelbach. London, British School of Archaeology in Egypt, 1927. 28p. (M913.32B831)

1509 Brunton, Guy and others. Lahun I and II. London, British School of Archaeology in Egypt, University College, 1920, 1923. 2 vols. (M913.32B831)

1510 Brunton, Guy and others. Qua and Badari, I and II. London, British School of Archaeology in Egypt, 1927. 2 vols. (M913.-32B839)

1511 Brunton, Winifred. Great ones of ancient Egypt. New York, Scribner's sons, 1930. 177p. (M932G79)

1512 Bryan, Cyril P. The papyrus Ebers. London, G. Bles, 1931. 167p. (M913.32P19)

1513 Brudge, Ernest Alfred Wallis. Annals of Nubian kings. London, Trubner, 1912. 176p. (M932B85a)

1514 Budge, Ernest Alfred Thompson Wallis. Cleopatra's needles and other Egyptian Obelisks ... London, The Religious Tract society, 1926. 308p. (M932B85c)

1515 Budge, Ernest Alfred Thompson Wallis. Egypt ... London, Thornton Butterworth Ltd. [1925] 256p. (M932B85e)

1516 Budge, Ernest Alfred Thompson Wallis. ... A history of Egypt from the end of the neolithic period to the death of Cleopatra VII, B.C. 30 [London, K. Paul, Trench, Trubner & co., ltd.] 1902. 8 vols. (M932B85)

1517 Budge, Ernest Alfred Thompson Wallis. The literature of the ancient Egyptians ... London, J. M. Dent & sons limited; New York, E. P. Dutton & co., 1914. 272p. (M932B851i)

1518 Budge, Ernest Alfred Thompson Wallis. The Nile. London, Cairo, T. Cook and son (Egypt), ltd., 1912. 1094p. (M932B85n)

1519 Budge, Ernest Alfred Thompson Wallis. Osiris and the Egyptian resurrection. London, P. L. Warner, 1911. 2 vols. (M932B85o)

1520 Budge, Ernest Alfred Thompson Wallis. The Rosetta stone in the British Museum; the Greek, demotic and hieroglyphic texts of the decree inscribed on the Rosetta stone conferring additional honours on Ptolmey V. Epiphanes (203-181 B.B.) with English translations and a short history of the decipherment of the Egyptian hieroglyphs, and an appendix containing translations of the stelae of Sân (Tanis) and Tall al-Maskhûtah ... with twenty-three plates. London, [etc.] The Religious tract society, [1929.] 325p. (M493.117B85)

1521 Burckhardt, John Lewis, tr. Arabic proverbs; or, The manners and customs of the Modern Egyptians, illustrated from their proverbial sayings current in Cairo, 2nd ed ... London, Quaritch, 1875. 283p. (M962B89)

1522 Butler, Alfred Joshua. The Arab conquest of Egypt and the last thirty years of the Roman dominion. Oxford, The Clarendon press, 1902. 563p. (M932B97a)

1523 Carpenter, Frank George. Cairo to Kisumu; Cairo, the Sudan, Kenya colony, Garden City, N.Y., Doubleday, Page and co., 1925. 313p. (M962C22c)

1524 Carter, Howard. The tomb of Tut-Ankh-Amen. London, Cassell & co., ltd., 1923. 40p. (M913.32C24)

1525 Caton-Thompson, Gertrude. Kharga Oasis in prehistory; with a physiographic introduction. London, University of London, 1952. 213p. (M932C29)

1526 Caulfeild, Algernon Thomas St. George. The temple of the kings at Abydos. London, B. Quaritch, 1902. 23p. (M913.32C31)

1527 Chabas, F. Etudes sur l'antiquité historique d'apres les sources Egyptiennes et les monuments reputés préhistoriques. Paris, Maison Neuve Cie, 1873. 606p. (M932C34e)

1528 [Chennells, Ellen.] Recollections of an Egyptian princess .... Edinburgh and London, W. Blackwood and sons, 1893. 2 v. (M932C42r)

1529 Childe, Vere Gordo. New light on the most ancient East. New York, D. Appleton-Century co., 1934. 326p. (AM913.3C43n)

1530 Chirol, V. The Egyptian problem. London, MacMillan & co., 1920. 331p. (M962C44)

1531 Cobern, Camden McCormack. The new archeological discoveries and their bearing upon the New Testament and upon the life and times of the primitive church. New York and London, Funk & Wagnalls co., 1917. 698p. (M225.93C63)

1532 Colvin, Auckland. The making of modern Egypt. London, 1910. 384p. (M916.2C72m)

1533 Cooper, Elizabeth. The women of Egypt. London, Hurst and Blackett, 1914. 380p. (M962C78w)

1534 Cormack, George. Egypt in Asia ... London, A. and C. Black, 1908. 280p. (AM913C81e)

1535 Cottrell, Leonard. The lost Pharaohs; the romance of Egyptian archaeology. New York, Philosophical Library, [1951] 256p. (M932C821)

1526 Crabitès, Pierre. Americans in the Egyptian army. London, G. Routledge and sons, [1938] 277p. (M962C84)

1537 Cromer, Evelyn Baring. Modern Egypt. New York, The Mac-Millan co., 1908. 2v. (M916.2C88m)

1538 Crowfoot, John Winter. The island of Meroe and Meroitic inscriptions. Part 1—Soba to Dangel, by F. L. Griffith. London, Office of the Egypt Exploration Fund, 1911. (M913.32C88)

1539 Davis, Simon. Race-relations in ancient Egypt: Greek, Egyptian, Hebrew, Roman. London, Methuen, 1951. 176p. (M932D29r)

1540 Davis, Theodore M. The tomb of Queen Tiyi. London, Constable & co., 1910. 45p. (M913.32D27)

1541 Dawood, Hassan Aly. Economic aspects of land tenure in Egypt. East Lansing, 1950. Microfilm copy of typescript. Negative. Thesis. Michigan State College of Agriculture and Applied Science. (M962D32e)

1542 Decoration Egyptieene. Paris, Ernest Henri, ed., n.d. 36 plates. (M932D35)

1543 Delany, Martin Robison. Principia of ethnology: the origin of races and color, with an archaeological compendium of Ethiopian and Egyptian civilization, from years of careful examination and enquiry. Philadelphia, Harper & brother, 1879. 95p. (M573.5D37)

1544 Delayen, Gaston. Cleopatra, translated from the French by Farrell Symons. New York, E. P. Dutton & co., 1934. 280p. (M932-D37)

1545 Denon, Dominque Vivant. Travels in upper and lower Egypt, in company with several divisions of the French army, during the campaigns of General Bonaparte in that country; and published under his immediate patronage. London, Printed for

T. N. Longman and O. Rees and Richard Philips, 1803. 2v. (M963D43t)

1546 Ditson, George. The Para papers on France, Egypt, & Ethiopia. New York, Mason broa., 1858. 496p. (M916.2D63)

1547 Duff-Gordon, Lucie (Austin) *lady.* Lady Duff Gordon's letters from Egypt. New York, McClure, Phillips & co., 1902. 383p. (M916.2G651)

1548 Dumas, Alexandre. Impressions of travel, in Egypt and Arabia Petraea. New York, J. S. Taylor, 1839. 318p. (M916.2D89)

1549 Dumont, Pierre Joseph. Narrative of thirty-four years slavery and travels in Africa. London, Sir Richard Phillips and co., 1819. 46p. (M326.8D89)

1550 Dumreicher, Andrè von. Trackers and smugglers in the deserts of Egypt. London, Methuen & co., ltd., 1931. 248p. (M916.2D89)

1551 Dunning, Harry Westbrook. To-day on the Nile. New York, J. Pott & co., 1905. 270p. (M962D92)

1552 Dust, Muhammed. The vision of Duse Mohamed Ali the Egyptian. [n.p., n.p. ca. 1924] 8p. (M962D94v)

1553 Dye, William M. Moslem Egypt and Christian Abyssinia .... New York, Atkin & Prout, 1880. 500p. (M916.2D98)

1554 Ebers, Georg Moritz. Aegyptische studien und verwandtes. Stuttgart und Leipzig, Deutsche verlags-anstalt, 1900. 517p. (M9-13.32Eb3)

1555 Ebers, Georg Moritz. Egypt: descriptive, historical and picturesque. Tr. from the original German by Clara Bell. With an introduction and notes by S. Birch ... London, Paris [etc.] Cassell & company, limited, [1878-79] 2vols (M932Eb3)

1556 Ebers, Georg Moritz. An Egyptian princess. New York, A. L. Burt, n.d. 518p. (M893.1Eb3e)

1557 Ebers, Georg Moritz. Uarda; a romance of ancient Egypt ...[tr. from the German by Clara Bill] New York, A. L. Burt, [1901] 485p. (M893.1Eb3u)

1558 Edgerton, William Franklin. The Thutmosid succession. Chicago, Univ. of Chicago press, 1933. 43p. (M913.32 Ed3)

1559 Edwards, Amelia Ann Blanford. Egypt and its monuments; Pharaohs, fellahs and explorers. New York, Harper and bros., 1891. 325p. (M962Edg)

1560 Edwards, Amelia Ann Blanford. Pharaohs, fellahs and explorers. New York, Harper and bros., [1891] 325p. (M932Ed9)

1561 Edwards, Amelia Ann Blanford. A thousand miles up the Nile. Copyright ed. Leipzig, B. Tauchnitz, 1878. 2 vols (M962Edg)

1562 Edwards, Amelia Ann Blandford. A thousand miles up the Nile. London, George Routledge, 1891. 499p. (M962Ed9)

1563 Egypt. Government press. . . . Almanac . . . Cairo. 1938

1564 Egypt Labour Office. Annual report, 1935. (M962Eg9)

1565 Egypt, the youngest republic in the world, 6000 years old. Washington, D.C. Egyptian Embassy, 1954. 31p. (M962Eg9)

1566 Engelbach, Reginald. . . . Harageh . . . inscriptions by Battiscombe Gunn. London, British school of Archaeology in Egypt [etc.] 1923. 40p. (M913.32En3h)

1567 Engelbach, Reginald. The problem of the obelisks; inscriptions by Battiscombe Gunn. London, T. F. Unwin, limited, 1923. 134p. (M913.32En3p)

1568 Engelbach, Reginald. Riqqeh and Memphis VI . . . with chapters by M. A. Murray, H. Flinders Petrie, London School of Archaeology in Egypt, University College, 1915. 38p. (M913.32En3)

1569 Erman, Adolf. Life in ancient Egypt. London and New York, MacMillan and co., 1894. 570p. (M913.32Er5)

1570 Erman, Adolf. The literature of the ancient Egyptians; poems, narratives, and manuals of instruction, from the third and second millannia B.C. Translated into English by Aylward M. Blackman. New York, E. P. Dutton and co. 1927. 318p. (M932ER5)

1571 Francis, René. Egyptian aesthetics. Chicago, Open Court Publishing co., 1912. 276p. (M916.2F84)

1572 Frankfort, Henri. The birth of civilization in the Near East. Bloomington, Indiana University Press, 1951. 116p. (M932-F84b)

1573 Frankfort, Henri. Kingship and the gods, a study of ancient Near Eastern religion as the integration of society & nature. Chicago, University of Chicago, 1948. 444p. (M932F85k)

1574 Frobenius, Leo. Hadschra maktuba, urzeitliche felsbilder Kleinafrikas. Munchen, K. Wolff, 1925. 61p. (AM913.3F92)

1575 Furniss, William. Waraga; or the charms of the Nile. New York, Baker and Scribner, 1850. (M916.2F98)

1576 Gardiner, Alan Henderson. Egyptian grammar; being an introduction to the study of hieroglyphs. Oxford, The Clarendon Press, 1927. 5959p. (M493.1G16)

1577 Gardner, John M. Pharaohs resurrected. New York, Sorg Publishing co., 1923. 71p. (M932G16p)

1578 Garstang, John. El Arábah: a cemetery of the Middle Kingdom; Survey of the old Kingdom Temenas; graffiti from the temple of Sety. London, B. Quaritch, 1901. 49p. (M913.32G19a)

1579 Garstang, John. Mahâsna and Bêt Kehallâf. With a chapter by Kurt Sethe. London, B. Quaritch, 1903. 42p. (M913.32G-19m)

1580 Gau, Francois Chrétien. Antiquités de la Nubie. Stuttgart, J. G. Cotta, 1822. [27.] 84p. (M932G23a)

1581 Gliddon, Goeerge R. Egyptian archaeology and hieroglyphical discoveries. London, James Madden, 1849. 148p.

1582 Golding, Louis. In the steps of Moses the lawgiver. New York, The Macmillan co., 1938. 355p. (M221.9G56)

1583 Gorringe, Henry Honeychurch. Egyptian obelisks. New York, Published by the author, 1882. 187p. (M913.32G68e)

1584 Gottheil, Richard James Horatio. The history of the Egyptian Cadis. Paris, Paul Geuthner, 1908. unnumbered leaves. (M-962G71h)

1585 Great ones of ancient Egypt; portraits by Winifred Brunton; historical studies by various Egyptologists. New York, C. Scribner's sons, 1930. 177p. (M932G79)

1586 Griffith, Francis Llewellyn. . . . Karanog; the Meroitic inscriptions of Shablul and Karanog . . . Philadelphia. . . . University Museum, 1911 181p. (M913.32G87)

1587 Groff, William N. Oeuvres Egyptologiques. Paris, Ernest Leroux, 1908. 503p. (M493.1G75)

1588 Hall, Trowbridge. Egypt in silhouette. New York, The Macmillan co., 1928. 278p. (M916.2H14)

1589 Hassan, Hassan Ibrahim. Relations between Egypt and the Caliphate. Cairo, Association of Authorship, Translation & Publication Press, 1940. 27p. (M962H27r)

1590 Hassan, Hassan Ibrahim. Relations between the Fatimids in North Africa and Egypt and the Umayyads in Spain during the 4th century A.H. (10th Century A.D.) Cairo, Fouad I University Press, 1948. 45p. (M962H27re)

1591 Hawks, Francis Lister. The monuments of Egypt; or Egypt a witness for the Bible . . . With illustrations. 4 ed., rev. and enl. New York, G. P. Putnam, 1854. 298p. (M913.32H31)

1592 Heeren, A. H. L. Historical researches into the politics, intercourse, and trade of the Carthaginians, Ethiopians, and Egyptians. London, H. G. Bohn, 1850. 520p. (M913.32H36)

1593 Hengenstenberg, E. W. Egypt and the books of Moses, or the book of Moses illustrated by the monuments of Egypt, with an appendix. From the German of R. D. C. Robbins. New York, Robert Carter and Brothers, 1850. 300p. (M220.93H39)

1594 Hichens, Robert Smythe. Egypt and its monuments. Illustrated by Jules Guérin and with photographs. New York, The Century co., 1923. 272p. (M932H52)

1595 Hichens, Robert Smythe. The spell of Egypt. New York, The Century co., 1911. 272p. (M932H52s)

1596 Ibrahim-Hilmy. The literature of Egypt and the Soudan from the earliest times to the year 1885 [i.e. 1887] inclusive. A bibliography: comprising printed books, periodical writings, and papers of learned societies; maps and charts; ancient papyri, manuscripts, drawings. London, Trubner and co., 1886-87. 2 v. (M016Ib7)

1597 Issawi, Charles Philip. Egyptian economic and social analysis, issued under the auspices of the Royal Institute of International Affairs, London, Oxford Univ. Press, 1947. 219p. (M962Is7)

1598 Jarvis, Claude Scudamore. Three deserts. New York, E. P. Dutton & co., 1937. 313p. (M916.2J29)

1599 Kandt, Richard. Caput Nili. Berlin, Dietrich Reimer, 1919. 2v. (M916.2K13)

1600 Kelly, Robert Talbot. Egypt. London, A. and C. Black, 1908. 86p. (M916.2K29)

1601 Kelly, Robert Talbot. Egypt painted and described. London A. and C. Black, 1902. 239p. (M932K29e)

1602 Kenrick, John. Ancient Egypt under the Pharaohs. London, B. Fellowes, 1850. 2v. (M932K41)

1603 King, Leonard William. History of Egypt, Chaldea, Syria, Babylonia and Assyria in the light of recent discovery. London, The Grolier Society, 1906. 468p. (M932K58h)

1604 Klunzinger, Karl Benjamin. Upper Egypt: its people and its products . . . New York, Scribner, Armstrong and Co., m1878. 408p. (M962K71)

1605 Knapp, Martin Wells. Out of Egypt into Canaan; or, lessons in spiritual geography. Boston, McDonald, Gill and Co.; Albion, Mich., The Revivalist Publishing Co., 1887. 196p. (M962K72)

1606 Lane, Edward William. The manners and customs of the modern

Egyptians. London, J. M. Dent and Co., New York, E. P. Dutton and Co., 1908. 630p. (M962L24)

1607 Lane, James Franklin. Some things we saw while abroad; a visit to Europe, the Holy Land and Egypt. Boston, The Christopher Publishing House [c1941.] 224p. (M910.4L24)

1608 Lane-Pool, Stanley. Social life in Egypt, a description of the country and its people with illustrations on steel and wood. New York, Collier. 138p. (M916.2L24)

1609 Lanoye, Ferdinand de. Rameses the Great. New York, Scribner and sons, 1885. 296p. (M932L28r)

1610 Legh, Thomas. Narrative of a journey in Egypt and the country beyond the cataracts. London, John Murray, 1816. 157p. (M962L52n)

1611 Lepsius, Richard. Letters from Egypt, Ethiopia, and the peninsula of Sinai. London, H. G. Bohn, 1853. 578p. (M13.32L55)

1612 Lhote, André. Les chefs-d'oeuvre de la peinture Égyptienne. Photographies de Hassia. Préface de Jacques Vandier. [Paris,] Harchette, [1954.] 245p. (M750L61)

1613 Lobo, Jeronymo. A short relation of the Nile, of its source and current: of its overflowing the campagnia of Egypt, till it runs into the Mediterranean; and of other curiosities; written by an eye-witness, who lived many years in the chief kingdoms of the Abyssine empire. London, J. Martyn, 1673. 104p. (M960L61s)

1614 Lokke, C. L. L'expédition d'Égypte et les projects de cultures coloniales, par C. L. Lokke et G. Debien. Egypt, Imprimé par l'Imprimerie, 1940. 337-56p. (M962L83)

1615 Low, Sidney James Mark. Egypt in transition. London, Smith, Elder and Co., 1914. 290p. (M962L95)

1616 Lucas, Alfred. Ancient Egyptian materials and industries. London, E. Arnold & Co., 1934. 447p. (M913.32L96)

1617 Lutz, Henry Frederick. Saitic myths in Arabic tradition. Berkley and Los Angeles, University of California Press, 1946. 312p. (M962L97s)

1618 McCoan, James Carlile. Egypt. With a supplementary chapter of recent events by Wilfred C. Lay. New York, The Cooperative Publication Society, [1900.] 478p. (M962M13e)

1619 McCoan, James Carlile. Egypt as it is. London, New York, Cassell, Petter & Galpin, [1877.] 433p. (M962M13)

1620 MacMillan, firm, publishers, London. Guide to Egypt and the Sudan, including a description of the route through Uganda to Mombasa. 5th ed. London, MacMillan and Co., 1908. (M962-M22)

1621   Madden, Richard R. Travels in Turkey, Egypt, Nubia and Palestine in 1824, 1825, 1826, and 1827. Philadelphia, Carey and Tea, 1830. 2v. (M916.2M26)

1622   Manning, Samuel. The land of the Pharaohs. Egypt and Sinai. London, The Religious Tract Society, [1875.] 223p. (M916.2M31)

1623   Marden, Philip Sanford. Egyptian days. Boston and New York, Houghton Miflllin Co., 1912. 329p. (M932M33)

1624   Marlowe, John. A history of modern Egypt and Anglo-Egyptian relations, 1800-1953. New York, Praeger, 1954. 440p. (M962M34)

1625   Martin, Richard A. Mummies. Chicago, Chicago Natural History Museum Press, 1945. 18p. (M962M36m)

1626   Maspero, Gaston Camille Charles. The dawn of civilization, Egypt and Chaldaea. New York, D. Appleton and Co., [1894.] 804p. (M930M38d)

1627   Maspero, Gaston Camille Charles. Egyptain archaeology. New York, Putnam's sons, 1887. 328p. (M913.32M38)

1628   Maspero, Gaston Camille Charles. History of Egypt. London, The Grolier Society, 1901? 9v (M962M38h)

1629   Maspero, Gaston Camille Charles. Ruines et paysages d'Égypte. Paris, E. Guilmoto, 1910. 326p. (M913.32M38r)

1630   Maspero, Gaston Camile Charles. The struggle of the nations, Egypt, Syria and Assyria. New York, D. Appleton & Co., 1897. 794p. (M930M38s)

1631   Mathews, Joseph James. Egypt and the formation of the Anglo-French entente of 1904. Philadelphia, University of Penna. Press, 1939. 141p. (M962M42e)

1632   Meadowcroft, Enid LaMonte. The gift of the river; a history of ancient Egypt. New York, Thomas Y. Crowell Co., 1937. 235p. (M932M46)

1633   Meier-Graefe, Julius. Pyramid and temple. London, New York, The Macaulay Co., 1934. 361p. (M916.2M47)

1634   Mercer, Samuel Alfred Broune. The religion of ancient Egypt. London, Luzac & Co., 1949. 260p. (M962M53r)

1635   Mertz, Richard Rolland. Some aspects of Egyptian autobiographies before the new kingdom. Chicago, University of Chicago Library, Dept. of Photographic Reproduction, 1953. Microfilm copy of typescript. Positive. Collation of original: 180 leaves. Dissertation.—M. A. Chicago University. (M962-M55)

1636 Mileham, Geoffrey S. Churches in lower Nubia. Philadelphia, The University Museum, 1910. 57p. (M913.32M59)

1637 Moorhead, Alan. Mediterranean front. New York, London, Whittlesey House, McGraw Hill Book Co., 1942. 306p. (M962M87)

1638 Moret, Alexandre. From tribe to empire . . . New York, A. A. Knopf, 1926. 371p. (M932M81f)

1639 Moret, Alexandre. In the time of the Pharaohs. New York and London, G. P. Putnam's Sons, 1911. 310p. (M932M81i)

1640 Moret, Alexandre. Kings and gods of Egypt. New York and London, G. P. Putnam's Sons, 1912. 290p. (M962M81k)

1641 Muir, William. The Mameluke; or, Slave dynasty of Egypt, 1260-1517. London, Smith, Elder and Co., 1896. 245p. (M932M89)

1642 Murray, G. W. Sons of Ishmael; a study of the Egyptian Bedouin. London, G. Routledge & Sons, 1935. 344p. (AM572.962M96)

1643 Murray, Margaret Alice. Index of names and titles of the old kingdom. London, Office of British School of Archaeology, 1908. 5p. (M913.32M96)

1644 Murray, Margaret Alice. The Osireion at Abydos. London, B. Quaritch, 1904. 47p. (M913.32M960)

1645 Murray, Margaret Alice. Saqqara mastabas, Part 1. London, B. Quaritch, 1905. 50p. (M913.32M96v)

1646 Murray, Margaret Alice. The splendour that was Egypt; a general survey of Egyptian culture and civilisation. New York, Philosophical Library, 1954. 354p. (M932M958)

1647 Murtadi, ibn al-Kafif. The Egyptian history, treating of the pyramids, the inundation of the Nile, and other prodigies of Egypt, according to the opinions and traditions of the Arabians. Written originally in the Arabian tongue by Murtadi the son of Gaphiphus. Rendered into the French by Monsieur Vattier Arabick Professor to the King of France. And thence faithfully done into English by J. Davies of Kidwelly. London, Printed by R. B. for Thomas Basset at the George, near Cliffords-Inn in Fleet Street, 1672. 226p. (M362M96e)

1648 Naville, Édouard Henri. Cemeteries of Abydes. Part 1. 1909-

1910. London, Egypt Exploration Fund, 1914. 54p. (M913.
32N22)

1649 Naville, Édouard Henri. Egypt Exploration Fund. The store-city
of Pithom and the route of the exodus. London, Trubner and
Co., 1903. 40p. (M932N22)

1650 Naville, Édouard Henri. The old Egyptian faith. London, Williams and Norgate, 1909. 321p. (M962N22o)

1651 Naville, Édouard Henri. The temple of Deir el Bahari. London,
Offices of the Egypt Exploration Fund, 1907. (M913.32N22d)

1652 Naville, Édouard Henri. The tomb of Hatshopsitu. London, A.
Canstable and Co., 1906. 112p. (M913.32N22t)

1653 New York public library. Ancient Egypt 1925-1941. A supplement to Ancient Egypt: Sources of information in the New
York public library, 1925, compiled by Ida A. Pratt. New
York, The New York public library, 1942. 340p. (MO15.
32N48)

1654 Norden, Frederic Lewis. The antiquities, natural history, ruins,
and other curiosities of Egypt, Nubia, and Theves. Exempli-
fied in near 200 drawings, taken on the spot. Member of the
Royal Societies of London, Paris, and Copenhagen, and com-
mander of a vessel sent by the King of Denmark to collect
materials towards explaining the history of those countries.
The whole engraved on 164 large plates including a portrait
of the author, by Martin Teuscher of Nuremberg. London,
Printed for Lockyer Davis, 1780. 164p. (M932N75)

1655 Norden, Frederick Lewis. Travels in Egypt and Nubia. London,
Davis & Reymers, 1757. 2v. (M916.2N75)

1656 Noshy, Ibrahim. The Coptic Church; Christianity in Egypt. Rev.
and ed. by Patricia Natirbov. Washington, Ruth Sloan Associates, [1955.] [23p.] (M962N84c)

1657 Pallme, Ignatius. Travels in Kordofan. London, Madden & Co.,
1844. 356p. (AM916.28P18)

1658 Pasha, Marcus H. Simaika. A brief guide to the Coptic Museum
and to the principal ancient Coptic Churches of Cairo. Cairo,
Government Press, Bulaq, 1938. 91p. (M962.16P26)

1659 Peel, Sidney Cornwallis. The binding of the Nile and the new
Soudan. London, E. Arnold, 1904. 288p. (M962P34)

1660 Peet, T. E. Cemeteries of Abydos. Pt. 3. 1912-1913. London,
Egypt, Exploration fund, 1913. 54p. (M913.32P34)

1661 Perrot, Georges. A history of art in ancient Egypt. London,

Chapman and Hall, limited, 1883. 14p. (M709P43)

1662 Perry, Walter S. Egypt, land of the Temple builders. Boston, N. Y., The Prang educational Co., [1898.] 249p. (M962P42)

1663 Petrie, William Matthew Flinders. Athribis. London, School of archaeology in Egypt, Univ. College, 1908. 26p. (M913.32-P44a)

1664 Petrie, William Matthew Flinders. Buttons and designs scarabs. London, British school of archaeology in Egypt, 1925. 34p. (M913.32P44b)

1665 Petrie, William Matthew Flinders. Corpus of prehistoric pottery and palettes. London, British school of archaeology in Egypt. Univ. college, 1921. 7p. (M913.32P44c)

1666 Petrie, William Matthew Flinders. Egypt and Israel. New York, E. S. Gorham, 1911. 150p. (M913.32P45e)

1667 Petrie, William Matthew Flinders. The formation of the alphabet. London, Macmillan and Co., 1912. 20p. (M913.32P44f)

1668 Petrie, William Matthew Flinders. Gerar. London, British school of archaeology in Egypt, 1928. 34p. (M913.32P44g)

1669 Petrie, William Mathew Flinders. Gizeh and Rifeh. London, School of archaeology, Univ. college, 1907. 49p. (M913.32-P44gi)

1670 Petrie, William Matthew Flinders. The Hawara portifolio: paintings of the Roman age, . . . 1888 and 1911. London, School of archaeology in Egypt, and Egyptian research account, nineteenth year, 1913. (M913.32P44ro)

1671 Petrie, William Matthew Flinders. Heliopolis, Kafr Ammar and Shurafa. London, School of archaeology in Egypt, Univ. college, 1915. 55p. (M913.32P44ho)

1672 Petrie, William Matthew Flinders. A history of Egypt. London, Methuen and Co., 1898-1905. 6v. (M932P44)

1673 Petrie, William Matthew Flinders. Hyksos and Israelite cities. London, School of Archaeology, Univ. college, 1906. 76p. (M913.32P44h)

1674 Petrie, William Matthew Flinders. The Labyrinth, Gerzeh, and Mazghunch. London, School of archaeology in Egypt, 1912. 59p. (M913.32P441)

1675 Petrie, Matthew Flinders. Memphis. London, School of archaeology in Egypt, 1909. (M913.32P44me)

1676 Petrie, William Matthew Flinders. Meydum and Memphis III.

London, School of archaeology in Egypt, 1910. 50p. (M913.-32P44m)

1677   Petrie, William Matthew Flinders and Quibell, J. E.   Naqada and Ballas. 1895 . . . with chapters by F. C. J. Spurrell. London, B. Quaritch, 1896. 79p. (M913.32P44n)

1678   Petrie, William Matthew Flinders. Objects of daily use. London, British School of Arch. in Egypt, 1927. 75p. (M913.32P44o)

1679   Petrie, William Matthew Flinders. . . . The palace of Apries (Memphis II) . . . with a chapter by Dr. J. H. Walker. London, School of archaeology in Egypt, University college, etc., 1909. 25p. (M913.32P44p)

1680   Petrie, William Matthew Flinders. Prehistoric Egypt. London, British School of arch. in Egypt. University college, 1920. 54p. (M913.32P44pr)

1681   Petrie, William Matthew Flinders. Qurneh. London, School of Archaeology in Egypt, 1909. 21p. (M913.32P44q)

1682   Petrie, William Matthew Flinders. . . . Roman portraits and Memphis (IV) . . . London, School of archaeology in Egypt, University college, 1911. 26p. (M913.32P44r)

1683   Petrie, William Matthew Flinders . . . Scarabs and cylinders with names. London, School of archaeology in Egypt. Univ. college, 1917. 45p. (M913.32P44sc)

1684   Petrie, William Matthew Flinders. Sedment. London, British school of archaeology in Egypt, 1924. (M913.32P44s)

1685   Petrie, William Matthew Flinders. Seventy years in archaeology. New York, H. Holt & Co., [c1932.] 307p. (M913.32P44se)

1686   Petrie, William Matthew Flinders. Tarkham I and Memphis V. London, School of acrhaeology in Egypt, 1913. 39p. (M913.-32P44t)

1687   Petrie, William Matthew Flinders.   Tarkham II, London. School of archaeology in Egypt, Univ. college, 1914. 29p. (M913.-32P44ta)

1688   Petrie, William Matthew Flinders. Tombs of the courtiers and Oxyrhynkhos. London, British school of archaeology in Egypt, 1925. 31p. (M913.32P44tom)

1689   Petrie, William Matthew Flinders. Tools and weapons. London, British school of archaeology in Egypt, 1917. 71p. (M913.-32P44to)

1690   Petrie, William Matthew Flinders. Wisdom of the Egyptians. London, British school of archaeology in Egypt and B. Quaritch, Ltd., 1940. 162p. (M913.32P44w)

1691 Pettigrew, Thomas Joseph. A history of Egyptian mummies. London, Longman, 1834. 264p. (M913.32P45h)

1692 Pollard, Joseph. The land of the monuments. London, Hodder and Stoughton, 1896. 456p. (M962P761)

1693 Prime, William Cowper. Boat life in Egypt and Nubia. New York, Harper & Brothers, 1857. 498p. (M962P63)

1694 Quibell, James Edward. Hierakonpolis. London, Bernard Quaritch, 1900-1902. 2v. (M913.32Q4)

1695 Quibell, James Edward. El Kab. London, B. Quaritch, 1898. 23p. (M913.32Q4e)

1696 Quibell, James Edward. . . . The Ramesseum, with translations and comments by W. Spiegelberg; and the Tomb of Ptah-hetep. Copied by R. F. E. Paget and A. A. Pine with comments by F. L. T. Griffith. London, B. Quaritch, 1898. 36p (M913.-32Q4r)

1697 Randall-MacIver, David. Mediaeval Rhodesia. London, New York, Macmillan and Co., Limited, 1906. 106p. (M913.32R15)

1698 Randall-MacIver, David and Wolley, C. L. Buhen. Philadelphia, University Museum, 1911. 2v. (M913.32R15b)

1699 Rappoport, Angelo Solomon. History of Egypt from 330 B. C. to the present time. London, the Grolier soc., 1904. 3v. (M962-R18h)

1700 Rawlinson, George. History of Ancient Egypt . . . New York, John B. Alden, publisher, 1890. 2vols. (M913.32R19)

1701 Records of the past. London, S. Bagster and Sons, 1874-81. 12vols. (M932R24)

1702 Reynolds-Ball, Eustace Alfred. The city of the caliphs. Boston, Estes and Lauriat, 1897. 335p. (M962.16R33c)

1703 Robichon, Clement. En Egypte. Paris, Hartman, 1937. plates. (M916.2R56)

1704 Romer, Mrs. Isabella Frances. A pilgrimage to the temples and tombs of Egypt. Nubia and Palestine. London, R. Bentley, 1846. 2v. (M916.2R66)

1705 Ross, Sir Edward Denision. The art of Egypt through the ages. London, The Studio, Ltd., 1931. 354p. (M913.32R73)

1706 Russell, Michael. View of ancient and modern Egypt; with an outline of its natural history. New York, Harper and Bros., 1842. 348p. (932R91)

1707 St. John, Bayle. Village life in Egypt; with sketches of the Sáid. Boston, Ticknor, Reed and Fields, 1853. 218p. (M916.2St2)

1708 St. John, James Augustus. Egypt and Nubia, their scenery and their people. London, Chapman & Hall, 1845. 472p. (M916.-2Sa2)

1709 Sandford, Kenneth S. First report of the prehistoric survey expedition. Chicago, Univ. of Chicago Press, 1928. 52p. (M-913.32Sa5f)

1710 Sandford, Kenneth Stuart. Paleolithic man and the Nile-Faiyum divide, Chicago, The Univ. of Chicago Press, 1929. 77p. (M913.32Sa5p)

1711 Sandford, Kenneth Stuart. Paleolithic man and the Nile valley in upper and middle Egypt. Chicago, Univ. of Chicago Press, 1934. 131p. (M913.32Sa5pa)

1712 Schodde, George H. Herma Nabi, the Ethiopic version of pastor hernae examined. Leipzig, F. A. Brockhaus, 1876. 45p. (M932Sch6)

1713 Seifert, Charles C. The three African saviour kings. New York, Charles C. Seifert, n.d. 20p. (M932Se4t)

1714 Seligman, Charles Gabriel. Egypt and Negro Africa; a study in divine kingship. London, G. Routledge and Sons, Ltd., 1934. (M321.6Se4)

1715 Sharpe, Samuel. The history of Egypt under the Ptolemies. London, Edward Moxon, 1838. 220p. (M932Sh2h)

1716 Sharpe, Samuel. The history of Egypt; from the earliest times till the conquest by the Arabs, A. D. 640. London, Edward Moxon, 1852. 2vols. (M932Sh2hi)

1717 Sharpe, Samuel. The history of Egypt, under the Romans. London, Edward Moxon, 1842. 276p. (M932Sh2)

1718 Simcox, Edith Jemima. Primitive civilizations; or, outlines of the history of ownership in arabic communities. New York, The Macmillan Co., 1897. 2vols. (M932Si4p)

1719 Smith, Earl Baldwin. Egyptian architecture as cultural expression. New York, Appleton-Century Co., Inc., 1938. 264p. (M913.-32Sm5)

1720 Smith, Grafton Elliot and Dawson, Warren R. Egyptian mummies with woodcuts by A. Horace Gerrard and K. Leigh-Pemberton and other illustrations. London, G. Allen & Unwin, Ltd., 1924. 189p. (M393.3Sm5)

1721 Smith, Jerome Van Crowninshield. A pilgrimage to Egypt . . .

Boston, Gould and Lincoln, 1852. 383p. (M916.2Sm5)

1722 Speke, John Hanning. Journal of the discovery of the source of
the Nile. New York, Harper, 1864. 480p. (M916.2sp3)

1723 Spence, Lewis. The mysteries of Egypt; or, the secret rites and
traditions of the Nile. London, Rider and Co., 1929. 285p.
(M962Sp3m)

1724 Spence, Lewis. Myths and legends of ancient Egypt. New York,
Frederick A. Stokes Co., 1915. 369p. (M913.32Sp3m)

1725 Spiegelberg, Wilhelm. Hieratic ostraka and papyri found by J. E.
Quibell in the Ramesseum, 1895-6. London, B. Quaritch, 1898.
99p. (M913.32Sp4)

1726 Steindorff, George. When Egypt ruled the East. Chicago, Univ.
of Chicago Press, 1942. 284p. (M932St34)

1727 Tabouis, G. R. The private life of Tutankhamen; love, religion,
and politics at the court of an Egyptian king. New York,
R. M. McBride & Co., 1929. 322p. (MB9T88t)

1728 Taylor, Bayard. A journey to Central Africa; or life and landscapes from Egypt to the Negro kingdoms of the White Nile.
New York, G. P. Putnam's Sons, 1867. 552p. (M962T21)

1729 Taylor, Issac. Leaves from an Egyptian note-book. London,
Kegan Paul, Trench & Co., 1888. 157p. (M962T211)

1730 Tien, Anton. Egyptian, Syrian, and North-African hand-book;
a simple phrase-book in English and Arabic... New York,
F. Ungar, 1943. 173p. (M492.7T44)

1731 Thompson, Arthur. The ancient races of the Thebaid . . . Oxford
Clarendon Press, 1905. 142p. (M932T38)

1732 Thurston, Arthur Blyford. African incidents; personal experiences
in Egypt and Unyoro. London, J. Murray, 1900. 331p.
(M967.6T42a)

1733 Uhlemann, M. A. Three days in Memphis; or sketches of the
public and private life of the old Egyptians. Philadelphia,
J. B. Lippincott and Co., 1858. 253. (M932Uh6)

1734 Wallace, Susan E. The repose in Egypt... New York, J. B. Alden,
1888. 391. (M916.2W15)

1735 Warburton, Eliot (ie.) Bartholomew Elliott George. The cresent
and the cross . . . Leipzig, B. Tauchnitz jun., 1852. 2 vols.
(AM916W19)

1736 Ward, John. Pyramids and progress; sketches from Egypt. Lon-

don, New York, Eyre and Spottiswoode, 1900. 288p. (M932-
W21p)

1737 Warner, Charles Dudley. My winter on the Nile. Boston, Houghton Mifflin & Co., 1899. 496p. (AM916W24)

1738 Weigall, Arthur Edward Pearse Brome. The glory of the Pharaohs
. . . with 17 illustrations. New York, London, G. P. Putnam's
Sons, 1923. 338p. (M913.32W429)

1739 Weigall, Arthur Edward Pearse Brome. A guide to the antiquities
of upper Egypt, from Abydos to the Sudan frontier. London,
Methuen & Co., Ltd., 1910. 594p. (M913.32W42gu)

1740 Weigall, Arthur Edward Pearse Brome. The life and times of
Aknaton, pharaoh of Egypt. New York, Putnam's sons, 1923.
255p. (M932W42)

1741 Weigall, Arthur Edward Pearse Brome. The life and times of
Cleopatra, queen of Egypt. London, T. Butterworth ltd.,
1923. 317p. (M932W421)

1742 Wertheimer, Oskar von. Cleopatra, a royal voluptuary. Philadelphia and London, J. P. Lippincott co., 1931. 325p. (M932-
W49)

1743 Westermann, William Linn. Upon slavery in Ptolemaic Egypt.
New York, Columbia University Press, 1929. 69p. (M3268EW52)

1744 Wilkinson, John Gardner. A popular account of the ancient Egyptians. London, J. Murray, 1854. 2 vols. (M932W65)

1745 Wilson, John Albert. The burden of Egypt; (an interpretation of
ancient Egyptian culture. Chicago, University of Chicago Press,
1951. 332p. (M932W69b)

1746 Worrell, William Hoyt. A short account of the Copts. Ann Arbor,
University of Michigan Press, 1945. 54p. (M932W89)

1747 Wood, Frederic H. This Egyptian miracle. Philadelphia, David
McKay co., 1939. 256p. (M913.32W85)

1748 Woolley, Charles Leonard. Karanog; the Romano-Nubian cemetery.
Philadelphia, the University Museum, 1910. 115p. (M913.-
32W83)

1749 Woolley, Charles Leonard. Karanog, the town. Philadelphia, University Museum, 1911. 51p. (M913.32W83k)

1750 Worsfold, William Basil. The redemption of Egypt. London,
George Allen & Unwin, 1899. 33p. (AM916W89)

1751 Wyndham, Richard. The gentle savage; a Sudanese journey in the
province of Bahr-el-Ghazal, commonly called "The Bog." New

York, W. Morrow and co., 1936. 278p. (AM9165.2W98)

1752 Yahuda, Abraham Shalom. The language of the Pentateuch in its
relation to Egyptian. London, Oxford University Press, H.
Milford, 1933. 24p. (M493.1Yal)

1753 Young, Thomas. An account of some recent discoveries in hieroglyphical literature and Egyptian antiquities. Including the
author's original alphabet, as extended by Mr. Champollion
with a translation of five unpublished Greek and Egyptian
manuscripts. London, J. Murray, 1823. 160p. (M419.25y85a)

SUDAN

1754 Abbas, Mekki. The Sudan question; the dispute over the Anglo-
Egyptian condominium, 1884-1951. London, Faber and Faber,
201p. (M962.4Ab2)

1755 Alford, H. S. L. The Egyptian Soudan, its loss and its recovery.
London, New York, Macmillan and co., ltd., 1898. 336p.
(AM962.4A12e)

1756 Allen, William. Picturesque views on the river Niger. London, J.
Murray, etc., 1840. 18p. (AM966.21A1p5)

1757 Arkell, Anthony John. A history of the Sudan: from the earliest
times in 1821. London, University of London, Athlone Press,
1955. 249p. (M962.4Ar4)

1758 Atteridge, A. H. Towards Khartoum, the story of the Soudan War
of 1896. London, A. D. Innes and co., 1897. 357p. (AM962.-
4At8t)

1759 Baker, Samuel White. The Albert N'yanza, great basin of the
Nile, and explorations of the Nile sources. London, Macmillan
and co., 1866. 2v. (M962B17)

1760 Baker, Samuel White. In the heart of Africa. New York, Funk
& Wagnalls, 1884. 286p. (AM962.6B17)

1761 Bernatzik, Hugo Adolf. Gari-Gari; the call of the African wilderness. Translated from the German by Vivian Ogilvie. New
York, H. Holt & co., [1936] 146p. (M916.24B45)

1762 Bingham, Rowland V. Seven sevens of years and a jubilee! Toronto,
New York, Evangelical publishers, 1943. 122p. (AM966.-
2B51s)

1763 Budge, Ernest Alfred T. W. The Egyptian Súdân, its history and
monuments. London, K. Paul, Trench, Trubner and co., ltd.,
1907. (AM962.6B85e)

1764 Burleigh, Bennet. Sidar and khalifa; or, The re-conquest of the

Soudan, 1898. London, Chapman & Hall, ltd., 1898. 305p.
(M962.6B92)

1765 Butt, Audrey J. The Nilotes of the Anglo-Egyptian Sudan and
Uganda. London, International African Institute, 1952. 198p.
(AM962.4P98)

1766 Carpenter, Frank George. Cairo to Kisumu; Cairo-the Sudan-
Kenya colony. Garden City, N.Y., Doubleday, Page & company, 1923. 313p. (M962C22c)

1767 Clapperton, Hugh. Journal of a second expedition into the Interior
of Africa, from the Bight of Benin to Soccatoo. London, J.
Murray, 1829. 355p. (AM966.2C53)

1768 Cooley, William Desborough. The Negro land of the Arabs exam-
imed and explained; or, An inquiry into the early history and
geography of Central Africa. London, J. Arrowsmight, 1841.
143p. (AM966.2C77)

1769 Crabitès, Pierre. Americans in the Egyptian army. London, G.
Routledge & sons, ltd., [1938] 277p. (M962C84)

1770 Crabitès, Pierre. Gordon, the Sudan and slavery. London. G.
Routledge and sons, ltd. 1933. 334p. (MC9G65c)

1771 Domville-Fife, Charles William. Savage life in the black Sudan; an
account of an adventurous journey of exploration amongst
wild & little-known tribes inhabiting swamps, dense forests,
mountain-tops & arid deserts hitherto almost unknown, with a
description of their manner of living, secret societies & mysterious & barbaric rites. London, Seeley, Service & co., limited,
1927. 284p. (M916.26D71)

1772 Duncan, J. S. R. The Sudan; a record of achievement. Edinburgh,
Blackwood, 1952. 283p. (M962.4D91s)

1773 English, George B. A narrative of the expedition to Dongola and
Sennaar, under the command of His Excellence Ismael Pasha,
undertaken by order of His Highness Mehemmed Ali Pasha,
Viceroy of Egypt. Boston, Welles and Lilly, 1923. 232p.
(M962.6En4)

1774 Evans-Pritchard, Edward Evan. The divine kingship of Shilluk of
the Nilotic Sudan. Cambridge, The University Press, 1948.
39p. (M962.6Ev1d)

1775 Evans-Pritchard, Edward Evan. Kinship and marriage among the
Nuer. Oxford, Clarendon Press, 1951. 183p. (AM572.962-
4Ev1k)

1776 Evans-Pritchard, Edward Evan. The Nuer, a description of the modes of livelihood and political institutions of a Nilotic people. Oxford, At Clarendon Press, 1940. 271p. (M962.4Ev1)

1777 Gessi, Romolo. Seven years in the Soudan. London, S. Low, Marston and co., 1892. 467p. (AM966.2G65s)

1778 Gordon, Charles George. The journals of Major General C. G. Gordon, C. B., at Khartoum. London, K. Paul, Trench and co., 1885. 587p. (AM962.6G65)

1779 Gordon Charles George. Lettres de Gordon a sa soeur ecrites du Soudan précédees d'une étude historique et biographique. Paris, J. Hetzel et cie. (n.d.) 332p. (AM966.2G551)

1780 Great Britain. British Information Services. Reference Division. The Sudan, 1899-1953. New York, Rockefeller Plaza, 1953. 58p. (M962.4G79)

1781 Great Britain. Central Office of Information. Growth of a nation, the story of the Sudan. London, Her Majesty's Stationery Office, 1953. 28p. (M962.5G79c)

1782 Griffiths, Vincent Llewellyn. An experiment in education; an account of the attempts to improve the lower stages of boys' education in the Moslem Anglo-Egyptian Sudan, 1930-1950. London, New York, Longman's Green, 1953. (M962.4G87)

1783 Guillebaud, Philippa F. School belts; letters from the southern Sudan. London, Church missionary society, 1949. 101p. (AM962.4G94s)

1784 Helser, Albert David. The hand of God in the Sudan. New York, London, etc., Fleming H. Revell Co., 1946. 144p. (AM266H-36h)

1785 Hill, Richard Leslie. A biographical dictionary of the Anglo-Egyptian Sudan. Oxford, Clarendon Press, 1951. 391p. (MBH55b)

1786 Hourst, Emile Auguste Leon. French enterprise in Africa; the personal narrative of Lieut. Hourst of his exploration of the Niger. London, Chapman and Hall, ltd. 1898. 520p. (AM-966.2H81f)

1787 Howell, Paul Philip. A manual of Nuer law, being an account of customary law, its evolution and development in the courts established by the Sudan Govt. London, New York, published for the International African Institute by the Oxford University Press, 1954. 256p. (M962.4H83m)

1788 Ibrahim-Hilmy, prince. The literature of Egypt and the Soudan from the earliest times to the year 1885 [i.e. 1887] inclusive.

A bibliography: comprising printed books, periodical writings, and papers of learned societies; maps and charts; ancient papyri, manuscripts, drawings, etc. London, Trubner and co, 1886-87. 2v. (M016Ib7)

1789   Jackson, H. C. Black ivory and white. Oxford, B. H. Blackwell, 1913. 118p. (AM962.6J13)

1790   James, Frank Linsly. The wild tribes of the Soudan. New York, Dodd, Mead and co., 1883. 280p. (AM962.6J23)

1791   Johnston, Harry H. History of the Slave. New York, George Munro, n.d. 120p. (AM966.2J64)

1792   MacMichael, Harold Alfred. The Sudan. London, Benn, 1954. 255p. (M962.4M22s)

1793   MacMichael, Harold Alfred. The tribes of northern and central Kordofan. Cambridge, University Press, 1912. 259p. (AM962.-8M22)

1794   Mann, Anthony. Where God laughed, The Sudan today. London, Museum Press, 1954. 221p. (M962.4M31)

1795   Martin, Percy F., The Sudan in evolution; a study of the economic, financial and administrative conditions of the Anglo-Egyptian Sudan. London, Constable and co., ltd., 1921. 559p. (M962-6M36)

1796   Mukherjee, Ramkrishna. The ancient inhabitants of Jebel Moya, Sudan. Cambridge, The University Press, 1955. 123p. (M962-6M89a)

1797   Nadel, Siegrried Frederick. The Nuba; an anthropological study of the hill tribes in Kordofan. London, New York, Oxford University Press, 1947. 527p. (M962.51N12m)

1798   Nalder, L. F. (ed.) A tribal survey of Mongalla province. London, New York, The Oxford University Press, 1937. 232p. (AM-572.9629N14)

1799   Newbold, Douglas. The making of the modern Sudan; the life and letters of Sir Douglas Newbold, K.B.E., of the Sudan Political Service, Governor of Kordofan, 1932-1938, Civil Secretary, 1939-1945. London, Faber and Faber [1953] 601p. (M962.-4N42)

1800   Niger, Valley Exploring Party. Official report of the Niger Valley exploring party. New York, T. Hamilton, 1861. 75p. (AM-916.66N56)

1801   Ohrwalder, Joseph. Ten years' captivity in the Mahdi's camp,

1882-1892. London, S. Low, Marston and co., ltd., 1892. 471p. (AM962.60h6)

1802 Pallme, Ignatius. Travels in Kordofan; embracing a description of that province of Egypt, and of some of the bordering countries, with a review of the present state of the commerce in those countries, of the habits and customs of the inhabitants, as also an account of the slave hunts taking place under the government of Mehemed Ali. London, J. Madden and co., 1844. 356p. (M916.28P18)

1803 Paul, Andrew. A history of the Beja tribes of the Sudan. Cambridge, Univ. Press, 1954. 163p. (M962.9P28)

1804 Peel, Sidney Cornwallis. The binding of the Nile and the new Soudan. London, E. Arnold, 1904. 288p. (M962P34)

1805 Russell, Henry, Journalist. The ruin of the Soudan, effect and remedy; a résumé of events, 1883-1891. London, S. Low, Marston and co., 1892. 407p. (M962.6R91r)

1806 Seligman, C. G. Pagan tribes of the nilotic Sudan. London, G. Routledge & sons, Ltd., 1932. 565p. (AM572.624Se4)

1807 Shibeika, Mekki. British policy in the Sudan, 1882-1902. London New York, Oxford University Press, 1952. 439p. (M962.4Sh-61)

1808 Simpson, William. A private journal kept during the Niger expedition. London, John F. Shaw, Edinburgh, J. Johnstone, 1843. 139p. (AM916.7Si5)

1809 Slatin, Rudolf Carl. Fire and sword in the Sudan. London, New New York, E. Arnold, 1896. 636p. (AM962.6S11f)

1810 Steevens, George W. With Kitchener to Kharum. New York, Dodd Mead and co., 1898. 326p. (AM962.4St3w)

1811 Streeter, Daniel Willard. Camels! New York, London, Putnam's sons, 1926. 277p. (AM799.2St8c)

1812 Sudan. Report on the administration of the Sudan for the year 1950-52. London, Her majesty's Stationery Office, 1952. 189p.

1813 Sudan. Self-determination in the Sudan; résumé of developments, November 15, 1851-January 1, 1956. London, Her Majesty's Stationery Office, 1956. 19p.

1814 Sudan, Egyptian. Governor-General. Report on the administration of the Sudan. London, H. M. Stationery Office, 1921. (M962-.4Su2)

1815 Sudan, Egyptian. The Sudan, a record of progress, 1898-1947. Sudan Government, 1947. 33p. (AM962.4Su2s)

1816 Sudan, Egyptian. Ministry of Agriculture. Annual report of the research division. 1948|49, 1949|50, 1950|51. Khartoum, Mc-Corquodale and co., Sudan, 1951. (M966.2Su2)

1817 Taylor, Bayard. A journey to Central Africa; or, Life and landscapes from Egypt to the Negro kingdom of the White Nile. New York, G. P. Putnam's sons, 1867. 552p. (M962T21)

1818 Theobald, Alan Buchan. The Mahiya: a history of the Anglo-Egyptian Sudan, 1881-1899. London, New York, Longmans, Green, 1951. 273p. (AM962.4T34m)

1819 Tothill, John Douglas. Agriculture in the Sudan. London, Oxford University Press, 1948. 974p. (AM962.6T66a)

1820 Tucker, Archibald Norman. The Eastern Sudanic languages. London, New York [etc.] Pub. for the International Institute of African languages & cultures by the Oxford university press, 1940- 2v. (AM496T79)

1821 Wauters, Alphonse Jules. Stanley's Emin Pasha expedition., London, J. C. Nimmo, 1890. 378p. (M966W35)

ETHIOPIA AND ERITREA

1822 Abyssinia and Italy. New York, Oxford University Press, Issued under the auspices of the Royal Institute of International Affairs, 1935. 48p. (M963Ab9)

1823 Asfa Yilma, princess. Haile Selassie, emperor of Ethiopia. London S. Low, Marston & Co., ltd. 1936. 305p. (M963As2)

1824 Azais, Francois. Cinq années de recherches archéologiques en Éthiopie, province du Hara et Ethiopie méridionale. Paris, Paul Geuthner, 1931. 348p. (M963Az1)

1825 Badoglio, Pietro. La guerra d'Ethiopia. Milano, A. Mondadori, 1936, 249p. (M963B14)

1826 Baker, Sir Samuel White. The Nile tributaries of Abyssinia and the sword hunters of the Hamran Arabs. Philadelphia, J. B. Lippincott & Co., 1868. 413p. (M916.3B17)

1827 Baratieri, Oreste. Memorie d'Africa (1892-1896) ... Torino, Fratelli Bocca, 1898. 487p. (M963.5B23)

1828 Baravelli, Giulio Cesare. The last stronghold of slavery: what Abyssinia is. Roma, Societa editrice di Novissima, 1935. 70p. (M963B23)

1829 Baum, James Edwin. Unknown Ethiopia, new light on darkest Abyssinia. New York, Grosset & Dunlap, 1935. 354p. (M916.-3B32u)

1830 Beke, Charles T. The British captives in Abyssinia. 2nd ed. London, Longmans, Green, Reader, and Dyer, 1867. 398p. (M963B39)

1831 Bent, James Theodore. The sacred city of the Ethiopians; being a record of travel and research in Abyssinia in 1893. With a chapter . . . On the inscriptions from Yeha and Aksum, and appendix, On the morphological character of the Abyssinians. London and New York, Longmans, Green and co., 1893. 309p. (M963B44)

1832 Berantzik, Hugo Adolf. Athiopen des westens. Wien, L. W. Seidel & Son, 1933. (AM572.9665B45)

1833 Bianchi, Gustavo. Alla Terra dei Galla. Milano, Fratelli Treves, Editori, 1884. 543p. (M963B38)

1834 Blanc, Henry. A narrative of captivity in Abyssinia. London, Smith Elder and Co., 1868. 409p. (M963B59)

1835 Blayechettai, Joseph Emanuel. The hidden mystery of Ethiopia. [m.p., n.d.] 74p. (M963B61)

1836 Bonneuil, Marie Edith de. Bivouacs aux étoiles. Paris, Plon. 1938. 280p. (M963B64)

1837 Bruce, James. Interesting narrative of the travels of James Bruce into Abyssinia . . . Boston, Samuel Etheridge, 1798. 388p. (M-963B83)

1838 Buchholzer, John. The land of burnt faces; translated from the Danish by Maurice Michael. London, A. Baker, 1955. 159p. (M963B851)

1839 Budge, Sir Ernest Alfred Thompson Wallis. A history of Ethiopia, Nubia & Abyssinia (according to the hieroglyphic inscriptions of Egypt and Nubia, and the Ethiopian chronicles . . . London, Methuen & Co., ltd. 1938. 2v. (M963B85h)

1840 Burns, Emile. Abyssinia and Italy. London, V. Gollanca, 1935. 223p. (M963B93)

1841 Buxton, David. Travels in Ethiopia. London, Lindsay Drummond, 1949. 200p. (M963B98)

1842 Carter, Boake. Black shirt, black skin. with illustrations by George P. Fayko, Jr. Harrisburg, Pa., Telegraph Press, 1935. 178p. (M916.3C24)

1843 Celarié, Henriette. Éthiopie xxe-siécle. Paris, Hachette, 1934. 252p. (M963C33)

1844 [Communist party of the United States of America] Harlem section War on Ethiopia; an interview with Tecle Hawariate, Ethiopian ambassador. [New York, 1936] 7p. (M963C73)

1845   Coon, Carleton Stevens. Measuring Ethiopia and flight into Arabia.
       Boston, Little, Brown & Co., 1935. (M916.3C78)

1846   Courlander, Harold. The fire on the mountain and other Ethiopian
       stories. Illustrated by Robert W. Kane. New York, Holt,
       1950. 141p. (M963C83)

1847   Cunard, Nancy. L'Ethiopie trahie; unité contre l'impérialisme. n.p.
       Nancy Cunard, 1936. 14p. (M963C91e)

1848   Currey, Muriel. A woman at the Abyssinian War. London, Hutchin-
       son and Co., 1936. 254p.

1849   Darley, Henry Algernon Cholmley. Slaves and ivory in Abyssinia:
       a record of adventure and exploration among the Ethiopian
       slave-raiders. New York, R. M. McBride & co., 1935. 219p.
       (M916.3D24)

1850   Del Valle, Pedro Augusto. Roman eagles over Ethiopia . . . Harris-
       burg, Pa., The Military Service Publishing Co. [c1940] 201p.
       (M963D37r)

1851   Denon, Dominque Vivant, baron. Travels in upper and lower Egypt.
       London, Printed for T. N. Longman and O. Rees and Richard
       Phillipp. 1803. (M963D43t)

1852   DeShands, Lottie B. Ethiopia's spiritual rise. Phila., A.M.E. Book
       concern [c1936] 157p. (M910D45e)

1853   Dillman, Freidrich August. Ethiopic grammar. London, Williams
       and Norgate, 1907. (492.8D85e)

1854   Dillman, Freidrich August. Verzeichniss der Abessinischen hand-
       schriften. Berlin, Buchdruckerei der Kongi, 1878. 85p. (M-
       963D58)

1855   Duchesne-Fournet, Jean. Mission en Éthiopie (1901-1903). Paris
       Masson et cie, 1908-09. 2v. (M963Dq5)

1856   Dufton, H. Narrative of a journey through Abyssinia. London,
       Chapman & Hall, 1867. 337p. (M963D87)

1857   Dye, William McEntyre. Moslem Egypt and Christian Abyssinia;
       or Military service under the kheduie, in his provinces and
       beyond their borders as experienced by the American staff . . . .
       New York, Atkin & Prout printers, 1880. 500p. (M916.2D98)

1858   Eschench, Georg. Im lande des Negus. Berlin, George Stilke, 1921.
       187p (AM916E16)

1859   [Esmenard, Jean d'] vicomte, A travers l'empire de Ménélik. Paris,
       Librairie Plon, 1928. 333p. (M963Es5)

1860   Ethiopia. The constitution of Ethiopia. [n.p., 1931?] 30p. (M963-
       Et3c)

1861 Ethiopia. Jimma Agricultural Technical School. Bulletin, Academic
      year 1955-56. Ethiopia, The Imperial Ethiopan College of
      Agricultural and Mechanical Arts, 1956. 30p. (M963Et3f)

1862 Ethiopia. Ministry of Education and Fine Arts. Yearbooks, E. C.
      1940-41 (1947-49) [Addis Ababa, Ethiopia] Ministry of Edu-
      cation, 1950. 140p. (M963Et3y)

1863 Ethiopia. Ministry of Finance. Duties and responsibilities of the
      various departments. Addis Ababa, 1943. 12p. (M963Et3f)

1864 Ethiopia. Ministry of Foreign Affairs. Empire of Ethiopia; digest
      of memoranda presented by the Imperial Ethiopian government
      to the Council of Foreign Ministers in London, September, 1945.
      Rev. ed. April 1946. 21p. (M963Et3)

1865 Ethiopia. The point 4 program in Ethiopia; a cooperative program
      of the Ethiopian and United States Governments. Addis Ababa,
      Ethiopia, Printed by the Cooperative Educational Program
      Press, 1954. unnumbered pages. (M963Ft3e)

1866 Ethiopia. This is Ethiopia; the new constitution. Ethiopia, Govt.,
      1956. 11p. (M963Et3t)

1867 Faitlovitch, Jacques. Proverbs Abyssins. Paris, Paul Geuthner,
      1907. 86p. (M963F17p)

1868 Faitlovitch, Jacques. Quer durch Abessinien meine zweite reise zu
      den Falaschas ... Berlin, Verlag von M. Poppelaver, 1910.
      188p. (M963F17)

1869 Farago, Ladislas. Abyssinia on the eve. New York, G. P. Putnam's
      sons, 1935. 286p. (M916.3F22)

1870 Ferret, Pierre Victor. Voyage en Abyssinie dans les provinces du
      Tigré, du Samen et de l'Amhara, Paris, Paulin, 1847-48. 3v.
      (M916.3F41)

1871 Forbes, Mrs. Rosita (Torr) From Red sea to Blue Nile. New York,
      Lee Furman, 1935. 280p. (M963F74)

1872 Frobenius, Leo. Under den unstraslichen Aethiopen. Berlin, Vita,
      Deutsches Verlagshaus, [1913] 508p. (M963F92u)

1873 Fuertes, Louis Agassiz. Artist and naturalist in Ethiopia. Garden
      City, N.Y. Doubleday, Doran & Co., Inc., 1936. 249p. (M962-
      F95)

1874 Geddes, Michael. The church history of Ethiopia ... London,
      Printed for Ro Chiswell, 1696. 488p. (M963G26c)

1875 Gentizon, Paul. La conquête de l'Éthiopie. Paris, Berger-Levrault,
      1936. 294p. (M963G28c)

1876 Gentizon, Paul. La revanche d'Adoua. Paris, Éditions Berger-

Levrault, 1936. 262p. (M963G28r)

1877   Glaser, Eduard. Bemerkungen zur geschichte altabessiniens und zu
       einer sabaischen vertragsinschrift. Säaz, 1894. 26p. (M963-
       G46)

1878   Glaser, Eduard. Die abessinier in Arabien und Afrika. München
       verlag von Hermann Lukaschik, 1895. 210p. (M963G46a)

1879   Gobat, Samuel. Journal of three years in residence in Abyssinia.
       New York, M. W. Dodd, 1850. 480p.

1880   Gt. Brit. War Office. Record of the expedition to Abyssinia. Lon-
       don, H. M. Stationery Office. [Harrison and sons, printers]
       1870. 2v. (M963G79r)

1881   Grebaut, Sylvain. Catalogue des manuscripts Ethiopiens de la col-
       lection. Graule. Paris, Institut D'Ethnologie, 1938. Université
       de Paris, 320p. (M963G79)

1882   Griaule, Marcel. Les flambeurs d'hommes. Paris, Clamann-Levy,
       1934. 205p. (M963G87f)

1883   Grühl, Max. The citadel of Ethiopia. London, J. Cape, 1932. 382p.
       (M916.3G92)

1884   Hammurabi, Frederick H. Where is black man headed in post war
       world? [n.p., n.d.] 104p. (M963H18)

1885   Hansberry, William Leo. Sources for the study of Ethiopian history.
       Washington, D.C., Howard University press, 1931. 21p. (M-
       378HMH83v.2)

1886   Harmsworth, Geoffrey. Abyssinia marches on. London and Mel-
       bourne, Hutchinson and co. ltd. [1941] 128p. (M963H22a)

1887   Harris, W. C. Highlands of Ethiopia. New York, J. Winchester,
       1844. 392p. (M916.3H24)

1888   Hartlmaier, Paul. Golden lion, a journey through Ethiopia, Lon-
       don, Geoffrey Bles, 1956. 186p. (M963H25)

1889   Hayter, Frank Edward. Gold of Ethiopia, by Frank Hayter . . .
       with 37 illustrations. London, S. Paul & Co., ltd. [1936] 256p.
       (M963H33g)

1890   Heeren, Arnold Hermann Ludwig. Historical researches into the
       politics, intercourse, and trade of the Carthaginians, Ethiopians,
       and Egyptians. Oxford, D. A. Talboys, 1832. 2v. (M913.-
       32H36)

1891   Hentze, Willy. Am hose des kaisers Menelik von Abessynien . . .
       Leipzig, Eduard Henrich Mayer, 1908. 214p. (M963H39)

1892   Hoare, Samuel. Italy and Ethiopia, collective action for security demanded . . . New York, Carnegie Endowment for International Peace, 1935. 24p. (M963H65)

1893 Howard, William Edward Harding. Public administration in Ethiopia; a study in retrospect and prospect. Groningen, J. B. Walters, 1956. 204p. (M963H83)

1894 Huggins, Willis N. An introduction to African civilizations, with main currents in Ethiopian History. New York, Ason House, 1937. 224p. (M9H87)

1895 L'llustration. La guerre Italo-Ethiopienne. Paris, L'illustration, 1936. 224p. (M963I16)

1896 International conciliation. Italy and Ethiopia . . . New York, Carnegie Endowment for International Peace, 1935. No. 314. Monthly. (M963In8)

1897 International conciliation. Sanctions of the Italo-Ethiopian conflict . . . New York, Carnegie Endowment for International Peace. No. 315. Monthly. (M963In8)

1898 Italian historical society. The Italo-Ethiopian controversy. New York, Italian Historical Society, 1935. 28p. (M963It1)

1899 The Italo-Ethiopian dispute. Abstract from the memorandum of the Italian government to the league of nations. Rome, Societa Editrice di Novissima, 1935. 24p. (M963It1d)

1900 Jackson, John G. Ethiopia and the origin of civilization . . . New York, The Blyden Society, 1939. 32p. (M963J13e)

1901 Johnson, Edward A. Adam vs. ape-man and Ethiopia. New York, J. J. Little & Ives Co., 1931. 293p. (M963J62)

1902 Johnston, Charles. Travels in Southern Abyssinia, through the country of Adal to the Kingdom of Shoa. London, J. Madden & Co., 1844. 2v. (M916.3J64)

1903 Jones, Arnold Hugh Martin. A history of Abyssinia. Oxford, the Clarendon Press, 1935. 188p. (M963J71)

1904 Jones, Arnold Hugh Martin. A history of Ethiopia, by A. H. M. Jones and Elizabeth Monroe. Oxford, Clarendon Press, 1955. 196p. (M963J71h)

1905 Jumilhac, Ethel (Barbey) comtesse de. Éthiopia moderne. Paris, Berger-Levrault, 1933. 166p. (M963J95e)

1906 Kuhn, DeProrok, Byron. Dead men do tell tales. New York, Creative Age Press, 1942. 328p. (M916.3K52d)

1907 Klein, Julius and Treatt, C. Court. Black cargo. Chicago, Lincoln Printing Co., 1935. 99p. (AM792K67)

1908 Kumm, H. K. W. Khont-hon-Nofer, the lands of Ethiopia. London & Edinburgh, Marshall Bros., Ltd., 1910. 291p. (AM·916K96)

1909 La Croze, Marthurin Veyssiére de. Historie du Christianisme d' Éthiope et d'Arménie. A la Haie, chés la Veuve le Vier, and Pierre Paupie, 1739. 402p. (M963L11)

1910 LaCroze, Mathurin Veyssiére de. Remarques de Monsieur de Lacroze conseiller, bibilothecaire et antiquaire de S. M. Le Roi de Prusse, sur son historie du Christianisme des Indes. A Amsterdam, chex Pierre Humbert, 1737. 42p. (M963L11)

1911 Le Roux, Hugues. Ménélik et nous. Paris, Nilsson, 1902. 446p. (M916.3L56)

1912 Leslau, Wolf. Falasha anthology. New Haven, Yale University Press, 1951. 222p. (AM896.8L56f)

1913 Liano, Alejandro. Ethiopie, empire des Négres Blancs. Paris, Editions Pierre Roger, [1929.] 291p. (M963L61e)

1914 The liturgy of the Ethiopian Church. Translated by the Rev. Margos Daoud . . . Ethiopia, Addis Ababa Berhanena Salam Print. Press of His Imperial Majesty Haile Selassie I., n.d. 252p. (M963L73)

1915 Lobo, Jeronymo. A short relation of the river Nile, of its source and current; of its overflowing the campagnia of Egypt, till it runs into the Mediterranean: and of other curiosities; written by an eyewitness, who lived many years in the chief kingdoms of the Abyssine empire. London, Printed for John Martin, Printed to the Royal Society at the Bell in St. Paul's Churchyard, 1673. 104p. (M960L61s)

1916 Lobo, Jeronymo. Voyage historique, du r. p. Jerome de la Compagnie de Jesus. Traduite du portugais, continuee and augmentee de plusieurs dissertations, lettres and memoires. Par m. Le Grand . . . A Paris, Chez la veuve d'A. U. Coustelier & J. Guerin, 1728. 514p. (M963L78)

1917 Ludolf, Hiob. A new history of Ethiopia. Being a full and accurate description of the kingdom of Abessinia, vulgarly, though erroneously called the empire of Prester John. In four books . . . By the learned Job Ludolphus . . . Made English, by J. P. gent. London, S. Smith, 1682. 398p. (M963L96)

1918 Ludolf, Hiob. A new history of Ethiopia. Being a full and accurate description of the kingdom of Abessinia, vulgarly, though, erroneously called the empire of Prester John. In four books . . . illus. with copper plates, by the learned Job

Ludolphus . . . Second edition, to which is added a new and exact map of the country; also, a preface, showing the usefulness of this history; with the life of Gregorious Abba; and the author's opinion of some other writers concerning Ethiopia. Made English by J. P., gent. London, Samuel Smith, 1684. 398p. (M963L96)

1919 Ludolf, Hiob. Iobi Ludolfi alias Leut-holf dicti Historia aethiopica, sive Brevis and succincta descriptio regni Habessinorum, quod vulgo male Presbyteri Iohannis vocatur. In qua libris quatuor agitur 1. De natura and indole regionis and incolarum. 11. De regimine politico, regum successione &'c. 111. De statu ecclesiastico, initio & progressu religionis christianae &c. iv. De rebus privatis, literatura, oeconomia, &c. Cum tabula capitum, & indicibus necesariis. Francofurti ad Moenum, prostat apud J. D. Zunner, 1681. 336p. (M963Y96i)

1920 Ludolf, Hiob. Iobi Ludolfi alias Leutholf dicti ad suam historiam Aethiopicam antehac editam commentarius in quo multa breviter dicta fusius narrantur: contraria refelluntur: Atque hac occasione praeter res Aethiopicas multa autorum, queeam ethiam S. Scripturae loca declarantur: aliaqur plurima geographica, historica et critica, imprimis vero antiquitatem ecclesiasticam illustrantia, alibi haud facile obvia, exponuntur; ut variarum observationum loco haberi possit cum tabula capitum, figuris, & variis indicibus locupletissimis. Francofurti ad Moenum, sumptibus Johannis David Zunneri, 1691. 631p. (M963L96ii)

1921 MacCallum, Elizabeth P. Rivalries in Ethiopia. Boston, World Peace Foundation, 1935. 64p. (M963M13)

1922 MacCreagh, Gordon. The last of free Africa; the account of an expedition into Abyssinia, with observations on the manners, customs and traditions of the Ethiopians with some pungent remarks on the anomalous political situation that at present obtains between this ancient kingdom and the nations of the world. New York and London, The Century Co., c1928. 361p. (M916.3M13)

1923 Maclean, R. John Hoy of Ethiopia. New York, Farrar & Rinehart, Inc., 1936. 264p. (M963M22)

1924 Marein, Nathan. The Ethiopian Empire; federation and laws. Rotterdam, Royal Netherlands Print. and Lithographing Co., 1954. 455p. (M963M33e)

1925 Marien, Nathan. Handbook to the laws of Ethiopia. Addis Ababa, Ethiopia, 1949. 207p. (M963.34M33h)

1926 Mahew, David. Ethiopia, the study of polity, 1540-1935. London,

Eyre & Spottiswoode, [1947.]   254p.   (M963M42)

1927   Matthews, Herbert L.   Two wars and more to come.   New York,
       Carrick and Evans, Inc., 1938.   318 p.   (M963M43)

1928   Mercer, Samuel Alfred Browne.   The Ethiopic liturgy; its sources,
       development, and present form, by the Rev. Samuel A. B.
       Mercer.   Milwaukee, The Young Churchman Co.; London, A. R.
       Mowbray and Co., 1915.   487p.   (M963M53e)

1929   Michel, Charles.   Vers Fachoda à la recontre de la mission marchand
       à travers l'Ethiopie.   Paris, Plonnourrit, 1900.   560p.   (M916.-
       3M58)

1930   Mikael, Kebbede.   Ethiopia and Western civilisation; Essay. Ethi-
       opia, n.p. 1949.   (M963M58e)

1931   Mikael, Kebbede.   Prophecy fulfilled.   [play.]   Translated from
       the Amharic by Stephen Wright.   Addis Ababa, 1953.   54p.
       (M963M58p)

1932   Montandon, George.   Au pays Ghimirra; recit de mon voyage à
       travers le Massif ethiopien (1909-1911).   Paris, A. Challamel;
       Neuchatel, Attinger fières, 1913.   424p.   (M916.3M76)

1933   Monfried, Henri de.   L'ile aux perles.   Paris, Editions Bernard
       Grasset, n.d. 103p.   (M963.5M74)

1934   Monfreid, Henri de.   Vers les terres hostiles de l'Éthiopie.   Paris,
       B. Grasset, 1933.   264p.   (M963M74)

1935   Nemours, Alfred.   Craignons d'etre un jour l'Ethiopie de quelqu'un;
       conflict Italo-Ethiopien 1935.   Port-au-Prince, Haiti, Imprim-
       erie du college vertieres, 1945.   82p.   (M972.94N34c)

1936   Nerazzini, Cesare.   La conquista mussulmana dell'Ethopia nel secolo
       XVI.   Roma, Forzani, 1891.   174p.   (M963N35)

1937   Newman, Polson.   Ethiopian realities.   London, G. Allen and Un-
       win, 1936.   134p.   (M963N46)

1938   Norden, Hermann.   Africa's last empire; through Abyssinia to Lake
       Tana and the country of the Falasha . . . with eighty-one photo-
       graphs and a map.   Philadelphia, Macrae-Smith Company,
       1930.   240p.   (M916.3N75)

1939   Orleans, Henri d'.   Une visite a l'Empereur Menelick.   Paris, Li-
       brarie Denter.   264p.   (M9630r5)

1940   Pankhurst, Estelle Sylvia.   Eritrea on the eve; the past and future
       of Italy's "firstborn" colony, Ethiopia's ancient sea province.
       Woodford Green, Essex.   "New Times and Ethiopia News"
       [1952] 72p.   (M963.5P19e)

1941 Parkyns, Mansfield. Life in Abyssinia. New York, D. Appleton and Co., 1854. 2v. (M916.63P23)

1942 Perham, Margery Freda. The government of Ethiopia. New York, Oxford University, 1948. 481p. (M963P41g)

1943 Pierre-Alype, François Julien. L'Empire des Négus. Paris, Plon-Nourrit et Cié, Imprimeurs-Editeurs. 1925. 307p.

1944 Pierre-Alype, François Julien. L'Ethiopie et les convoitises allemandes. Paris, Berger-Levrault, 1917. 285p. (M963P61e)

1945 Pierre-Alype, François Julien. Sous la couronne de Salomon. L'empire des négus, de la reine de Saba à la Société des nations, par Pierre-Alype. Preface de Henry de Jouvenel. Avec sept illustrations hors texte et une carte. Nouv. éd. mise à jour. Paris, Plon, 1935. 312p. (M963P61s)

1946 Playne, Beatrice . . . St. George for Ethiopia. London, Constable [1954] 200p. (AM726.5P69)

1947 Plowden, Walter Chichele. Travels in Abyssinia and the Galla country with an account of a mission to Rao Ali in 1848. London, Longmans, Green & Co., 1868. 485p. (M963P72)

1948 Quinton, A. G. H. Ethiopia and the evangel; A record of "the things which happened . . . unto the furtherance of the gospel" in Ethiopia. London, Marshall, Morgan and Scott, 1949. 71p. (M963.2Q4e)

1949 Rassam, Hormuzd. Narrative of the British mission to Theodore, King of Abyssinia. London, J. Murray, 1869. 2v. (M963R33i)

1950 Rathjens, Carl. Die Juden in Abessinien. Hamburg, W. Gente, 1921. 97p. (M963R18j)

1951 Rebeaud, Henri. Chez le roi des rois d'Éthiopie. Paris, Editions Victor Attincer, 1934. 199p. (M963R24)

1952 Rey, Charles Fernand. In the country of the Blue Nile. London, Duckworth, 1927. 296p. (M963R33i)

1953 Rey, Charles Fernand. The real Abyssinia. Philadelphia, J. B. Lippincott Co., 1935. 291p. (M916.3R33)

1954 Rey, Charles Fernand. The romance of the Portuguese in Abyssinia. London, H. F. & G. Witherby [1929] 319p. (M963R33r)

1955 Rogers, Joel Augustus. The real facts about Ethiopia. New York, F. Jubner & Co., n.d. 51p. (M963R63)

1956 Roman Roads in East Africa . . . Roma, Società editrice di "Novissima," [1936] 4p. (M963R66)

1957 Rosen, Felix. Eine Deutsche gesandtschaft in Abessinien. Leipzig,

Verlag von veit und Comp. 1907. 496p. (M963R72)

1958 Russell, Michael . . . Nubia and Abyssinia comprehending their civil history, antiquities, arts, religion, literature, and natural history . . . Illustrated by a map, and several engravings. New York, J. & J. Harper, 1833. 331p. (M916R91)

1959 Salt, Henry. A voyage to Abyssinia, and travels into the interior of that country, executed under the orders of the British government, in the years 1809 and 1810; in which are included, an account of the Portuguese settlements on the east coast of Africa visited in the course of the voyage; a concise narrative of late events in Arabia Felix; and some particulars respecting the aboriginal African tribes, extending from Mozambique to the borders of Egypt; together with vocabularies of their respective languages. London, F. C. & J. Rivington, 1814. 506p. (M963Sa3v)

1960 Sanceau, Elaine. The land of Prester John, a chronicle of Portuguese exploration. New York, A. A. Knopf, 1944. 243p. (M963Sa5)

1961 Simon, Gabriel. L'Ethiopie, ses moeurs, ses traditions . . . Paris, Challamel Aine, 1885. 374p. (M963Si5e)

1962 Skinner, Robert Peet. Abyssinia of today. New York, Longmans, Green & Co., 1906. 227p. (M916.3Sk3)

1936 Skordiles, Kimon. Kagnew: the story of the Ethiopian fighters in Korea. Tokyo, Radiopress, 1954. 244p. (M963Sk5)

1964 Snowden, Frank M. Rome and the Ethiopian warrior. Reprinted from the Studies Presented to David Moore Robinson. pp. 906-917. (M963Sn6)

1965 Sorenson, Manuel James. A study of Anglo-Ethiopian relations from 1800-1936. Abstract of a dissertation presented to the graduate college in partial fulfillment of the requirements for the degree of Doctor of Philosophy. Lincoln, Nebraska, Univ. of Nebraska, Dept. of History, 1950. 9p. (M963So6)

1966 Stanley, Sir Henry Morton. Coomassie and Magdala: the story of two British campaigns in Africa. New York, Harper and Bros., 1874. 510p. (M963St2c)

1967 Steer, George Lowther. Sealed and delivered; a book on the Abyssinian campaign. London, Hodder and Stoughton limited, 1942. 256p. (M963St4s)

1968 Talbot, David A. Contemporary Ethiopia. New York, Philosophical Library, 1952. 267p. (M963T14c)

1969 Temple, Richard Carmac. The itinerary of Ludovico di Varthema
       of Bologna from 1502 to 1508 as translated from the original
       Italian edition of 1510. F. S. A. in 1863 for the Hakluyt
       society with a discourse on Varthema and his travels in southern
       Asia. London, The Argonaut Press, 1928. 121p. (M960T24i)

1970 Trimingham, John Spencer. Islam in Ethiopia. London, New
       York, Oxford University Press. 299p. (AM297T73)

1971 The Truth about Ethiopia. A nation blocked from the sea. New
       York, The Universal Ethiopian students' association, 1936.
       24p. (M963T77)

1972 United aid for Ethiopia. Ethiopia. New York, n.p. 1936. (M963-
       Un3)

1973 U. S. Dept. of Commerce. Office of International trade. Ethiopia
       (summary of current economic information. Prepared by the
       Foreign service of the United States of America. Washington,
       D. C., Government printing office, 1947. 4p. (M973Un31)

1974 Varley, Douglas Harold. A bibliography of Italian colonisation in
       Africa, with a section on Abyssinia. London, The Royal em-
       pire society and the Royal institute of international affairs,
       1936. 92p. (AM01V42)

1975 Vigoni, Pippo. Abissinia; gomaldei un viaggio . . . Milano, etc.,
       Ulrico Hoepli. 1881. 246p. (M916.3V68)

1976 Vitelleschi, Mutio. Lettere annue die Ethiopia del. 1642, 1625,
       1626. Roma Perl' Herede di Bartolomeo Zanneti, 1628. 232p.
       (M963V83)

1977 Walker, Craven Howell. The Abyssinian at home. London, The
       Sheldon Press, 1933. 220p. (M916.3W15)

1978 The war danger over Abyssinia. London, League against imperial-
       ism and for national independence, n.d. 28p. (M963W19)

1979 Wellby, Montagu Sinclair. 'Twixt sirdar & Menelik. London and
       New York, Harper & Bros., 1901. 408p. (M916.3W45)

1980 Wheller, Post. The golden legend of Ethiopia; the lovestory of
       Maqeda, virgin queen of Axum and Sheba and Solomon the
       great king, by Post Wheeler . . . New York, London, D. Apple-
       ton-Century Company, Incorporated, 1936. 184p. (M896.-
       3W57g)

1981 Woolf, Leonard Sidney. The League and Abyssinia. London, L.
       and Virginia Woolf at the Hogarth Press, 1936. 35p. (M963-
       (W88)

1982 Work, Ernest. Ethiopia, a pawn in European diplomacy. New

Concord, O., the Author, 1935.   354p.   (M963W89)

1983   Yaltasamma.   Les amis de Menilek II, roi des rois d'Ethiopie avec
documents sur la conquete du nil par les Anglais et l'incident
de fachoda.   Paris, Augustin Challamel, 1899. 63p. (M963Y13)

1984   Zervos, Adrien.   L'Empire d'Ethiopie . . . Alexandrie (Égypte),
Impr. de l'École professionnelle des frères, 1936.   503p.   (M916.
3Ze5)

SOMALILAND

1985   Burton, Richard Francis.   First footseps in East Africa; or, an
exploration of Harar.   London, Longman, Brown, Green, and
Longmans, 1856.   648p.   (M967.7B95f)

1986   Ethiopia.   Ministery of foreign affairs.   Empire of Ethiopia; digest
of memoranda presented by the Imperial Ethiopian government
to the Council of Foreign ministers in London, Sept., 1945.
21p.   (M963Et3)

1987   Galaal, Muuse Haaji Ismaa'iil.   Hikmad Soomaali.   London, Oxford University Press, 1956.   150p.

1988   Hamilton, Angus.   Somaliland.   London, Hutchinson and Co., 1911.
366p.   (M967.6H18s)

1989   Herbert, Agnes.   Two Dianas in Somaliland; the record of a shoot-
ing trip.   London, New York, J. Lane, 1908.   306p.   (AM-
967.7H41t)

1990   Pankhurst, Estelle Sylvia.   Ex-Italian Somaliland.   London, Watts,
1951.   460p.   (M967.73P19e)

1991   Smith, A Donaldson.   Through unknown African counties, the first
expedition from Somaliland to Lake Lamu.   London, Edward
Arnold, 1897.   417p.   (AM967.6Sm5t)

WESTERN AFRICA

GENERAL

1992   Ademola, Adenenkan.   The new West Africa; problems of independence.   London, Allen and Unwin, 1953.   184p.   (M966Ad3)

1993   L'Afrique occidental française.   Agence économique.   L'Afrique occidentale française.   Paris, Agence économique de l'Afrique occidentale française.   n.d.   31p.   (M966Af83n.1)

1994   Agbebi, Mojola.   An account of Dr. Mojola Agbebi's work in West
Africa, comprising Yorubaland, Fantiland, the Ekiti country,
Central Nigeria, Southern Nigeria and the Cameroons.   n.p.,
n.p., n.d.   36p.   (MB9Ag3)

1995 Agyeman, Nana Yaw Twum Duah. West Africa on the March, an intimate survey of problems and potentialities. New York, William-Frederick Press, 1952. 73p. (M966Ag9u)

1996 Ajibola, J. O. Economic development of West Africa. London, West African Society, 1948. 48p. (M966Aj5c)

1997 Ankermann, Bernhard. Ostafrika. Stuttgart, Strecker und Schroder, 1929. 379p. (M967An6)

1998 Armattoe, Raphael Ernest Grail. The golden age of West African civilization. Londonderry, The Londonderry Sentinel, 1946. 98p. (AM966.81Ar5g)

1999 Austin, Dennis. West Africa and the commonwealth. London, Penguin Books, 1957. 124p.

2000 Awoonor-Renner, Bankole. West African Soviet Union. London, Wans Press, 1946. 31p. (M966Aw6w)

2001 Baker, Richard St. Barbe. Sahara challenge. London, Lutterworth Press, 1954. 152p. (M966.11B17s)

2002 Batson, Alfred. African intrigue. Garden City, N.Y., Garden City Publishing co., 1933. 307p. (M916.61B32)

2003 Bauer, Peter Tamas. West African trade; a study of competition, oligopoly and monopoly in a changing economy. Cambridge, University Press, 1954. 450p. (M966B32)

2004 Beato, González, Vicente. Capacidad méntal del Negro. Los métodos de Binet-Bobertag y de Yerkes, para determinar la edad y coeficiente mental, aplicados al Negro, 2.ed. Madrid, Consejo Superior de Investigaciones Científicas, Instituto de Africanos, 1953. 116p. (M966B37)

2005 Beaver, Philip. African memoranda; relative to an attempt to establish a British settlement of the island of Bulama, on the western coast of Africa, in the year 1792. London, C. and R. Baldwin, 1805. 500p. (AM966B38a)

2006 Belshaw, Harry. Facing the future in West Africa. London, Cargate Press, 1951. 128p. (AM966B41f)

2007 Birmingham, Walter. Introduction to economics. London, Penguin Books, 1955. 123p.

2008 Blake, John William. European beginnings in West Africa, 1454-1578 ... London, New York, Longmans, Green and Co., 1937. 212p. (AM966B58)

2009 Blake, John William. Europeans in West Africa, 1450-1560; documents to illustrate the nature and scope of Portuguese enterprise in West Africa ... London, The Hakluyt Society, 1942. (AM966B58e)

2010 Blyden, Edward W. African life and customs. London, C. M. Phillips, 1908. 91p. (AM90B62a)

2011 Blyden, Edward W. Christianity, Islam and the Negro race. London, W. B. Whittingham & Co., 1888. 3p. (M960B62)

2012 Blyden, Edward W. From West Africa to Palestine. Freetown, Sierra Leone, T. J. Sawyer, 1873. 201p. (M915.69B62)

2013 Blyden, Edward W. West Africa before Europe. London, C. M. Phillips, 1905. 158p. (AM960B62w)

2014 Boateng, E. A. Tomorrow's map of West Africa. London, Staples, 1952. 17p. (M966B63)

2015 Bodley, Ronald Victor Courtenay. Wind in the Sahara. New York, Coward-McCann, 1944. 224p. (AM966.11B63)

2016 Bolitho, Hector. The British Empire. London, New York, B. T. Batsford, 1948. 246p. (AM960B63b)

2017 Bosman, William. A new and accurate description of the coast of Guinea; divided into the Gold, the Slave, and the Ivory Coasts. London, Printed for J. Wren, 1754. 456p. (M916.-6B65)

2018 British Africa. London, Kegan Paul, Trench, Trubner and co., 1899. 413p. (AM960B77a)

2019 British Information Services, Africa challenge. New York, British Information Services, 1945. 64p. (AM960B77a)

2020 British Justice in Africa; developed in official and other documents, concerning certain recent proceedings at the British forts on the coast of Guinea: to which is prefixed an introduction, by the English editor. London, Printed by and for J. Ines, n.d. 49p. (M326.9Ab77)

2021 British Museum. Department of British and mediaeval antiquities and ethnography. Antiquities from the city of Benin and from other parts of West Africa in the British museum. London, British Museum, 1899. 3p. (M913.6B77)

2022 Burton, Richard Francis. Wanderings in West Africa from Liverpool to Fernando Po. London, Tinsley bros., 1863. 2v. (AM-966B95w)

2023 Butt-Thompson, Frederick William. West African secret societies, their organisations, officials and teaching. London, H. F. & G. Witherby, 1929. 320p. (M966B98)

2024 Cameron, I. D. The West African councillor. London, Oxford University Press, 1954. 168p. (M966C14w)

2025 Cansdale, George. Reptiles of West Africa. London, Penguin Books, 1955. 103p.

2026 Carlin, John. Gulla the tramp. London, J. Cape, 1937. 407p. (AM916.711C19)

2027 Cary, Joyce. Britain and West Africa. London, New York, Longmans, Green, 1947. 79p. (AM966C25b)

2028 Cecchi, Antonio. Funf jahre in Ostafrika. Leipzig, Brockhaus. 1888. 541p. (M916C32)

2029 Chadwick, E. R. Community development. London, Bureau of Current Affairs, 195? 15p. (M966C34)

2030 Cooksey, J. J. Religion and civilization in West Africa; a missionary survey of French, British, Spanish and Portuguese West Africa, with Liberia. London, World Dominion Press, 1931. 277p. (M966C77)

2031 Crone, Gerald R. H. The voyages of Cadamosto and other documents of Western Africa in the second half of the fifteenth century. London, Printed for the Hakluyt Society, 1937. 159p. (AM916.6C88)

2032 Dallimore, H. A geography of West Africa. 3rd ed. rev. London, United Society for Christian Literature. [1949] 113p. (AM966D16)

2033 Davey, T. H. Trypanosomiasis in British West Africa. [London] Published for the colonial office by his majesty's stationery office, 1948. 15p. (M966D31t)

2034 Davidson, Basil. The new West Africa; problems of independence. London, Allen & Unwin [1953] 184p. (M96.7D28n)

2035 Davis, Jackson. Africa advancing; a study of rural education and agriculture in West Africa and the Belgian Congo. New York, The Friendship press; London, The International committee on Christian literature for Africa, 1945. 230p. (M966J29)

2036 Davis, Shelby Cullom. Reservoirs of men: a history of the black troops of French West Africa, by Shelby Cullom Davis.... Geneva, Librairie Kundig, 1934. 025p. (M966.8D29)

2037 Decle, Lionel. Three years in savage Africa. New York, M. F. Mansfield, 1898. 594p. (M966D35)

2038 DeGraft-Johnson, John Coleman, African glory; the story of vanished Negro civilizations. London, Watts [1954] 209p. (M960D36a)

2039 Denne, R. E. At the back of the black man's mind. London, Macmillan and co., 1906. 288p. (AM572D41)

2040 Du Chaillu, Paul. The country of dwarfs ... Illustrated by Erick Berry. New York and London, Harper & Brothers, 1871. 261p. (M966D85c)

2041 DuChaillu, Paul Belloni. Explorations and adventures in equatorial Africa, with accounts of the manners and customs of the people, and of the chase of the gorilla, the crocodile, leopard, hippopotamus, and other animals. New York, Harper & brothers, 1861. 531p. (M916D86)

2042 DuChaillu, Paul Belloni. Lost in the jungle. Narrated for young people. New York, Harper & brothers, 1872. 260p. (M916.-62D85)

2043 East, D. J. Western Africa; its condition, and Christianity, and means of its recovery. London, Houlston & Stoneman, 1844. 400p. (M966Ea7w)

2044 Elias, T. Olawale. The nature of African customary law. Oxford Road, Manchester, University of Manchester, Manchester University Press, 1956. 318p. (M960E14)

2045 Ellis, George [Washington] Negro cultures in West Africa; a social study of the Negro group of Vai-speaking people, with its own invented alphabet and written language shown in two charts and six engravings of Vai script, twenty-six illustrations of their arts and life, fifty folklore stories, one hundred and fourteen proverbs, and one map ... Introduction by Frederick Starr ... New York, The Neale publishing Company, 1914. 290p. (M966E15)

2046 Evans, Ifor Leslie. The British in tropical Africa. Cambridge, (Eng.), The university Press, 1929. 396p. (M960E15)

2047 Fage, J. D. An introduction to the history of West Africa. [School ed.] Cambridge [Eng.] University Press, 1955. 209p. (M-966F13)

2048 Foote, Andrew H. African and the American flag. New York, D. Appleton & Co., 1854. 390p. (M960F737)

2049 Ford, Henry A. Observations on the fevers of the West coast of Africa. New York, E. O. Jenkins, 1856. 48p. (AM616.92F-75)

2050 Fraser, Donald. African idylls; portraits and impressions of life on a Central African mission station. London, Seeley, Service and Co., ltd., 1923. 229p. (M966F86)

2051 Frobenius, Leo. Auf dem wege nach Atlantis; bericht über den verlauf der zweiten reise-periode der D.i.a.f.e. in den jahren 1908 bis 1910 . . . mit. 48 tafeln, . . . Berlin-Charlottenburg, Vita deutsches verlagshaus, [c1911] 410p. (M960F92a)

2052 Frobenius, Leo. The voice of Africa, being an account of the travels of the German inner African exploration expedition in the years 1910-1912. London, Hutchinson & co, 1913. 2v. (M916-F921)

2053 Gardiner, R. K. The development of social administration [by] Robert Kweku Gardiner [and] Helen O. Judd. London, Oxford University Press, 1954. 208p. (M966G17)

2054 Gaunt, Mary Eliza Bakewell. Alone in West Africa. London, T. W. Laurie, 1912. 404p. (AM916G23)

2055 Golbéry, Sylvain Meinrad Xavier de. Travels in Africa . . . 2d ed. London, Printed for Jones & Bumford, 1808. (AM966.3G56t)

2056 Gorer, Geoffrey. Africa dances, a book about West African Negroes. Harmondsworth, Middlesex, Eng., New York, Penguin books [1945] 224p. (M96G661949)

2057 Graves, Anna Melissa, ed. Benvenuto Cellini had no prejudice against bronze. Baltimore, Waverly press, 1943. 176p. (M-916.6G78g)

2058 Great Brit. Colonial Office. Report of West African oilseeds mission. London, His Majesty's Stationery Office, 1948. 60p. (M966G79r)

2059 Great Brit. West African court of appeal. Selected judgments of the West African court of appeal . . . v.1, 1930|33-Accra, Government printing dept. 1936. Library has v.7, 1941. (M966-G79s)

2060 Griaule, M. Dieu d'eau, entretiens avec Ogotemmêli. Paris, Éditions du Chêne [1948] 263p. (M966.2G87d)

2061 Hailey, William Malcolm Hailey, baron. West Africa: Nigeria, Gold Coast, Sierra Leone, Gambia. London, H. M. Stationery Office, 1951. 350p. (AM354H12n)

2062 Hayford, Marc. C. West Africa and Christianity. London, Baptist Tract & Book Society, 1900. 68p. (AM916.1H33w)

2063 Heard, William H., The Missionary fields of West Africa. [Philadelphia A.M.E. Book Concern, printers, n.d.] 28 plates. (AM-260H35)

2064 Herskovits, Melville Jean. Native self-government. Reprinted from Foreign Affairs, an American Quarterly Review, April,

1944. 13p. (M966H43)

2065 Horn, Alfred Aloysius. Trader Horn; being the life and works of Alfred Aloysius Horn: an "old visiter" ... the works written by himself at the age of seventy-three and the life, with such of his philosophy as is the gift of age and experience, taken down and here edited. New York, The Literary Guild of America, 1927. 302p. (M916H78v.1)

2066 Horton, James Africanus Beale. West African Countries and peoples, British and Native. With the requirements necessary of etablishing that self government recommended by the Committee of the House of Commons, 1865; and a vindication of the African race, by James Africanus B. Horton. London, W. J. Johnson, 1868. 287p. (M960H78w)

2067 Howard, C., ed. West African explorers. London, New York, Oxford University Press, 1952. 598p. (M966H83)

2068 Huxley, Eelspeth Joscelin (Grant). Four Guineas; a journey through West Africa,. London, Chatto and Windus, 1954. 303p. (M966H98f)

2069 Ingrams, William Harold. Seven across the Sahara; from Ash to Accra. London, J. Murray, 1949. (M916.61In4s)

2070 Irvine, Frederick Robert. A text-book of West African agriculture, soils and crops. 2nd ed. London, New York, Oxford University Press, 1953. 367p. (M966Ir8t)

2071 Jobson, Richard. The golden trade; or a discovery of the river Gambia, and the golden trade of the Aethiopians. Teignmouth, Devonshire, E. E. Speight and R. H. Walpole, 1904. 209p. (M966J57g)

2072 Johnson, Joseph William de Graft. Towards nationhood in West Africa. Thoughts of young Africa addressed to young Britain. London, Headley, 1928. 158p. (M966J63)

2073 Jones-Quartey, K. A. B. Problems of the press. London, Bureau of Current Affairs, 195? 15p. (M966J73)

2074 Kilham, Hannah. The claims of West Africa to Christian instruction, through the native languages. London, Harvey and Darton, 1830. 28p. (M370K55)

2075 Kimble, David. The machinery of self-government. London, Penguin Books, 1953. 124p.

2076 King, William Joseph Harding. A search for the masked Tawareks. London, Smith, Elder & co., 1903. 334p. (M966.11K58)

2077 Kingsley, Mary Henrietta. The story of West Africa. London, H.

Marshall & son, 1899. 169p. (M966K61)

2078 Koelle, Sigiemund Wilhelm. Narrative of an expedition into the
      Vy country of West Africa; and the discovery of a system of
      syllabic writing recently invented by the natives of the Vy
      tribe. London, Suleys, 1859. 34p. (M966K81n)

2079 Lee, Sarah (Wallis) Bowditch. Adventures in Fanti-land. Illus-
      trations by John Gilbert. New York, E. P. Duton & co., n.d.
      190p. (M966L51)

2080 Lenz, Oskar, i.e. Henrich Oskar. Skizzen aus Westafrika. Berlin,
      A. Hofmann & co., 1878. 346p. (AM916L54)

2081 Leonard, Peter. Western coast of Africa; journal of an officer
      under Captain Owen. Philadelphia, Mielke, 1833. 177p. (AM-
      916L55)

2082 Lewin, Julius. The recognition of native law and custom in British
      Africa. Journal of the Royal African Society, 1938. 8p. (AM-
      960L58)

2083 Lewis, L. J. Equipping Africa. Educational development in Brit-
      ish colonial Africa. London, Edinburgh House Press, 1948.
      42p. (M916L58e)

2084 Library of Congress. Division of Bibliography. British West
      Africa: a selected list of reference compiled by Helen F. Con-
      over ... Dec. 1, 1942. 32p (M01L61b)

2085 Londres, Albert. A very naked people. Translated by Sylvia Stuart.
      New York, H. Liveright, c1929 267p. (M966L84)

2086 MacArthur, David Wilson. The desert watches. 1st American ed.
      Indianapolis, Bobbs-Merril, 1954. 350p. (M966.11M11)

2087 Macmillan, William Miller. Africa emergent; a survey of social,
      political and economic trends in British Africa. Harmonds-
      worth, Middlesex, Penguin Books, 1949. 352p. (M960M22a)

2088 Mansfield, Alfred. Westafrika aus urwald und steppe zwischen
      crossfluss und benue. München, Bei Georg Müller, 1928.
      144p. (AM572M31)

2089 Martin, Eveline Christiana. The British West African settlements.
      1750-1821; a study in local administration. New York, Long-
      mans, Green and co., 1927. 186p. (M960M36b)

2090 Mbadiwe, Kingsley Ozuomba. British and Axis aims in Africa.
      New York, Malliet and co., 1942. 248p. (M960M45b)

2091 McKay, Vernon. British rule in West Africa. New York, Foreign
      Policy Assn., 1948. 80p.

2092   McKay, Vernon. Nationalism in British West Africa. New York, Foreign Policy Assn., 1948. 12p.

2093   Meek, Charles Kingsley. Europe and West Africa; some problems and adjustments. London, New York, Oxford University Press, 1940. 143p. (M966M47e)

2094   Milburn, Stanley. The growing cost of education. London, Staples, 1952. 17p. (M966M59)

2095   Milligan, Robert H. The fetish folk of West Africa. New York, Fleming H. Revell co., 1912. 328p. (M966M62)

2096   Meckler-Ferryman, Augustus Ferryman. Up the Niger. London, G. Philip & son, 1892. 326p. (M966.96M71)

2097   Morel, Edmund Dene. Affairs of West Africa. London, W. Heinemann, 1902. 382p. (M966M81)

2098   Mulira, E. M. K. Thoughts of a young African. London, United Society for Christian Literature, 1945. 64p. (M960M89t)

2099   Nash, Thomas Arthur Manly. Tsetse flies in British West Africa. London, Published for the Colonial Office, 1948. 77p. (M966-N17t)

2100   Nassau, Robert Hamill. Fetichism in West Africa; forty years' observation of native customs and superstitions. New York, C. Scribner's sons, 1904. 389p. (AM291.211N18)

2101   Nassau, Robert Hamill. My Ogowe. New York, The Neal Publishing co., 1914. 708p. (AM966N18)

2102   O'Donovan, Patrick Anthony. Africa: which way now? London, Africa Bureau, 1952. 16p. (AM3230d5)

2103   Officer, Morris. Western Africa, a mission field of the moral and physical condition of Western Africa ... Pittsburgh, W. S. Haven, 1856. 44p. (M966f2w)

2104   Onabamiro, Sanya Dojo. Why our children die; the causes, and suggestions for prevention, of infant mortality in West Africa. London, Methuen [c1949] 195p. (M9660n1w)

2105   Ossendowski, Ferdinand. Slaves of the sun. New York, E. P. Dutton and co., 1928. 489p. (AM916.620s7)

2106   Parrinder, Geoffrey. West African psychology ... London, Lutterworth Press, 1951. 229p. (AM966P24w)

2107   Parrinder, Geoffrey. West African religion; illustrated from the beliefs and practices of the Yoruba, Ewe, Akan, kindred peoples. London, Epworth Press, 1949. 223p. (M290P24w)

2108   Pedler, F. J., Economic Geography of West Africa. London, New

York, Longmans, Green [1955] 232p. (M916.6P34e)

2109 Pedler, F. J. West Africa. New York, F. A. Praeger, 1951, 208p. (M916.6P34w)

2110 Perham, Margery F. Africans and British rule. London, Oxford, University Press, 1941. 98p. (M960P41a)

2111 Phillips, Thomas. A journal of a voyage made in the Hannibal of London, ann 1693-94 ... London, 1732. 239p. (AM916.6P53j)

2112 Pim, Alan W. The financial and economic history of the African tropical territories. Oxford, The Clarendon Press, 1940. 234p. (AM966P64)

2113 Puleston, F. African drums. New York, Farrar and Rinehart inc., 1930. 318p. (AM966P96)

2114 Scott, (Mrs.) A. M. Day dawn in Africa, or; Progress of the Protestant Episcopal Mission at Cape Palmas, West Africa. New York, Protestant Episcopal Society for the promotion of evangelical knowledge, 1858. 314p. (M266Sco8)

2115 Seabrook, William Buehler. Jungle ways. New York, Harcourt, Brace & Co., 1931. 308p. (AM572.67Se1)

2116 Seabrook, William Buehler. Secrets de la jungle. Paris, Crasset, n.d. 102p. (AM966Se1s)

2117 Singer, Caroline. White Africans and black. Cape Coast, Gold Coast, Methodist Book Depot, 1929. 3p. (M966Si6)

2118 Smith, A. Agricultural problems. Growing more food. London, Staples Publication, 195? 18p. (M966Sm5)

2119 Smith, Charles Spencer. Glimpses of Africa, West and Southwest coast. Nashville, Tenn., Publishing House A.M.E. Church Sunday School Union, 1895. 288p. (AM966Sm5)

2120 Smith, William. A new voyage to Guinea, describing the customs, manners, soil, climate, habits, buildings, education, manual arts, agriculture, trade, employments, languages, ranks of distinction, habitations, diversions, marriages, and whatever else is memorable among the inhabitants. London, Printed for John Nourse, n.d. 276p. (M966Sm5n)

2121 Tete-Ansá, Winfried. Africa at work. New York, 1930. 94p. (M966T29a)

2122 Thomas, Charles W. Adventures and observations on the west coast of Africa, and its islands. Historical and descriptive sketches of Madeira, Canary, Biafra and Cape Verd islands; their climates, inhabitants and productions. Accounts of places, peoples, customs, trade, missionary operations, etc., etc., on that part

of the African coast lying between Tangier, Morocco and
Benguela. New York, Derby & Jackson, 1860. 479p. (M916-
T36)

2123 Thompson, George. The palm land, or West Africa, illustrated ...
Cincinnati, Moore, Wilstach, Keys and Co., 1859. 456p. (AM-
966T37)

2124 Thompson, George. Thompson in Africa, or, An account of the
missionary labors, sufferings, travels, and observations. Cleve-
land, Printed for the author, 1852. 356p. (AM966T37t)

2125 Tracey, Joseph. Colonization and missions. Boston, Press of T. R.
Marvin, 1944. 40p. (AM966T67)

2126 Travassons Valdez, Francisco. Six years of a traveller's life in
western Africa. London, Hurst and Blackett, 1861. 2vols.
(AM966T69s)

2127 Tristram, Henry Baker. The great Sahara; wanderings south of
the Atlas mountains. London, J. Murray, 1860. 435p. (AM-
966.11T73g)

2128 Trull, George Harvey. The tribe of Zambe. New York, Board of
Foreign Missions of the Presbyterian Church in the U.S.A.,
1917. 107p. (AM966T76t)

2129 Vaillant, Auguste Nicolas. Voyage de monsieur le Vaillant dans
l'interieur de l'Afrique, par le Cap de Bonne-Esperance. Dans
les annes 1780-85. Chez Mourer, 1790 (AM966V24v)

2130 Wauters, Alphonse Jules. Stanley's Emin Pasha Expedition. London, J. C. Nimmo, 1890. 378p. (M966W35)

2131 Ward, William Ernest Frank. African education; a study of educational policy and practice in British tropical Africa. London,
Crown Agents for the Colonies, 1953. 187p. (AM370W21)

2132 West Africa. Court of Appeals. Rules made under West African
Court of Appeal order in council, 1948. n.p., 1951. 47p.

2133 The West African expedition, November, 1936-June, 1937. In University bulletin, vol. 7, November, 1937. 30p. (M966W52)

2134 West African Institute of Social and Economic Research. Annual
conference First, Third, Fourth and fifth proceedings. Ibadan,
University Press, 1956. (M966.7W52)

2135 The Western coast of Africa. Journal of an officer under Captain
Owen. Records of a voyage in the ship Dryad, in 1830, 1831,
and 1832. Philadelphia, E. C. Mielke, 1833. 177p. (M916L55)

2136 Williams, Joseph John. Hebrewism of West Africa; from Nile to
Niger with the Jews. New York, Lincoln MacVeagh, The

Dial Press, 1931. 443p. (AM572W67)

2137   Willis, Colin. White traveler in black Africa. London, D. Dobson,
       1951. 207p. (AM966W68w)

2138   Wilson, John Leighton. Western Africa; its history, condition, and
       prospects. New York, Harper & Bros., 1856. 527p. (AM-
       966W69)

2139   Wrong, Margaret. For a literate West Africa. New York, Friend-
       ship Press, 1946. 64p. (AM916W94b)

2140   Wrong, Margaret. The land and life of Africa. London, Edin-
       burgh House Press, 1935. 144p. (M960W941)

2141   Wrong, Margaret. West African journey in the interests of literacy
       and Christian literature, 1944-45. London, The Livingstone
       Press, 1946. 79p. (AM276.6W94)

2142   Zook, George Frederick. The company of royal adventurers trading
       into Africa. Lancaster, Pa. Press of the New Era Printing
       co., 1919. 105p. (AM966Z7)

NIGERIA

2143   Abraham, Roy Clive. Dictionary of the Hausa language. London,
       Published on behalf of the Govt. of Nigeria by the Crown
       Agents for the Colonies, 1949. 992p. (M493.5Ab8d)

2144   Abraham, Roy Clive. A dictionary of the Tiv language. London,
       Pub. on behalf of the Government of Nigeria by the Crown
       Agents for the Colonies, 1940. 331p. (M496.4Ab8d)

2145   Abraham, Roy Clive. The principles of Tiv. London, Published
       on behalf of the government of Nigeria, by the Crown Agents
       for the Colonies, 1940. 102p. (M496.4Ab8p)

2146   Abraham, Roy Clive. The Tiv people. London, Published on behalf
       of the government of Nigeria by the Crown agents for the
       colonies . . . , 1940. 177p. (AM496.4Ab8p)

2147   An account of Dr. Mojola Agbedi's work in West Africa, comprising
       Yorubaland, Fantiland, the Ekiti country, Central Nigeria,
       and the Cameroons. [1903?] [40]p. (MB9Ag3)

2148   Achonu, Thomas A. A study of some housing programs and how
       they apply to Nigeria. Washington, D.C., Howard University,
       (type written thesis), 1955. 75p. (M378.242So)

2149   Ajisafe, Ajayi Kowawole. Gbadebo Alake (lati Ogosti 8, 1898
       Titi de May 28, 1920) nipa, Ajayi Kilawole Ajisafe. Bungay,
       Suffolk, Printed for the author Richard Clay & Sons ltd., 1922.
       26p. (M896.1Ag5g)

2150   Ajisafe, Ajayi Kolawole. History of Abeokuta. Bungay, Suffolk, Richard Clay and sons, ltd., 1924. 225p. (AM966.9Aj5h)

2151   Ajisafe, Ajayi Kolawole. Iwe itan Abeokuta. Bungay, Suffolk, Richard Clay and sons, 1924. 192p. (AM966.9Aj5i)

2152   Ajisafe, Ajayi Kolawole. Laws and customs of the Benin People, by A. K. Ajisafe. Lagos, Kash & Klare Bookshop, 1945. 101p. (M966.9Aj51a)

2153   Ajisafe, Ajayi Kolawole. The laws and customs of the Yoruba people. London, George Routledge and sons, ltd., 1924. 97p. (M966.9Aj51)

2154   Akiga. Akiga's story; the Tiv tribe as seen by one of its members. London, New York, Oxford Univ. press, 1939. 436p. (AM-966.9AK5a)

2155   Akjintan, E. A. Training in English: Iwe akomolede gesi. Lagos, C.M.S. Bookshop, 1933. 142p. (M496Ak56)

2156   Akinyele, I. B. The outlines of Ibadan history, by Chief I. B. Akinyele. Lagos, Alebiosu printing press, 1946. 135p. (M-966.6Ak5c)

2157   Akpan, Ntieyong U. Epitaph to indirect rule. London, Cassell and Co., 1956. 204p.

2158   Aluko, S. A., The problems of self-government for Nigeria; a critical analysis. Devon, A. H. Stockwell, ltd., 1955. 62p. (M966.9A18)

2159   Anstruther, Ian. I presume. Stanley's triumph and disaster. London, G. Bles, 1956. 207p. (MC9St2i)

2160   Atundaolu, H. Awon enia inu bibeli. Lagos [n.p.] 1906. 208p. (AM966.9At8a)

2161   Awolowo, Obafemi. Path to Nigerian freedom. London, Faber and Faber [1947] 137p. (AM966.9Aw6p)

2162   Awoonor-Renner, Bankole. West African Soviet Union. London, Wans press, 1946. 36p. (M896.1Aw6t)

2163   Azikiwe, Benjamin Nnamdi. Assassination story: true or false. Onitsha, Nigeria, African Book Company, 1946. 3-15p. (MB9-Az3)

2164   Azikiwe, Benjamin Nnamdi. Renascent Africa. Accra, Gold Coast, West Africa, The author, 1937. 313p. (AM966.9Az2r)

2165   Azikiwe, Benjamin Nnamdi. Suppression of the press in British West Africa. Onitsha, Nigeria, African Book Company, 1945. 15p. (AM966.98Az3s)

2166 Babamuboni, I. E. Ojo Oluwa (Sunday) lati owo M.I.E. Babamuboni. Lagos, Tanimola printing and bookbinding works, 1927.
12p. (M966.9B11o)

2167 Backer-Beall, R. W. C. Our economy. Lagos, Public Relations
Department. n.d. 16p. Crownbird Series no. 26. (M966.9-
B170)

2168 Bargery, George Percy. A Hausa-English dictionary and English-
Hausa vocabulary compiled for the government of Nigeria.
London, Oxford University Press, 1934. 1226p. (AM493.5B23)

2169 Basden, George Thomas. Among the Ibos of Nigeria, an account
of the curious & interesting habits, customs & beliefs of a
little known African people by one who has for many years
lived amongst them on close & intimate terms. With thirty-
seven illustrations & map. Philadelphia, J. B. Lippincott company; London, Seeley, Service & Co., ltd., 1921. 315p. (M966-
B29)

2170 Bittinger, Desmond Wright. An educational experiment in northern
Nigeria in its cultural setting. Philadelphia, 1941. 343p.
(AM370B54)

2171 Blay, J. Benibengor. Dr. Bengia wants a wife. London, The
Blackheath Press, ltd., 1953. 23p. (M966.7B61d)

2172 Blyden, Edward Wilmot. Appendix to Ben [amin] Anderson's
journey to Musadu. New York, Lithographing, engraving &
printing co., 1870. 14p. (AM966.1B62)

2173 Bohannan, Laura. The Tiv of central Nigeria. London, International African Institute, 1953. 100p. (AM966.9B63)

2174 Bowdich, Thomas Edward. Mission from Cape Coast Castle to
Ashantee, with a statistical account of that kingdom, and geographical notices of other parts of the interior of Africa. London, John Mueray, 1819. 512p. (M916.674B67)

2175 Bowen, T. Grammar and dictionary of the Yoruba language. With
a description of the country and people of Yoruba. Washington, Smithsonian Institute, 1858. (M496.4B67)

2176 Bower, Penelope A. The balance of payments of Nigeria in 1936.
Oxford, B. Blackwell, 1949. 86p. (M966.9B67b)

2177 Brady, Michael, pseud. Our pioneers. Part I. Lagos, Public Relations Department, n.d. 19p. (M966.9B72o Pt. 1)

2178 Brady, Michael, pseud. Our pioneers Part II. Lagos, Public Relations Department, n.d. 16p. (M966.9B72o Pt.2)

2179 Brilliant, Hugh C. Our progress in the air. Lagos, Public Relations

Department, n.d., 16p. Crownbird Series no. 25. (M966.9B760)

2180 British West African Meteorological Services. Reports. 1949, 1952, 1953. Lagos, Federal Government Printer. (M966.9B77)

2181 Buchanan, Keith M. Land and people in Nigeria; the human geography of Nigeria and its environmental background [by] K. M. Buchanan and J. C. Pugh, with a contribution by A. Brown and a foreword by L. Dudley Stamp. London, University of London, Press, [1955] 252p.

2182 Bulifant, Josephine C. 40 years in the African bush. Grand Rapids, Zondervan [1950] 185p. (AM266B87f)

2183 Bunting, J. R. Thoughts on the aims of secondary education in West Africa; a paper read at the inaugural meeting of the Nigerian Conference of Principals. Lagos, Federal information service, [1957] 14p.

2184 Burns, Alan Cuthbert. History of Nigeria. [4th ed.] London, G. Allen & Unwin, [1948] 332p. (AM966.9B93)

2185 Calvert, Albert Frederick. Nigeria and its tin fields. London, E. Stanford, 1910. 488p. (M966.9C13)

2186 Cameron, Donald. Native administration in Nigeria and Tanganyika. Extra supplement to the "Journal of the Royal African Society." Vol. 36, Nov. 30, 1937. 29p. (AM966.9C14)

2187 Campbell, Robert. A few facts relating to Lagos, Abbeokuta, and other sections of Central Africa. By Robert Campbell . . . of the Niger Valley Exploring party. Philadelphia, King & Baird printers, 1860. 18p. (M966.9C15f)

2188 Campbell, Robert. A pilgrimage to my motherland. An account of a journey among the Egbas and Yorubas of Central Africa, in 1859-60. By Robert Campbell . . . of the Niger Valley exploring party. New York, T. Hamilton; Philadelphia, The author, 1861. 145p. (M966.9C15p)

2189 Cardinall, Allan Wolsey. In Ashanti & beyond. London, Seeley, Service & co., ltd., 1927. 288p. (AM572.966C17)

2190 Carlyle, G. G. Budget Speech. 1st March, 1956. Lagos, Federal Government Printer, 1956. 13p. (M966.9C19)

2191 Chadwick, E. R. Our community effort in the east. Lagos, Public Relations Department. Crownbird Series, no. 30 (Special). 32p. (M966.9C34o)

2192 Chalmers, Tom. Our broadcasting service. Lagos, Public Relations Department, n.d. 16p. Crownbird Series no. 21. (M966-9C35o)

2193   Chatterji, Suniti Kumar. The culture and religion of the Yorubas
       of West Africa. Calcutta, Swami Pavitrananda, 1945. 12p
       (M966.1C39c)

2194   Christopherson, Paul. Bilingualism; an inaugural lecture delivered
       on foundation day, November 17, 1948. London, Methuen and
       co., for University College, Ibadan, 1948. 16p. (M410 C46b)

2195   Chukwuemeka, Nwankwo. African dependencies, a challenge to
       western democracy. New York, William-Frederick Press, 1950.
       207p. (AM966.9C47a)

2196   Chukwuemeka, Nwankwo. Industrialization of Nigeria. [New
       York, William-Frederick Press] c1952. 64p. (AM966.9C47i)

2197   Clarke, J. D. Omu, an African experiment in education. London,
       New York, Longmans, Green & co., 1937. 167p. (AM370C55)

2198   Coker, Increase. Our oil palm industry. Lagos, Public Relations
       Department. n.d. 16p. Crownbird Series, no. 20. (M966.9C66c)

2199   Cook, Arthur N. British enterprise in Nigeria. Philadelphia, 1943.
       330p. (AM966.9C77)

2200   Crocker, Walter Russel. Nigeria; a critique of British colonial ad-
       ministration. London, G. Allen and Unwin ltd., 1936. 277p.
       (AM966.9C87n)

2201   Crowther, Samuel Adjai. The first seven chapters of the gospel
       according to St. Matthew, in Nupe. Translated by the Rev.
       Samuel Crowther. London, Printed for the British and Foreign
       Bible Society, 1860. 20p. (M966.9C88f)

2202   Crowther, Samuel Adjai. The gospel on the banks of the Niger.
       Journals and notices of the native missionaries accompanying
       the Niger expedition of 1857-1859. By the Rev. Samuel Crow-
       ther and the Rev. John Christopher Taylor. London, Church
       Missionary House, 1859. 451p. (M966.9C88g)

2203   Crowther, Samuel Adjai. A grammar and vocabulary of the Yoruba
       language, compiled by the Rev. Samuel Crowther, together with
       introductory remarks by O. E. Vidal. London, Seeleys, 1852.
       291p. (M966.9C88g)

2204   Crowther, Samuel Adjai. Journal of an expedition up the Niger and
       Tshadda rivers, undertaken by Macgregor Laird Esq. in con-
       nection with the British government in 1854. By the Rev.
       Samuel Crowther. With map and appendix. London, Church
       missionary house, 1855. 233p. (M966.9C88j)

2205   Crowther, Samuel Adjai. Journals of the Rev. James Frederick
       Schon and Mr. Samuel Crowther, who, with the sanction of

her majesty's government, accompanied the expedition up the
Niger in 1941 in behalf of the church missionary society. With
appendices and map. London, Hatchard and son, 1842. 393p.
(M966.9C88jo)

2206   Crowther, Samuel Adaji. Labari wangi yan yohanu. The Gospel
according to St. John, translated into Nupe, by the Right Rev.
Samuel Crowther. London, Church Missionary House, 1877.
72p. (M966.9C88L)

2207   Crowther, Samuel Adjai, bp. Omode erú-kunrin ti o di bisopu,
tabi itan Samuel Adjai Crowther. 5th ed. Lagos, C.M.S.
boókshop, 1931. 31p. (M966.9C88o)

2208   Crowther, Samuel Adjai. Slave trade-African squadron. Letters
from the Rev. Samuel Crowther ... and the Rev. Henry Townsend ... London, John Martimer, 1850. 15p. (M966.9C88s)

2209   Crowther, Samuel Adjai. Vocabulary and dictionary of the Yoruba
language. London, W. M. Watts, 1856. 254p. (M966.9C88w)

2210   Currey, Muriel. A woman at the Abyssinian war. London, Hutchinson and co., 1936. 254p. (M963C93)

2211   Davis, Alexander. The native problem in South Africa. London,
Chapmann and Hall, 1903. 242p. (M968D29n)

2212   De Gaye, Jules A. Yoruba grammar ... London, K. Paul, Trench,
Trubner & Co., 1923. 966p. (M496.4D34)

2213   Delano, Isaac O. An African looks at marriage. London and Redhill, United society for Christian literature, 1944. 47p. (M966-
9D37a)

2214   Delano, Isaac O. Notes and comments from Nigeria. London, and
Redhill, The society for Christian literature, 1944. 63p. (AM-
966.9D37)

2215   Delano, Isaac O. One church for Nigeria. London, United Society
for Christian literature [1945] 48p. (AM966.9D37o)

2216   Delano, Isaac O. The singing minister of Nigeria; the life of the
Rev. Canon J. J. Ransome-Kuti. London, United Society for
Christian literature, 1942. 63p. (MB9R17)

2217   Delano, Isaac O. The soul of Nigeria. London, T. Werner Laurie
[1937] 251p. (M966.9D37s)

2218   Dennett, R. E. Nigerian studies or "The religious & political system of the Yoruba." ... London, Macmillan and co., ltd., 1910.
235p. (AM966.9D41n)

2219   Desplagnes, Louis. ... Le plateau central Nigerien. Une mission
archeologique et ethnographique au Soudan francais ... Paris,

Emile Larose, 1907. 504p. (AM966.9D46p)

2220 Dictionary of the Yoruba language. 2nd ed. Lagos, Church Missionary society Bookshop. 1937. 243p. (M496.4D56)

2221 Dike, K. Onwuka. Trade and Politics in the Niger Delta, 1830-1885. Oxford, Clarendon Press, 1956.

2222 Eaglesfield, Carrol Frederick. Listen to the drums; Nigeria and its people. Nashville, Broadman Press, 1950. 82p. (M966.9Ea31)

2223 East, R. . A vernacular bibliography for the languages of Nigeria. Zaria, Literature Bureau, 1941. 85p. (AM496Ea7v)

2224 Edegbe, Joshua E. Benin-English grammar. Lagos, C.M.C. Bookshop, 1936. 62p. (M966.9Ed4b)

2225 Educational studies and documents. African languages and English in education; a report of a meeting of experts on the use in education of African languages in relation to English, where English is the accepted second language, held at Jos, Nigeria, November, 1952. n.p. Education Clearing House, June 1953. 91p. (M496Ed8)

2226 Egharevba, Jacob U. A short history of Benin. Benin, Published by the author, 1953. 118p. (M966.93Eg3)

2227 Egharevba, Jacob U. A short history of Benin. Lagos, Church Missionary society bookshop, 1936. 104p. (M966.9Eg35s)

2228 Elias, Taslim Olawale. Groundwork of Nigerian law. London, Routledge & Paul, 1954. 374p. (M966.9E142g)

2229 Elias, Taslim Olawale. Nigerian land law and custom. London, Routledge & K. Paul, 1951. 326p. (M966.9E142)

2230 Emeruwa, Obonnaya N. The Nigerian monetary system: a study in the operation of the West African currency board. Washington, D.C., Howard University, (type written thesis), 1952. 99p. (M378.242EcEm3)

2231 Epelle, Kiea. Our folklore and fables. Part II. Lagos, Public Relations Department. n.d. 16p. (Crownbird Series, no. 37. (AM398Ep2-0Part2)

2232 Epelle, Kiea. Our land and people. Part I. The East. Lagos, Public Relations Department, n.d. 16p. Crownbird Series, no. 31. (M966.9Ep20)

2233 Falconer, John Downie. The geology and geography of Northern Nigeria. London, Macmillan and co., ltd., 1911. 295p. (966.9-F18g)

2234 Falconer, John Downie. On horseback through Nigeria; or, Life and travel; in the central Sudan. London, T. F. Unwin, 1911. 312p. (AM966.9F18)

2235　Forde, Cyril Daryll. The Ibo and Ibibio-speaking peoples of south-eastern Nigeria, by Daryll Forde and G. I. Jones. London, New York, Published for the International African Institute by Oxford University Press, 1950. 94p. (M966.9F75i)

2236　Forde, Cyril Daryll. Marriage and the family among the Yako in South-eastern Nigeria. London, P. Lund, Humphries and co., ltd., 1941. 121p. (AM966.9F75)

2237　Forde, Cyril Daryll. The Yoruba-speaking peoples of south-western Nigeria. London, International African Institute, 1951. 102p. (M966.9F75y)

2238　Farrow, Stephen S. Faith, fancies and fetich; or, Yoruba Paganism. London Society for Promoting Christian Knowledge, 1924. 180p.

2239　Fraser, Douglas. Impressions: Nigeria 1925. London, Herbert Jenkins, 1926. 188p.

2240　Frobenius, Leo. Die Atlantische Gotterlebre. Jena, Verlegt bei Eugen Diederichs, 1926. 318p. (AM966.92F92)

2241　Fuller, Francis. A vanished dynasty Ashanti. London, John J. Murray, 1921. 241p. (M966.74F95)

2242　Galletti, R. ... Nigerian cocoa farmers; an economic survey of Yoruba cocoa farming families. London, Oxford University Press, 1956. 744p. (M966.92 G13)

2243　Gana, Mallam Abba. Our land and people; Part II—The North. Lagos, Public Relations Department. n.d. 16p. Crownbird Series, no. 32. (M966.9G15o)

2244　Gibson, Thomas Ogbe. A handbook on West African native laws and customs (with particular reference to Southern Nigeria [n.p., n.d.] 26p. (AM966.9G35h)

2245　Goubadia, B. A. A. Our olympic adventure. Lagos, Public Relations Department, n.d. 12p. Crownbird Series, no. 17. (M966-9G72o)

2246　Great Britain. Colonial Office. Annual report on Nigeria, 1946-47, 1951-52. (M966.9G79a)

2247　Great Britain. Commission of Enquiry into the disorders in the Eastern Provinces of Nigeria. London, H.M. Stationery Office, 1950. (AM331G79d)

2248　Green, M. M. Ibo village affairs, chiefly with reference to the vil-

lage of Umeke Agbaja. London, Sidgwick and Jackson, 1947.
262p. (AM966.9G82ib)

2249   Greenberg, Joseph. The influence of Islam on a Sudanese religion.
New York, J. J. Augustin, 1947. 73p. (AM966.9G82i)

2250   Gunn, Harold. Peoples of the Plateau area of Northern Nigeria.
Western Africa, Part VII. London, International African Institute, 1953. 110p. (M966.9G95)

2251   Haig, E. F. G. Nigerian sketches. London, George Allen and Unwin, ltd., 1931. 251p. (AM966.9H12n)

2252   Hambly, Wilfrid Dyson. ... Culture areas of Nigeria. Frederick
H. Rawson-Field museum ethnological expedition to West Africa, 1929-30. Chicago, 1935. 365-502p. (AM572.669H17c)

2253   Harris, Jack. Human relationship to the land in Southern Nigeria.
Rural sociology, 1942. Pp. 89-92 (M966.9H24h)

2254   Hassan, Malam. A chronical of Abuja, translated and arranged
from the Hasua of Malam Hassan, Sarkin Ruwa, Abuja and
Malam Shuaibu, Mkaddamin Makarantar, Bida. Published for
the Abuja Native Administration by the Ibadan University
Press, 1952. 92p. (M966.9H27c)

2255   Hastings, Archibald Charles Gardiner. Nigerian days. London,
John Lane, 1925. 255p. (AM916.69H27n)

2256   Helser, Albert David. Education of primitive people. New York,
etc. Fleming H. Revell company, 1934. 136p. (AM370H36)

2257   Hennessy, Maurice. Our marketing boards. Lagos, Public Relations Department, n.d. 15p. Crownbird Series, no. 2. (M966-
9H39o)

2258   Hines, Frank. Ju-Ju- and justice in Nigeria. London, John Lane,
[1930] 254p. (AM572.669H64)

2259   Hogarth, Randal F. Our next generation. Part I. Lagos, Public
Relation Department. n.d. 14p. Crownbird Series no. 3. (M-
966.9 H67 no. 1)

2260   Hogarth, Randal F. Our next generation. Part II. Lagos, Public
Relations Department. n.d. 12p. Crownbird Series no. 7.
(M966.9 H7 no. 2)

2261   Howeidy, A. Concise Hausa grammar. Wheatley, G. Ronald, 1953.
232p. (M496H83c)

2262   Ibadan University College. Annual report of academic board to the
provisional council session. Ibadan, University College, 19—.
48p. (AM378 Ibla)

2263 Ibadan University College. Department of Extra-mural studies. Report, 1949. Ibadan, Nigeria. (AM378Ib1)

2264 Ihaza, Daniel E. Foreign trade of Nigeria. Washington, D.C., Howard University, (type written thesis), 1954. 97p. (M378-242Ec)

2265 Ikoli, Ernest. Our council of ministers. Lagos, Public Relations Department, n.d. 22p. (M966.9Ik7o)

2266 Ikoli, Ernest. Our northern warriors. Lagos, Public Relations Department, n.d. 12p. Crownbird series no. 15. (MB9 Ik7)

2267 Imrie, J. ... Report of the West Africa Survey Mission on the training of civil servants in Nigeria (Central Government) by Lt. Col. J. Imrie and D. G. Lee. Lagos, Federal Govt Printer, 1954. 15p. (M966.9Im8)

2268 International African Institute. Peoples of the Niger-Benue confluence; The Nupe by Daryll Fored; the Igbira, by Paula Brown; The Igala, by Robert G. Armstrong; The Idoma-speaking peoples by Robert G. Armstrong. London, 1955. 160p.

2269 International Bank for Reconstruction and Development. Economic development of Nigeria. Lagos, Government Printer, 1954. 438p. (AM966.9In8)

2270 Irvine, William H. Our cocoa industry. Lagos, Public Relations Department, n.d. 16p. Crownbird Series no. 18. (M966.9 Ir8oc)

2271 Irvine, William H. Our groundnut industry. Lagos, Public Relations Department, n.d. 16p. Crownbird Series no. 27 (M966.9-Ir80g)

2272 Ita, Eyo. The assurance of freedom. Calabar, W.A.P.O. press, 1949. 62p. (AM966.9It2a)

2273 Ita, Eyo. Reconstructing towards wider integration; a theory of social symbiosis. Calabar, W.A.P.I. press. 9p. (AM966.-9It2r)

2274 Itayemi, Phebean Ajibola. Folk tales and fables, collected by Phebean Itayemi and P. Gurrey. London, Penguin Books [1953] 133p. (AM398It1)

2275 Johnson, Samuel, d. The history of the Yorubas from the earliest times to the beginning of the British protectorate. Ed. by Dr. O. Johnson ... London, G. Routledge & Sons, Ltd., 1921. 648p. (M966.9J63h)

2276 Jones, Melville, bp. Isin Kristi ati Isin Monodu-Christianity and Mohammedanisn. Lagos, printed and published by the C.M.S. Press, 1920. 62p. (AM966.9J71i)

2277 Kennedy, James Domone. Forest flora of Southern Nigeria. Lagos, The Govt. Printer, 1936. 242p. (AM966.9K38f)

2278 Kisch, Martin Schlessinger. Letters and sketches from Northern Nigeria. London, Chatto and Windus, 1910. 232p. (M966.-9K64)

2279 Kleiss, Lee. Community life on the coast of Nigeria. (In: The plough, the quarterly of the Bruderhof Communities, 3:42-46). (M966.9K67)

2280 Kuye, J. G. English principia, or grammar Gési for primary schools and private tuition, containing copious exercises for translation with vocabularies. Fifth edition. Lagos, published by the author, 1925. 15p. (M966.9K96e)

2281 Langa, Langa. Up against it in Nigeria. London, George Allen and Unwin, 1922. 224p.

2282 Leith-Ross, Sylvia. Beyond the Niger. London, Lutterworth Press, 1951. 123p. (M966.7L53b)

2283 Leonard, Arthur Glyn. The lower Niger and its tribes. London, Macmillan and Co., Ltd., 1906. 564p. (AM966.9L551)

2284 Lijadu, E. M. Ifa: imole re ti ise ipile isin ni ile Yoruba, [Sayings of the Yoruba.] Exeter, James Towsend and Sons, 1923. 72p. (AM966.9L62i)

2285 Lobagola, Bata Kindai Amgoza ibn. The folk tales of a savage. New York, A. A. Knopf, 1930. 199p. (AM966.9L78f)

2286 Lobagola, Bata Kindai Amgoza ibn. LoBagola; an African savage's own story. New York, A. A. Knopf, 1930. 402p. (AMB9L78)

2287 Longley, E. O. Contagious caprine pleuro-pneumonia. London, H. M. Stationery Office, 1951. 26p. (AM966.9L86c)

2288 Lois, John B. Ogunjimi. History of Abeokuta. Lagos, Nigeria, Bosere Press, 1924. 176p. (AM966.9L89hi)

2289 Lois, John B. Ogunjimi. Itan Abeokuta. Lati owo Prince John B. O. Ogunjimi. 2d. impression. Exeter, James Towsend and Co., 1920. 135p. (AM966.9L89hi)

2290 Losi, John B. Ogunjimi. Itan eko. 3d. ed. Lagos, Church missionary society's press, 1921. 60p. (AM966.9L89h)

2291 Losi, John B. Ogunjimi. History of Lagos. 2d ed. Lagos, C.M.C. Bookshop, 1921. 75p. (AM966.9L89h)

2292 Lugard, Flora Louise. A tropical dependency. An outline of the ancient history of the western Soudan, with an account of the modern settlement of Northern Nigeria. London, J. Nisbet & Co., 1905. 508p. (M966.9L96)

2293	Maddocks, K. P. Report on local government in the Northern
	Provinces of Nigeria. 14th December, 1950. Kaduna, Gov-
	ernment Printer, 1951. 35p. (M966.9M26)

2294	Marshall, Percival G. The people's right in democracy. Accra,
	Lona Press, Itd., 1950. 36p. (M966.7M35p)

2295	Mbadiwe, Kingsley Ozuomba. British and Axis aims in Africa.
	New York, W. Malliet and Co., 1942. 248p. (AM966.9M45b)

2296	Meek, Charles Kingsley. Law and authority in a Nigerian tribe; a
	study in indirect rule, by C. K. Meek ... lately anthropological
	officer, Nigerian administrative service ... With a foreword
	by the Right Hon. Lord Lugard . . . London, New York, etc.
	Oxford University Press, 1937. 372p. (M966.9M471)

2297	Meek, Charles Kingsley. The northern tribes of Nigeria; an ethno-
	graphical account of the northern provinces of Nigeria together
	with report on the 1921 decennial census commissioner, Nigeria
	. . . London, Oxford University Press, H. Milford, 1925. 2v.
	(AM572M47)

2298	Meek, Charles Kingsley. A Sudanese kingdom; an ethnographical
	study of the Jukun speaking peoples of Nigeria . . . with in-
	troduction by H. R. Palmer . . . with 2 maps and 147 illustra-
	tions. London, K. Paul, Trench, Trubner & Co., Ltd., 1931.
	548p. (AM572.669M47)

2299	Meek, Charles Kingsley. Tribal studies in nothern Nigeria. London,
	K. Paul, Trench, Trubner & Co., 1931. 108p. (AM572.-
	699M47t)

2300	Mellanby, Kenneth. An address to the academic staff at the open-
	ing of the first term of the 1950-1951 session, by the principal.
	Ibandan, Nigeria, University college, 1950. 15p. (AM378-
	M48a)

2301	Mellanby, Kenneth. Our university college. Lagos Public Rela-
	tions Department. n.d., Crownbird Series No. 16. (M966.9M-
	480)

2302	Meniru, Godwin Udegbunem. African-American cooperation, a
	study in tropical development; a survey of the natural re-
	sources and industrial development; a survey of the natural
	resources and industrial potentialities of Nigeria. Glen Gard-
	ner, N. J., Libertarian Press. [c1945] 120p. (M966.9M52a)

2303	Messinger, Susan F. Witchcraft in two West African Societies.
	Chicago, University of Chicago Library, Dept. of Photographic
	Reproduction, 1953. Microfilm.

2304	Miller, Walter R. For Africans only. London, United Society for

Christian literature, Lutterworth Press, 1950.   79p.   (AM-966.9M61f)

2305   Miller, Walter R.   Success in Nigeria: Assets and possibilities. London, United Society for Christian literature, Lutterworth Press, 1948.   96p.   (AM966.9M61s)

2306   Mockler-Ferryman, Augustus-Ferryman.   British Nigeria; a geographical and historical description of the British possession adjacent to the Niger River, West Africa . . . with map, illustrations, and appendix.   London, New York, etc.   Cassell and Co., Ltd., 1902.   351p.   (M966.9M71)

2307   Mockler-Ferryman, Augustus Ferryman.   Up the Niger.   Narrative of Major Claude MacDonald's mission to the Niger and Benue rivers, West Africa . . . to which is added a chapter on native musical instruments.   London, G. Philip & Son, 1892.   326p.   (M966.96M71)

2308   Murray, K. C.   Our art treasures.   Lagos, Public Relations Department.   n.d.   (Crownbird Series No. 28) 16p.   (M966.9M960)

2309   Nadel, Siegfried Ferdinand.   A black Byzantium; the kingdom of Nupe in Nigeria.   With a foreword by the Right Hon. Lord Lugard . . . London, New York, [etc.] Pub. for the International Institute of African languages and cultures by the Oxford University Press, 1942.   420p.   (AM916.69N12)

2310   Newlyn, W. T. and Rowan, D. C.   Money and banking in British Colonial Africa; a study of the monetary and banking systems of eight British African Territories.   Oxford, Clarendon Press, 1954.   301p.   (AM332.1N46m)

2311   Nicol, B. M.   Feeding Nigeria.   Lagos, Produced and Published by the Federal Information Service and printed by the Federal Government Printer, 195?   17p.   (M966.9N54)

2312   Nigeria.   The accounts of quasi-commercial undertakings operated by government by means of bank current accounts which were opened with grants of working capital.   Lagos, Government Printer, 1956.   64p.   (M966.9N56ACl1956)

2313   Nigeria.   The accounts of quasi-commercial undertakings operated by government by means of bank current accounts which were opened with grants of working capital.   Lagos, Government Printer, 1957.   7p.   (M966.9N56AC11957)

2314   Nigeria.   The capital structure of the electricity corporation of Nigeria.   Lagos, Government Printer, 1957.   7p.   (M966.9N-56C1)

2315   Nigeria.   The criminal procedure ordinance, 1945.   [Lagos, Government Printer, 1945] 190p. (AM966.9N56cr)

2316 Nigeria. Estimates of revenue and expenditures of the government
of Nigeria . . . (excluding Nigerian railway) . . . Nigeria, Government Printer, 1954-55. (M966.90N56Es8)

2317 Nigeria. Food in relation to health . . . Lagos, Printed by the Government Printer, 1946. 10p. (AM966.9N568)

2318 The Nigeria handbook. London, The Crown Agents for Overseas
Governments and Administrations. 1956. 339p.

2319 Nigeria. The international tin agreement; Participation by Nigeria.
Lagos, Government Printer, 1957. 1p. (M966.9N561n1)

2320 Nigeria. Man o'war bay. Nigeria. Government Printer, 1953.
3p. (M966.9N56T2)

2321 Nigeria. Memorandum on the estimates of revenue and expenditure. Lagos, Government Printer, 1954-55. (M966.90N56-
Es8m)

2322 Nigeria. An ordinance to create facilities for the fixing of minimum
wages, the regulating of conditions of employment generally
and the registration of industrial workers for the purposes of
employment. [Lagos, Government Printer], 1943. 14p. (AM-
966.9M560)

2323 Nigeria. Proposals for the development of medical and health
services in Lagos. Lagos, Government Printer, 1956. 5p.
(M966.9N56P1)

2324 Nigeria. Report by the committee to advise the federal government on the stimulation of industrial development by affording
relief from import duties and protection to Nigerian industry.
Lagos, Government Printer, 1956. 24p. (M966.9N56R1)

2325 Nigeria. Report of the committee appointed to advise on the ade-
quacy of pensions. Lagos, Government Printer, 1956. 12p.
(M966.9N56R2)

2326 Nigeria. Report of a committee appointed to examine the salary
structure of non-government teachers in the Federal territory
of Lagos. Lagos, Government Printer, 1956. 14p. (M966.-
9N56R4)

2327 Nigeria. Report of the director of federal audit on the statement
of the university college (Capital) account for the year ended
30th June, 1955. Lagos, Federal Government Printer, 1955.
8p. (M966.9N56di)

2328 Nigeria. Staff list. Lagos, Government Printer, 1956. (M966.-
9N56St1)

2329   Nigeria. Statement of policy of the government of the federation
       on the Nigerianisation of the Federal Public Service and the
       higher teaching of Nigerians, 1956-60. Lagos, Government
       Printer, 1956. 20p. (M966.9N56St2)

2330   Nigeria. Statement on the policy proposed by the government of
       the Federation for the development of telecommunications with-
       in Nigeria. 9p. (M966.9N56St8)

2331   Nigeria. Statement of the policy proposed by the Government for
       the establishment of the Nigerian Naval Force. Lagos, Gov-
       ernment Printer, 1956. 8p. (M966.9N56St4)

2332   Nigeria. State of the policy proposed by the Government of the
       Federation for the establishment of an inland waterways de-
       partment. Lagos, Government Printer, 1956. 5p. (M966.-
       9N56St6)

2333   Nigeria. Statement of the policy proposed by the Government of
       the Federation for the establishment of Post Offices within
       Nigeria. Lagos, Government Printer, 1957. 10p. (M966.-
       9N56St7)

2334   Nigeria. Statement of the policy proposed by the Government of
       the Federation for Navigation in the Ports of the Western
       Delta and on the Niger and Benu Rivers. Lagos, Government
       Printer, 1956. 2p. (M966.9N56St5)

2335   Nigeria. Statement of policy proposed by the Federal Government
       on the report by a committee appointed to advise on the stimu-
       lation of industrial development by affording relief from im-
       port duties and protection to Nigerian Industry. Lagos, Gov-
       ernment Printer, 1956. 4p. (M966.9N56St3)

2336   Nigeria. Statement on the policy and reorganisation of the posts
       and telegraphs department. Lagos, Government Printer, 1956.
       26p. (M966.9N56St1)

2337   Nigeria. Supplementary estimates [of revenue and expenditure]
       Lagos, Government Printer, 1954-55. (M966.90N56Es8s)

2338   Nigeria. Supplementary memorandum on the revised estimates of
       revenue and expenditure. Lagos, Government Printer, 1954-55.
       (M966.90N56Es8sm)

2339   Nigeria. The training of Nigerians for the representation of their
       country overseas; a statement of policy by the Government of
       the Federation of Nigeria. Lagos, Government Printer,
       1956. 7p. (M966.9N56t1)

2340   Nigeria. White paper on education. Lagos, Government Printer,
       1956. 5p. (M966.9N56W1)

2341 Nigeria. White paper on federal fisheries service. Lagos, Government Printer, 1957. 4p. (M966.9N56W4)

2342 Nigeria. White paper on further financial provisions required for the University College Hospital, Ibadan. Lagos, Government Printer, 1956. 10p. (M966.9N56W3)

2343 Nigeria. White paper on natural resources. Lagos, Government Printer, 1956. 6p. (M966.9N56W2)

2344 Nigeria. Year book 1953. Lagos, Nigerian Printing and Publishing Co., 1953. (AM966.9N569)

2345 Nigeria. Accountant General. Report of the Accountant-General with financial statements. Lagos, Government Printer, 1951-53. (M966.90N56Ac2r)

2346 Nigeria. Administrator-General's Department. Report. Lagos, Government Printer, 1953-55. (M966.90N56Ad6a)

2347 Nigeria. Agriculture. Reports. 1951-2, 1953, 1954. Lagos, Government Printer. (M966.9 Govt. Doc.)

2348 Nigeria. Agricultural Research Department. Report. Lagos, Government Printer, 1954-55. (M966.90N56Ag8r)

2349 Nigeria. Agriculture Department. Reports. Lagos, Government Printer, 1952-54. (M966.90N56Ag8a)

2350 Nigeria. Antiquities Service. Reports. Lagos, Government Printer, 1953-54. (M966.90N56An7a)

2351 Nigeria. Audit Department. Electricity Corporation of Nigeria. Report on the accounts of the Electricity Corporation of Nigeria. Lagos, Government Printer, 1952-53. (M966.90N56Au2e)

2352 Nigeria. Audit Department. Government Railway. Report. Lagos, Government Printer, 1953-55. (M966.90N56Au2g)

2353 Nigeria. Audit Department. Report on the accounts of the Nigerian Coal Corporation. Lagos, Government Printer, 1955. (M966.9N56au)

2354 Nigeria. Audit Department. Report of the Director of Audit on the Accounts of the Government of Nigeria. Lagos, Government Printer, 1953-56. (M966.90N56Au2go)

2355 Nigeria. Chemistry Department. Reports. Lagos, Government Printer, 1945, 1953-56. (M966.90N56C42a)

2356 Nigeria. Civil Aviation Department. Reports. Lagos, Government Printer, 1952-55. (M966.90N56C49a)

2357 Nigeria. Coal Corporation. Reports. Lagos. Federal Government Printer, 1954-55. (M966.90N56C63r)

2358   Nigeria.   Cocoa Marketing Board.   Reports.   Lagos, Nigerian Information Service, 1952-54.   (M966.90N56C64a)

2359   Nigeria.   Colonial Office.   Enquiry into the cost of living and the control of the cost of living in the colony and protectorate of Nigeria.   London, H.M.S.C., 1946.   (M966.9G79e)

2360   Nigeria.   Colony Development Board.   Reports.   Lagos, Federal Government Printer, 1954-56.   (M966.90N56C71a)

2361   Nigeria.   Commerce and Industries Department.   Handbook of commerce and industry in Nigeria.   Lagos, Government Printer, 1952.   (M966.9N56C73h)

2362   Nigeria.   Commerce and Industries Department.   Reports.   Lagos, Government Printer, 1951-54.   (M966.90N56C73a)

2363   Nigeria.   Cooperative Office.   Report on the progress of cooperation in Nigeria, 1944-45.   Lagos, Government Printer, 1944-45.   (M966.90N56C78a)

2364   Nigeria.   Cotton Marketing Board.   Reports. 1952-53, 1953-54.   Lagos, Government Printer, 1952-54.   (M966.90N56C82a)

2365   Nigeria.   Costums and Excise Department.   Reports.   Lagos, Government Printer, 1953-54.   (M966.90N56C96a)

2366   Nigeria.   Development and Welfare Schemes.   Development finance, 1955-56.   Lagos, Government Printer, 1956.   (M966.90N56-D49re)

2367   Nigeria.   Development and Welfare Schemes.   Report on the general progress of development and welfare schemes.   Lagos, Government Presses, 1952-53.   (M966.90N56D49r)

2368   Nigeria.   Education Department.   Reports.   Lagos, Government Printer, 1944-45, 1951-53.   (M966.90N56Ed8a)

2369   Nigeria.   Federal House of Representatives.   Debates in the Federal House of Representatives.   First session, 17th to 30th August, 1955.   Lagos, Federal Government Printer, 1955- (M-966.9N56fe)

2370   Nigeria.   Federal Information Service.   Report.   Lagos, Federal Government Printer, 1954-55.   (M966.90N56F81a)

2371   Nigeria.   Forest Research and the Forest School.   Report.   Lagos, Government Printer, 1954-56.   (M966.90N56F76f)

2372   Nigeria.   Forestry Department.   Report.   Lagos, Federal Government Printer, 1952-53.   (M966.90N56F76a)

2373   Nigeria.   Full court.   Law reports. vol. 1-3.   A selection from the cases decided in the Full court and the Divisional courts of the Colony and Protectorate of Nigeria, 1881-1911 - 1911-1914 1914-1922 1922-. Lagos, Printed by the Government Printer, 1915. (M966.9N561a)

2374 Nigeria. Geological Survey Department. Records. Lagos, Government Printer, 1954. (M966.90N56G29r)

2375 Nigeria. Geological Survey Department. Report. Lagos, Government Printer 1951-56. (M966.90N56G29a)

2376 Nigeria. Government Coastal Agency. Report. Lagos, Federal Government Printer, 1954-56. (M966.90N56G74c)

2377 Nigeria. Grading Teams and Reviewing Body for the Federal Public Service (including the Southern Cameroons). Conclusions. Lagos, Government Printer, 1956. (M966.90N56G75re)

2378 Nigeria. Grading Teams and Reviewing Body for the Federal Public Service (including the Southern Cameroons). Report. Lagos, Government Printer, 1956. (M966.90N56G75r)

2379 Nigeria. Groundnut Marketing Board. Report. Lagos, Government Printer, 1952-54. (M966.90N56G91a)

2380 Nigeria. House of Representatives. Debates. Lagos, Government Printer, 1954-57. (M966.90N56H81d)

2381 Nigeria. House of Representatives. The economic programme of the government of the Federation of Nigeria 1955-60. Lagos, Government Printer, 1956. 75p. (M966.9N56H1)

2382 Nigeria. House of Representatives. First progress report on the economic programme 1955-60. Lagos, Government Printer, 1957. 34p. (M966.9N56H2)

2383 Nigeria. House of Representatives. Proposals for the establishment of a Nigerian Broadcasting Corporation together with an outline of the projected further development of Broadcasting in Nigeria. Lagos, Government Printer, 1956. 7p. (M966.-9N56P2)

2384 Nigeria. House of Representatives. Public Accounts Committee. Report. Lagos, Government Printer, 1954-57. (M966.90N56-H81p)

2385 Nigeria. House of Representatives. Standing Committee on Finance. Report. Lagos, Government Printer, 1954-55. (M966.-90N56H81f)

2386 Nigeria. House of Representatives. Tribunal of Inquiry. Lagos, Government Printer. 2v. (M966.9N56J81t)

2387 Nigeria. Labour Department. Report. Lagos, Government Printer, 1944, 1952-55. (M966.90N56L11a)

2388 Nigeria. Land Department. Report. Lagos, Federal Government Printer, 1954-55. (M966.90N56L22a)

2389 Nigeria. Laws, statutes, etc. Annual volume of the laws of Nigeria and of the Federation of Nigeria 1954; containing the ordinances and subsidiary legislation of Nigeria enacted until 30th September, 1954, and of the Federation enacted thereafter to the end of the year. Lagos, Federal Government Printer, 1954. (M966.9N56L)

2390 Nigeria. Marine Department. Reports. Lagos, Government Printer, 1952-55. (M966.90N56M33a)

2391 Nigeria. Marine Department. Tide tables . . . Lagos, Federal Government Printer, 1955. (M966.90N56M33t)

2392 Nigeria. Marketing and Exports Department. Report. Nigeria, Government Printer, 1950-53. (M966.90N56M34a)

2393 Nigeria. Medical Services. Report. Lagos, Government Printer, 1944, 1949-55. (M966.90N56M46a)

2394 Nigeria. Mines Department. Report. Lagos, Government Printer, 1944, 1950-51, 1954-55. (M966.90N56M66a)

2395 Nigeria. Police Department. Report. Lagos, Government Printer, 1945, 1950-54. (M966.90N56P75a)

2396 Nigeria. Post and Telegraph Department. Grading Commissioners. Conclusions. Lagos, Government Printer, 1956. (M966.90N-56P84gr)

2397 Nigeria. Post and Telegraph Department. Grading Commissioners. Report. Lagos, Government Printer, 1956. (M966.90N56P84g)

2398 Nigeria. Post and Telegraphs Department. Report. Lagos, Government Printer, 1952-54. (M966.90N56P84r)

2399 Nigeria. Post Office Savings Bank. Report. Lagos, Government Printer, 1951-53, 1955. (M966.90N56P84a)

2400 Nigeria. Prisons Department. Report. Lagos, Government Printer, 1944. (M966.90N56P93a)

2401 Nigeria. Public Relations Department. Report. Lagos, Government Printer, 1948, 1951-54. (M966.90N56P96r)

2402 Nigeria. Public Works Department. Report. Lagos, Government Printer, 1950-54. (M966.90N56P96w)

2403 Nigeria. Social Welfare Department. Report. Lagos, Federal Government Printer, 1954-56. (M966.90N56Sola)

2404 Nigeria. Statistics Department. Report. Lagos, Government Printer, 1953-55. (M966.90N56St2a)

2405   Nigeria.   Statistics Department.   Trade report.   Lagos, Government Printer, 1952-54.   (M966.90M56St2t)

2406   Nigeria.   Treasury.   Accounts and Finances.   Lagos, Government Printer, 1944-45.   (M966.90N56T71a)

2407   Nigeria.   Treatment of Offenders.   Report.   Lagos, Government Printer, 1952-54.   (M966.90N56T71r)

2408   Nigeria.   University College.   Audit Dept.   Report of the Director of Federal Audits on the Statements of the University College (Capital) Accounts.   Lagos, Government Printer.   (M966.-90N56Un3r)

2409   Nigeria.   University College Hospital, Ibadan: Recurrent costs. Lagos, Government Printer, 1957.   5p.   (M966.90N56Un3)

2410   Nigeria.   Veterinary Department.   Report.   Lagos, Government Printer, 1950-53.   (M966.90N56V64a)

2411   Nigeria.   Eastern Region.   Estimates of revenue and expenditures of the Eastern Region.   Lagos, Government Printer, 1954-55. (M966.90EN56Es8)

2412   Nigeria.   Eastern Region.   Memorandum on the estimates of revenue and expenditure of the Eastern Region.   Enugu, Government Printer, 1954-55.   (M966.90EN56Es8m)

2413   Nigeria.   Northern Province.   Native Courts.   Commission of Inquiry.   Native Courts Commission of Inquiry 1949 to 1952. Appendix and Summary of Conclusions and Recommendations. Lagos, Government Printer, 1949.   (M966.90NN56N21re)

2414   Nigeria.   Northern Province.   Native Courts.   Commission of Inquiry.   Report of the Native Courts (Northern Provinces) Commission of Inquiry.   Lagos, Government Printer, 1952. 190p.   (M966.90NN56N21r)

2415   Nigeria.   Northern Region.   Address by ... B. E. Sharwood Smith ... Northern Region to the Budget Session of the Northern Legislature, February 1952.   Nigeria, Government Printer, 1952.   50p.   (M966.90NN56L62a1953)

2416   Nigeria.   Northern Region.   Address by ... Bryan Sharwood Smith ... Northern Region, to the Budget Meeting of the Northern Regional Legislature, 1953.   Nigeria, Government Printer, 1953 35p.   (M966.90NN56L62al1953)

2417   Nigeria.   Northern Region.   Executive Council.   Yakin Jahilci Committee.   Report.   Nigeria, Government Printer, 1953.   10p. (M966.90NN56Ex3)

2418   Nigeria.   Northern Region.   House of Assembly.   Debates.   Kaduna,

Government Printer, 1952. (M966.90NN56H81d)

2419 Nigeria. Northern Region. Referendum on the Constitution to Provincial Conferences and Subsidiary Meetings. Nigeria, Government Printer, 1953. 13p. (M966.90NN56R25)

2420 Nigeria. Northern Region. Speech by ... Sir Bryan Sharwood-Smith to the Northern House of Assembly, 15th January, 1953. Lagos, Government Printer, 1953. 15p. (M966.90NN56L62s)

2421 Nigeria. Northern Region. Report on the Kano disturbances, 16th, 17th, 18th, and 19th of May, 1953. Nigeria, Government Printer, 1953. 51p. (M966.9N569r)

2422 Nigeria. Western Region. Estimates [of revenue and expenditure] of the Western Region. Ibadan, Government Printer, 1954-55. (M966.90WN56s8)

2423 Nigeria. Western Region. Memorandum on estimate [of revenue and expenditure] of the Western Region. Ibadan, Government Printer, 1954-55. (N966.90WN56Es8m)

2424 Niven, Cyril Rex. Nigeria, outline of a colony. London, New York, [etc.] T. Nelson and sons, ltd. [1946] (M966.9N64n)

2425 Niven, Cyril Rex. Our emirates. Lagos, Public Relations Department. n.d. 16p. Crownbird Series no. 36. (M966.9N64o)

2426 Niven, Cyril Rex. A short history of Nigeria. London, New York, [etc.] Longmans, Green and co., [1937] 262p. (M966.9N64)

2427 Obasa, Denrele Adetimkan. Iwe kinni ti awon Akewi (Yoruba philosophy) nipa Denrele Adetimkan Obasa. Published by Egbe Agba-'O-Tan. Ibaden, The Illard, 1927. 61p. (M896.-10B1i)

2428 Odunjo, J. F. Iwe-Kini A B D Alawiye, fun awon omode ati awon agbalagb. Lagos, The Ife-Olu Printing works 1946. 32p. (AM496.40d8i)

2429 Oghe Edo (Benin reader, Book I) Lagos, Church Missionary Society Bookshop, 1934. 24p. (M4960g2)

2430 Oghe Edo (Benin reader, Book II) Church Missionary Society Bookshop, 1934. 32p. (M496Og2)

2431 Ogumefu, M. I. Yoruba legends. London, The Sheldon Press [1929] 87p. (AM966.90g9y)

2432 Ogumefu, M. I. Yoruba melodies, adapted by Ebun Ogumefu. London, Society for promoting Christian Knowledge, 1929. 16p. (AM7840g9y)

2433 Ogumefu, M. I. The staff of Oranyan and other Yoruba tales. London, The Sheldon Press, [1930] 32p. (AM966.90g9s)

2434   Ogumefu, M. I. Tales of tortoise, Yoruba tales. London, The Sheldon Press, [n.d.] 32p. (AM966.90g9t)

2435   Ogunbiye, Thomas A. J. Awon Serafu. Lagos, C.M.S. Press, 1926. 14p. (AM966.90g9a)

2436   Ojike, Mbonu. My Africa. New York, The John Day co., [1946] 350p. (AM966.90j3m)

2437   Ojike, Mbonu. Portrait of a boy in Africa. New York, East and West association. [c1945] 36p. (AM966.90j3p)

2438   Okotie-Eboh, Festus Sam. Report on the International Labour Conference 38th Session, held in Geneva from 1st to 23rd June, 1955, by the Minister of Labour and Welfare, Federation of Nigeria. Lagos, Government Printer, 1956. 38p. (M3310k5r)

2439   Olaleye, Amos Mobolaji. A philosophy of the Yoruba Religion. Washington, D.C., Howard University, 1956. 54p. (M378.-242ph 1956)

2440   Onabamiro, Sanya Dojo. Why our children die; the causes and suggestions for prevention, of infant mortality in West Africa. London, Methuen [1949] 195p. (AM966.90n1w)

2441   Oresanya, A. O., compiler. An outline of the system of administration in Nigeria; being excerpts from the Nigeria handbook and other publications. 6th ed. Lagos, The Ife-Olu Printing Works, 1942. 45p. (AM966.90r3)

2442   Orizu, Akweke Abyssinia Nwafor. Without bitterness; western Nations in postwar Africa. New York, N. Y., Creative age press, inc. [1944] 395p. (AM966. 90r1w)

2443   Osadebay, Dennis Chukude. Africa sings. Illfracombe, Arthur II. Stockwell, 1952. 104p. (AM7840s2)

2444   Page, Jesse. The black Bishop, Samuel Adjai Crowther. London, Hodder and Stoughton, 1908. 440p. (AM966.9C88p)

2445   Palmer, Sir Herbert Richmond. The Bornu Sahara and Sudan. London, J. Murray, 1936. 296p. (AM966.98P18)

2446   Partridge, Charles. Cross river natives... London, Hutchinson, 1905. 332p. (AM966.9P25)

2447   Perham, Margery Freda. The economics of a tropical dependency. London, Pub. under auspices of Nuffield College by Faber and Faber. 2v. 1946-48. (M966.9P41e)

2448   Perham, Margery Freda. Native administration in Nigeria. London, New York, Oxford University Press, 1937. 404p. (AM-966.9P41)

2449 Perron, Michel. L'ere Nigérienne; Préface de Maurice Delafosse. Paris, Editions de la Pensée Latine, 1926. 235p. (M841.-91P42)

2450 Phillips, T. A. An agricultural note book (with special reference to Nigeria). London, Longmans, Green and co., ltd. 1956. 218p. (M966.9P54)

2451 Pott, D. A. Progress report on local government in the Northern Region of Nigeria. Nigeria, Government Printer, 1953. 22p. (AM966.9P85)

2452 Prest, Alan Richmond. The national income of Nigeria, 1950-51, by A. R. Prest and I. G. Stewart. London, H.M. Stationery Office, 1953. 124p. (M966,9P92)

2453 Radley, Thomas Bertram. Our revised constitution. Lagos, Nigeria, Pub. by the Public Relations Dept., 1954. 24p. (M966.9R11)

2454 [Ransome-Kuti, Josiah Jesse] Awon orin mimo ni eded ati ohùn ile wa. Yoruba sacred songs. Lagos, C.M.S. Bookshop, 1925. 556-617p. (AM784Aw6)

2455 Raphael, John R. Through unknown Nigeria. London, T. W. Laurie ltd., [1914] 361p. (AM966.9R18t)

2456 Rattray, Robert Sutherland. Ashanti. Oxford, The Clarendon Press, 1923. 348p. (M966.74R18a)

2457 Rattray, Robert Sutherland. Ashanti law and constitution. Oxford, The Clarendon Press, 1929. 420p. (M966.74R18al)

2458 Rattray, Robert Sutherland, ed, and tr. Ashanti Proverbs (the primitive ethics of a savage people) tr. from the original with grammatical and anthropological notes ... with a preface by Sir Hugh Clifford ... Oxford, The Clarendon Press, 1916. 191p. (M966.74R18ap)

2459 Rattray, Robert Sutherland, ed and tr. Hausa folk-lore, customs, proverbs, etc., collected and transliterated with English translation and notes ... with a preface by R. R. Marett ... Oxford, The Clarendon Press, 1913. 2v. (M493.5R18)

2460 Rattray, Robert Sutherland. Religion & art in Ashanti ... with chapters by G. T. Bennett, Vernon Blake, H. Dudley Buxton, R. R. Marett, C. G. Seligman. Oxford, The Clarendon Press, 1927. 414p. (M966.74R18r)

2461 Rattray, Robert Sutherland. The tribes of the Ashanti hinterland with a chapter by Professor D. Westermann ... Oxford, The Clarendon Press, 1932. 298p. (AM572.66R18)

2462 Robertson, James Wilson. Speech by His Excellency the Governor-

General . . . to the House of Representatives on the 25th February, 1956. Lagos, Government Printer, 1956. 7p. (M966-9R541956)

2463 Robertson, James Wilson. Speech by His Excellency the Governor-General . . . to the House of Representatives on the 18th February 1957. Lagos, Government Printer, 1957. 7p. (M966.9R-541957)

2464 Robinson, Charles Henry. Dictionary of the Hause language. 3d ed. rev. and enl. Cambridge, University Press, 1913-14. (AM-496.5R56d)

2465 Robinson, Charles Henry. Hausa grammar, with exercises, readings and vocabularies, and specimens of Hausa script. 5th ed. rev. London, K. Paul Trench, Trubner, 1942. 218p. (AM492-R56)

2466 Robinson, Charles Henry. Nigeria, our latest protectorate. London, H. Marshall and son, 1900. 223p. (AM916.69R56)

2467 Robinson, Charles Henry. Specimens of Hausa literature. Cambridge, University Press, 1896. 112p. (AM492.5R56)

2468 Rosevear, D. R. Our forests. Lagos, Public Relations Department, n.d. 16p. (M966.9R720) Crownbird Series no. 23)

2469 Roth, Henry Ling. Great Benin; its customs, art and horrors. Halifax, England, F. King and sons, ltd., 1903. 234p. (AM966.-93 R74)

2470 Ryan, Isobel. Black man's country. London, Cape, 1950. 276p. (M966.9R95b)

2471 St. Croix, F. W. de. The Fulani of northern Nigeria. Lagos, [The Government Printer, 1945] 74p. (AM966.9Sa2f)

2472 Saunders, John Tennant. Report to the Nuffield Foundation on a visit to Nigeria, by J. T. Saunders, R. L. Turner and D. Veale. London, Published for the Nuffield Foundation by Oxford University Press, 1946. 67p. (M966.9Sa8)

2473 Sciortino, J. C. Notes on Nassarawa province, Nigeria. London, Warerlow and sons, ltd., 1920. 32p. (AM96 9Sc6n)

2474 Schon, James Frederick. Dictionary of the Hausa language. London, Church Missionary House, 1876. 142p. (AM496.5Sc6d)

2475 Simpson, A. The Nigerian coalfield; the geology of parts of Onitsha, Owerri and Benue Provinces; with 4 maps, 19 figures, 24 tables and 5 plates. Lagos, Published by authority of the Nigerian Government, 1954. 85p. (M966.9Si5)

2476 Sise, Ogbin Pépèpè. Iwe-kika fun lilo ni awon ile-eko kekeke no

iha gusu Nigeria. (Elementary agriculture—a book for use as
a reader in Southern Nigerian elementary (schools). Exeter,
England, James Townsend & sons, 1930. 31p. (AM630Si8)

2477 Sowummi, Akintunde. Our land and People. Part III—the west.
Lagos, Public Relations Department, n.d. 16p. (M966.9So5o)

2478 Stocker, John. Our festival of the arts. Lagos, Public Relations
Department, n.d. 19p. (M966.9St6o)

2479 Talbot, Percy Amaury. In the shadow of the Bush. London, W.
Heinemann, 1912. 500p. (AM916.69 T14)

2480 Talbot, Percy Amaury. The peoples of Southern Nigeria. London,
Oxford University Press, H. Milford, 1926. 4v. (AM572.-
669T14)

2481 Talbot, Mrs. D. Amaury. Woman's mysteries of a primitive people,
the Ibibios of Southern Nigeria. London, New York, Cassell
and co., ltd., 1915. 251p. (AM966.9T14w)

2482 Temple, Charles Lindsay. Native races and their rulers; sketches
and studies of official life and administrative problems in Nigeria, with illustrations by the author. Cape Town, Argus
printing & publishing company, ltd., London, agents, Way &
co., ltd., 1918. 252p. (M966.9T24n)

2483 Temple, Charles Lindsay. Notes on the tribes, provinces, emirates
and states of the northern provinces of Nigeria. Cape Town,
The Argus Printing and Publishing Co., ltd., 1919. 577p. M-
966.9 T24)

2484 Temple, O. Notes on the tribes, provinces emirates & states of the
Northern provinces of Nigeria. Nigeria, C.M.S. Bookshop,
1922. 577p. (AM572.9669T24)

2485 Thanni, Ade. Our coronation visitors. Lagos, Public Relations Department, n.d. 32p. (M966.9T32o)

2486 Thomas, A .V. ... Report on the existing fire services in Nigeria
and the needs and requirements of the principal towns and
rural areas. Lagos, Federal Government Printer, 1954. 84p.
(M966.9T36r)

2487 Thomas, Northcote Whitridge. Anthropological report on the Edo-
speaking peoples of Nigeria. London, Harrison & sons, 1910
2v. (AM966.9T36)

2488 Thorn, G. W. P. Our inland waterways. Lagos, Public Relations
Department, n.d., 13p. Crownbird Series no. 19. (M966.9T390)

2489 Tremearne, Arthur John Newmann. Hausa superstitions and customs; an introduction to the folklore and the folk, with forty-

one illustrations, over two hundred figures in the text, and a map. London, J. Bale, sons & Danielsson, ltd., 1913. 548p. (M966.9T72h)

2490 Tremearne, Arthur John Newmann. The tailed head-hunters of Nigeria. London, Seeley, Service & co., ltd., 1912. 341p. (AM-966.9T71)

2491 Tucker, Charlotte Maria. Abbeokuta; or, Sunrise within the Tropics. London, J. Nisbet & co., 1853. 278p. (AM916T79)

2492 Urvoy, Yves Francois Marie Aime. Histoire de l'empire du Bornou. Paris, Larose, 1949. 166p. (AM966.98Ur9h)

2493 Uzo, T. M. The Nigerian political evolution. Lagos, C.M.S. Bookshops, 1950. 80p. (M966.9Uz7n)

2494 Walker, Hubert. Our roads. Lagos, The Public Relations Department, n.d. 16p. (M966.9W15o)

2495 Ward, Edward. ... Marriage among the Yoruba. Washington, D.C. The Catholic University of America, 1937. 55p. (M-966.9W21m)

2496 Ward, Edward. The Yoruba husband-wife code. Washington, D.C., The Catholic University of America, 1938. 178p. (M-572.66W21y)

2497 Ward, Ida Caroline. An introduction to the Yoruba language. Cambridge, W. Heffer, 1952. 255p. (M496.4W21)

2498 Welch, James. Religious studies in an African university. Ibadan University Press, 1950. 21p. (M268W44r)

2499 Wheare, Joan. The Nigerian Legislative Council. London, pub. under the auspices of Nuffield College by Faber and Faber 1950. 265p. (M966.9W56n)

2500 Wilson-Haffenden, James Rhodes. The red men of Nigeria, an account of a lengthy residence among the Fulani, or "red men", & other pagan tribes of central Nigeria, with a description of their headhunting, pastoral & other customs, habits & religion. With a foreword by Bronislaw Malinowski ... Philadelphia, J. B. Lippincott company [1930] 318p. (AM966.9W69r)

GHANA

2501 Abedi-Boafo, J. Modern problems in Gold Coast elementary schools. Mampong Akwapim, Gold Coast, The author, 1951. 53p. (M966.7Ab3m)

2502 Abraham, Roy Clive. Dictionary of the Hausa language. Abraham and Malam Mai Kano. [London] Published on behalf of the

Government of Nigeria by the Crown Agents for the Colonies,
1949. 992p. (M496Ab8d)

2503 Accra, High School. Report for the year 1924-1925, with the sermon preached by the principal. Accra, Gold Coast, 1925. 15p.
(M966.7Ac2s)

2504 Accra. Public Relations Department. The Gold Coast. Accra,
Public Relations Department, 1950. 32p. (M916.67A28g)

2505 Accra Town Council. Your questions answered by the Accra Town
Council. Accra, Gold Coast, Regional Information Office, British West Africa, [1948] 71p. (M966.7Ac2y)

2506 Acquaah, Gaddiel Robert. Mfantse amabra. Cape Coast, Methodist Book Depot, 1947. 32p. (M966.7Ac7m)

2507 Acquaah, Gaddiel Robert. Oguaa Aban. Cape Coast, Methodist
Book Depot, 1946. 32p. (M966.7Ac7o)

2508 Adams, David Thickens. An elementary geography of the Gold
Coast. London, University of London, ltd., 1931. 240p. (M-
916.67Ad1)

2509 Africa Today. March-April 1957 from Gold Coast to Ghana. Freedom Issue. Vol. 4. No. 2. 31p. (M966.7Af8)

2510 Agyeman, Nana Yaw Twum Duah. West Africa on the march, an
intimate survey of problems and potentialities. New York, William-Frederick Press, 1952. 73p. (M966.7Ag9w)

2511 Alicoe, Thomas. The evolution of Gold Coast Chiefship. Stockport, Stockport Express, n.d. 102p. (M966.7A14c)

2512 Alleyne, Cameron Chesterfield. Gold Coast at a glance. With an
introduction by Bishop Paris Arthur Wallace. New York, The
Hunt Printing co., 1931. 143p. (M966.7A15g)

2513 Ankrah, Roy. My life story. Accra, West African Graphic co.,
1952. 30p. (MB9An6)

2514 Apeadu, Kwafo. The co-operative movement. London, Bureau of
Current Affairs, 1951. 15p. (M966.7Ap4c)

2515 Apter, David Ernest. The Gold Coast in transition. Princeton,
Princeton University Press, 1955. 355p. (M96.7Ap8)

2516 Armattoe, Raphael Ernest Grail. The golden age of West African
civilization. With an introduction by Prof. Dr. E. Schroeding-
er. Londonderry, Published for the Lomeshire research centre
by "The Londonderry Sentinel", 1946. 116p. (M966.7A5g)

2517 Asekre, B. A. An analysis of the Gold Coast evolution. New York,
Ira Rosenberg, 1937. 8p.

2518   Balmer, William Turnbull. A history of the Akan peoples of the Gold Coast. With foreword by the Hon. C. W. Welman. London, The Atlantic Press, [1926] 208p. (M966.7B21h)

2519   Barker, W[illiam] H[enry]. The Gold Coast Colony and protectorate. Manchester, Sherratt & Hughes, 1922. 174p. (M966.-7B24g)

2520   Barker, William Henry. West African folk-tales, collected and arranged by W. H. Barker and Cecelia Sinclair. London, George G. Harrap and co., 1917. 184p. (M966.7B24w)

2521   Bartels, F. L. and J. A. Annobil. Mfantse nkasafua dwumadzi: A Fanti grammar of function. Cape Coast, Methodist Book Depot, 1952. 182p. (M966.7B28m)

2522   Blay, J. Benibengor. Dr. Bengia wants a wife. London, The Blackheath Press, ltd., 1953. 23p.

2523   Boatang, E. A. Tomorrow's map of West Africa. London, Staples Press, 1951. 15p. (M966.7B63t)

2524   Botsio, Kojo. Progress in education in the Gold Coast. Accra, Published by the Department of Education and Printed by the Government Printing Department, 1953. 20p. (M966.7B65)

2525   Bourret, Florence M. The Gold Coast and British Togoland, 1919-1946. Stanford, California, Stanford University Press, 1949. 231p. (AM966B66g)

2526   Bourret, Florence M. The Gold Coast; a survey of the Gold Coast and British Togoland, 1919-1951. 2nd ed. Stanford, California, Stanford University Press, 1952. [c1949] 248p.

2527   Brewster, Sydney Pentekol. Gold Coast income tax. [Takoradi] Brewster, 1954. 64p. (M966.7B75)

2528   Busia, Kofi Abrefa. Education for citizenship. London, The Bureau of Current Affairs. 15p. (M966.7B96e)

2529   Busia, Kofi Abrefa. The position of the chief in the modern political system of Ashanti; a study of the influence of contemporary social changes on Ashanti political institutions. London, New York, Published for the International African Institute, by the Oxford University Press, 1951. 233p. (M966.7B96p)

2530   Busia, Kofi Abrefa. Report on a social survey of Sekondi-Takoradi. London, Crown Agents for the Colonies on behalf of the Government of the Gold Coast, 1950. 164p. (M966.7B96r)

2531   Busia, Kofi Abrefa. Self-government. London, Bureau of Current Affairs, 195? 15p. (M966.7B96s)

2532   Butler, William Francis. Akim-foo: the history of failure. London,

S. Low, Marston, Low and Searle, 1875. 300p. (M966.-74B97a)

2533 Cardinall, Allan Wolsey. A bibliography of the Gold Coast. Accra, Gold Coast colony, Printed by the Government Printer [1932] 383p. (AM01C17)

2534 Cardinall,, Allan Wolsey. The natives of the Northern Territories of the Gold Coast. London, G. Routledge and sons, New York, E. P. Dutton and co., 1920. 158p. (M572C17n)

2535 Carr-Gregg, John Ralph Edward. Self-rule in Africa; recent advances in the Gold Coast. New York Carnegie Endowment for International Peace. [1951] 382p. (M966.7C23s)

2536 Chamberlain, George Digby. A brief account of the Brissa language. Accra, Gold Coast, Printed at the Government Printing Office, 1930. 53p. (M496C35)

2537 Claridge, William Walton. A history of the Gold Coast and Ashanti from the earliest times to the commencement of the 20th century. London, J. Murray, 1915. 580p. (M966.74C54)

2538 Coffee, Mary. The self-government movement in the Gold Coast, West Africa. Washington, D.C., Howard University (type written thesis), 1954. 153p. (M378.242G)

2539 Colbourne, M. J. Health in the village. London, Bureau of Current Affairs, 195? 15p. (M966.7C67)

2540 Convention People's Party. Foreward to freedom with the common people. Manifesto for the general election, 1954. Vote C.P.P. and we shall finish the job. 104—freedom. Accra, Convention People's Party, 1954. 20p. (M966.7C76f)

2541 Cruickshank, Brodie. Eighteen years on the Gold Coast of Africa, including an account of the native tribes, and their intercourse with Europeans. London, Hurst and Blackett, 1853. 2v. (M916.67C88)

2542 Cudjoe, Seth Dzifanu. Aids to African autonomy; A review of education and politics in the Gold Coast. London, College Press, 1949. 62p. (AM350C89a)

2543 Curtis, L. C. Liberia and the Gold Coast. Orlando, Fla., Sentine-Reporter Print 1904. 36p. (M966.6C94)

2544 Danquah, Joseph Boakye. The Akan doctrine of God, a fragment of Gold Coast ethics and religion. With 9 illustrations by Kofi Antubam. London, Lutterworth Press, [1944] 206p. (M966.7D23a)

2545 Danquah, Joseph Boakye. Ancestors, Negroes and God, the principles of Akan-Ashanti ancestor-worship. Gold Coast, George Boakie Publishing co., 1938. 46p. (M966.7D23ak)

2546 Danquah, Joseph Boakye. Cases in Akan Law Decisions delivered by the Hon. Nana Sir Ofori Atta. Edited with introduction, synopses, and notes by J. B. Danquah, London, George Routledge, 1928. 26p. (M966.7B23ca)

2547 Danquah, Joseph Boakye. Gold Coast: Akan laws and customs and the Akim Abuakwa constitution. London, G. Routledge and sons, 1928. 272p. (M966.7D23g)

2548 Danquah, Joseph Boakye. The third woman; a play in five acts. London and Redhill, United Society for Christian Literature, 1943. 151p. (M966.7D23t)

2549 Davidson, Basil. ed. The new West Africa. London, Allen and Unwin, 1953. 184p. (M966.7D28n)

2550 De Graft-Johnson, John Coleman. African glory; the story of vanished Negro civilizations. New York, Praeger, 1955, c1954. 209p. (M966.7D36a)

2551 Dei-Anang, M. F. Cocoa comes to Mampong. Brief dramatic sketches based on the story of cocoa in the Gold Coast and some occasional verses. Cape Coast, Methodist Book Depot, 1949. 47p. (AM966.7D36c)

2552 Delafosse, Maurice. Les frontieres de la Cote d'Ivoire de la Cote d'or et du Soudan. Paris, Masson et cie., 1908. 256p. (M-966.68D37)

2553 Dove, Gordon F. K. The political philosophy of Kwame Nkrumah. (Thesis) Washington, D.C., Howard University, 1955. 87p. (M378.242g)

2554 Dovlo, C. K. Africa awakes. Some of the problems facing Africa today as seen from the Christian point of view. Accra, Scottish Mission Book Depot, 1952. 78p. (M966.7D75)

2555 Edu, John E. How Dr. Kwame Nkrumah conquered colonialism. Accra, The Heal Press, n.d. 44p. (M966.7Ed8h)

2556 Edu, John E. Your share in local government. Accra, Published by the author, 1952. 41p. (M966.7Ed8y)

2557 Ellis, Alfred Burdon. The Tshi-speaking peoples of the Gold Coast of West Africa. Their religion, manners, customs, laws, languages, etc. London, Chapman & Hall ltd., 1887. 343p. (AM572.9667E15)

2558 Ellis, Alfred Burdon. A history of the Gold Coast of West Africa. London, Chapman & Hall ltd., 1893. 400p. (M966.7E15h)

2559 Field, Margaret Joyce. Adim-Kotoku; an oman of the Gold Coast.
      London, Crown Agents for the Colonies, 1948. 211p. (M966-
      7F45a)

2560 Fortes, Meyer. The dynamics of clanship among the Tallensi,
      being the first part of an analysus of the social structure of
      a trans-Volta tribe. London, Oxford University Press, 1945.
      270p. (AM527F77)

2561 Fortes, Meyer. The web of kinship among the Tallensi. London,
      Oxford University Press, 1949. 358p. (AM527.96F77w)

2562 Fuller, Francis. A vanished dynasty, Ashanti. London, John
      Murray, 1921. 241p.

2563 Gardiner, Robert Kweku Atta. The development of social ad-
      ministration. London, Oxford University Press, 1954. 208p.
      (M966G17)

2564 The Gold Coast. London, Hudson & Kearnes, n.d. 56p. (M966-
      7G56c)

2565 Gold Coast and the Constitution. Accra, The West African Graphic
      co., 1952. 31p. (AM966.7G56c)

2566 Gold Coast. Committee on Constitutional Reform. Report to His
      Excellency the Governor, 1949. London, H.M. Stationery
      Office, 1949. 103p. (M966.7G564)

2567 Gold Coast. Department of Social Welfare and Community De-
      velopment. Literacy Campaign, 1952. Gold Coast, 1952. 52p.

2568 Gold Coast. Department of Social Welfare and Community De-
      velopment Report. Accra, Government Printing Department,
      1946-51- (M966.7g56w)

2569 Gold Coast. Development progress report, 1955. Accra, Govern-
      ment Printer, 1956. 46p. (M966.7G563d)

2570 Gold Coast. Education Department. Mfantsa nkasafuka nykerewee
      nye ho Mbra: A Fanti word list with principles and rules of
      spelling. Cape Coast, Methodist Book Depot, 1951. 90p.
      (M966.7C56m)

2571 Gold Coast. Education Department. Reports. Gold Coast, Gov-
      ernment Document, 1952. (M966.6 Gov. Doc.)

2572 Gold Coast. The Gold Coast cocoa marketing board at work.
      Accra, Gold Coast, Government Printer, 1956. 19p. (M966-
      7G56go)

2573 Gold Coast. Golden harvest; the story of the Gold Coast cocoa
      industry. Gold Coast, A publication of the Information Serv-
      ices Department, 1953. 56p. (M966.7G56g)

2574   Gold Coast. The government's proposals for constitutional reform. Accra, Printed by the Government Printing Department, 1953. 74p. (M966.7G56go)

2575   Gold Coast. Information Department. Nurses in training. Accra, Department of Information Services, 1952. 22p. (Vertical file)

2576   Gold Coast. Laws of the Gold Coast containing all legislation enacted during the year 1949. Accra, Gold Coast, Government Printing Department, 1950. 498p. (AM966.7G561)

2577   Gold Coast. Legislative Assembly. Debates, 1954-. Accra, Government Printing Department. (M966.7)

2578   Gold Coast. Legislative Council, Select Committee. Report appointed to make recommendation concerning local government in Ashanti. London, C. F. Roworth, 1951. 64p. (M966.74-G561)

2579   Gold Coast. Library Board. An introduction to the library services available. Accra, n.d. 15p.

2580   Gold Coast. Ministry of Commerce, Industry and Mines. Handbook of trade and commerce, 1951. Accra, Government Printing Department, 1952. (M966.7)

2581   Gold Coast. Ministry of Finance. Economic survey, 1953. Accra, Office of the Government Statistician, 1953. (M966.7g56e)

2582   Gold Coast. Proposals on constitutional reform. Gold Coast, The West African Graphic Co., 1952. 28p. (M966.7G56p)

2583   Gold Coast. Public Relations Department. Achievements in the Gold Coast; aspects of development in a British West African territory. Accra, Gold Coast, 1951. 96p. (M966.7G56Pa)

2584   Gold Coast. Public Relations Department. A plan in action. Produced for the Ministry of Education by the Information Services Department and the Government Printer, Accra, 1955. 20p.

2585   Gold Coast. Public Relations Department. The Gold Coast, a brief description for presentation at the Gold Coast stand, British Industries Fair, 1950. Accra, 1950. [11u.] (M966.7)

2586   Gold Coast. Public Relations Department. Kofi the good farmer. Accra, Gold Coast, W. S. Cowell, Ltd., 1950. 51p.

2587   Gold Coast. Public Relations Department. News bulletin. Accra, 1950. (M966.7G56pn)

2588   Gold Coast. Report by the select committee on local government, 1950. London, C. F. Roworth, 1951. 52p. (M966.6G563)

2589   Gold Coast. A statement on the programme of the Africanisation
         of the public service. Accra, Government Printing Depart-
         ment, 1954. 75p. (M966.7G563s)

2590   Gold Coast. University College. Annual report by the principal,
         1948-52, 1952-53, 1953-54, 1954-55. Edinburgh, Thomas Nel-
         son and Sons, 1948. (M966.7G56a)

2591   Gold Coast. University College. Library bulletin, 1955-56. Gold
         Coast, 1955. (M966.9G56)

2592   Gold Coast. Year book, 1953. Accra, Daily Graphic, 1953. 126p.
         (AM966.7G56y)

2593   Gold Coast. Your government; the story of the Gold Coast general
         elections of 1954. Accra, West African Graphic Co., 1955.
         64p. (M966.7G56y)

2594   Goody, Jack. The ethnography of the northern territories of the
         Gold Coast, west of the white Volta. London, Colonial Office,
         Research Department, 1954. 59p. (M966.7G63e)

2595   Great Britain. Colonial office. Gold Coast report. 1947, 1949,
         1950, 1951. (M966.7)

2596   Hamilton, John A. Crime and punishment. London, Staples, 1951.
         19p. (M966.7H18c)

2597   Hayford, Casely i.e., Joseph Ephraim Casely. Gold Coast native
         institutions. With thoughts upon a healthy imperial policy
         for the Gold Coast and Ashanti. London, Sweet and Max-
         well, Ltd., 1913. 304p. (M966.7H33)

2598   Hinden, Rita. Plan for Africa; a report prepared for the Colonial
         bureau of the Fabian Society. London, G. Allen & Unwin,
         Ltd., [1941.] 223p. (M960H58p)

2599   Hodgson, Frederich. Seize of Kumassi. New York, Longmans,
         Green, 1901. 366p. (AM966.74H66)

2600   Irvine, Frederick Robert. Plants of the Gold Coast. London,
         Oxford University Press, 1930. 521p. (M966.71r8)

2601   Kemp, Dennis. Nine years at the Gold Coast. London, Macmillan
         and Co., 1898. 279p. (M966.9K32n)

2602   Kessie, Ohanenana Cobina. Colonies; what Africa thinks. London,
         The African Economic Union, 1939. 28p. (M966.7K48c)

2603   Kimble, David. The machinery of self-government. London, Pen-
         guin Books [1953] 124p. (M966.7K56m)

2604   Laing, George E. F. A king for Africa. London, Redhill, United
         Society for Christian Literature, 1945. 63p. (M200Li4K)

2605   Leeson, Frank. Identification of snakes of the Gold Coast. London, Crown Agents for the Colonies, 1950. 142p. (M498.-12L51i)

2606   Leith-Ross, Sylvia. Beyond the Niger. London, Lutterworth Press, 1951. 123p. (M966.7L53b)

2607   Lerner, L. D. The language we speak. London, Bureau of Current Affairs, 195-. 15p. (M966.7L56)

2608   Lewis, L. J. Perspectives in mass education and community development. London, Thomas Nelson and Sons, [1955.] 101p. (M966.7L58)

2609   Lewis, William Arthur. Report on industrialisation and the Gold Coast. Accra, Government Printing Department, 1953. 23p. (M966.7L58r)

2610   MacDonald, George. The Gold Coast, past and present; a short description of the country and its people. New York, Longmans, Green and Co., 1898. 352p. (M916M14)

2611   Manoukian, Madeline. Akan and Ga-Adangme peoples of the Gold Coast. London, Oxford University Press, 1950. 112p. (M966M31a)

2612   Manoukian, Madeline. The Ewe-speaking people of Togoland and the Gold Coast. London, International African Institute, 1952. 63p. (AM966.81M31e)

2613   Manoukian, Madeline. Tribes of the northern territories of the Gold Coast. London, International African Institute, 1951. 102p. (M966.7M31t)

2614   Meyerowitz, Eva L. R. The sacred state of the Akan. London, Faber and Faber, 1951. 222p. (M966.7M57s)

2615   Musson, M. Aggrey loka Achimota. Nairobi, The Eagle Press, 1951. 42p.

2616   Musson, M. Aggrey of Achimota. London and Redhill, United Society for Christian Literature, 1944. 56p. (MB9Ag8m)

2617   Nimako, Gyasi. Sukuufos twi I. London, Oxford University Press, 1954. 44p.

2618   Nimako, Gyasi. Sukuufos twi II. London, Oxford University Press, 1954. 44p.

2619   Nimako, Gyasi. Sukuufos twi III. London, Oxford University Press, 1954. 48p.

2620   Nketia, J. H. Funeral dirges of the Akan people. Achimota, James Townsend & Sons, Ltd., 1955. 296p.

2621 Nkrumah, Kwame. Ghana: The autobiography of Kwame Nkrumah. New York, Nelson, 1957. 302p.

2622 Nkrumah, Kwame. Motion for Gold Coast independence made by the Prime minister in the legislative assembly of 3rd August, 1956. (VFS)

2623 Nortley, Kobina. Britain's future in the Gold Coast "Torchlight" supplement. London, 1953. 14p.

2624 Ofori, David. Kibi "Ritual murder". Accra, Heal Press, 1954. 36p.

2625 Ogundele, Joseph Ogunsina. Ibu Olókun. London, University of London Press, 1956. 128p.

2626 Ogunlesi, J. S. Ni Ale ojo kan; Die ninu awon itan ile wa Lati owo. London, Sidgwick and Jackson, 1948. 46p.

2627 Okae, J. D. Why so stories; Twi stories. London, The Sheldon Press, n.d. 16p. (M966.70kiw)

2628 Owusu, Seth Amoako. Political institutions of the Coastal areas of the Gold Coast as influenced by European contact. [1954.] (M966.70w7)

2629 Padmore, George. The Gold Coast revolution; the struggle of an African people from slavery to freedom. London, Dennis Dobson, 1953. 272p. (M966.7P13g)

2630 Price, J. H. The Gold Coast election. London, Bureau of Current Affairs. 195-. 15p. (M966.7P93)

2631 Quartey, K. A. B. Jones. Problems of the press. London, The Bureau of Current Affairs. 15p. (M966.7Q2p)

2632 Rattray, Robert Sutherland, Jr. Ashanti proverbs (the primitive ethics of a savage people). Oxford, The Clarendon Press, 1916. 190p. (M966.74R18a)

2633 Rattray, Robert Sutherland, Jr. The tribes of the Ashanti hinterlands. Oxford, The Clarendon Press, 1932. 129p. (AM-572.66R18)

2634 Redmayne, Paul. The Gold Coast yesterday and today. London, Chatto and Windus, 1938. 124p. (M916.67R24)

2635 Reindorf, Carl Christian. History of the Gold Coast and Asante, based on traditions and historical facts comprising a period of more than three centuries from about 1500 to 1860. Basel, Switzerland, Basel Mission, Book Depot, [1951.] 349p. (M966.7R27)

2636 Roberts, J. T. A hymn of thanksgiving and other songs. London, The Curwen Press, 1953. 10p.

2637 Roper, J. I. The labour and trade union ordinances of the Gold
        Coast, ed. by J. I. Roper and R. B. Davison. London, Staples
        Publication, 195? 19p. (M966.7R68)

2638 Sarbah, John Mensah. Fanti customary laws. A brief introduction
        to the principles of the native laws and customs of the Fanti
        and Akan districts of the Gold Coast. London, W. Clowes
        and Sons, 1897. 295p. (M966.7Sa7fa)

2639 Sarbah, John Mensah. Fanti law report of decided cases on Fanti
        customary laws. Second selection. Long, William Clowes
        and Sons, Ltd., 1904. 189p. (AM966.7Sa7fa)

2640 Seers, Dudley. Report on financial and physical problems of de-
        velopment in the Gold Coast. Accra, Office of the Govern-
        ment Statistician, 1952. 63p. (M966.7Se3)

2641 Sitwell, Edith. Gold Coast customs. London, Duckworth, [1929.]
        63p. (M821.91Si8)

2642 Smith, Edwin William. Aggrey of Africa. New York, Doubleday,
        Doran and Co., 1929. 292p. (MB9Ag8s)

2643 Sutherland, D. A. State emblems of the Gold Coast. Illustrated
        by Amon Kotei. Gold Coast, Government Printing Office,
        1954. 70p. (M966.9Su84)

2644 Tete-Ansa, Winfred. Africa at work, n.p. n.d. c1930. 95p.
        (M966.7T29a)

2645 Tidsley, Alfred. The remarkable work achieved by Dr. Mark C.
        Rayford, in promotion of the spiritual and material welfare of
        the natives of West Africa, and proposed developments. Lon-
        don, Morgan and Scott, 1926. 36p. (AM966.7T45r)

2646 Timothy, Bankole. Kwame Nkrumah; his rise to power. London,
        George Allen and Unwin, 1955. 198p. (MB9N65)

2647 Tooth, Geoffrey. Studies in mental illness in the Gold Coast.
        London, H. M. Stationery Office, 1950. 71p. (M966.7T61s)

2648 Tooth, Goeffrey. A survey of juvenile delinquency in the Gold
        Coast. n.p. n.d. December 1946. 27p. (M364T61)

2649 Ward, Ida Caroline. Report of an investigation of some Gold
        Coast language problems. London, Published on behalf of
        the Government of the Gold Coast by the Crown Agents for
        the colonies, 1945. 74p. (M966.7W21r)

2650 Ward, William Ernest Frank. A history of the Gold Coast. Lon-
        don, G. Allen and Unwin, [1948.] 387p. (M966.7W21h)

2651 West African Institute of Social and Economic Research. Annual
        conference. [Third, Fourth and Fifth] Proceedings, 1956.

Ibadan, University College Ibadan, 1956. 3v. (M966.7W52)

2652 Wight, Martin. The Gold Coast Legislative Council. London,
Faber, [1947.] 285p. (M966.7W63g)

2653 Wright, Richard. Black power; a record of reactions in a land of
pathos. [1st ed.] New York, Harper, [1954.] 358p. (M966.-
7W93)

2654 Wright Richard. Puissance noire. Traduit de l'Américain par
Roger Giroux. Paris Corrêa, Butchet Chastel, 1955. 400p.
(M813.5W93p)

2655 Yen, Kwesi. The achievements of Dr. Kwame Nkrumah. Accra,
The Hel Press, [1954.] 19p. (M966.7Ye3a)

2656 Yen, Kwesi. The street boys on the march to freedom. Accra,
The Quality Press, 1954. 23p. (M966.7Ye3s)

SIERRA LEONE

2657 Alldridge, Thomas Joshua. The Sherbro and its hinterland. London, The Macmillan Co., 1901. 356p. (AM966.4A53s)

2658 Alldridge, Thomas Joshua. A transformed colony, Sierra Leone, as
it was, and as it is . . . London, Seeley & Co., Ltd., 1910. 368p.
(AM966.4A53)

2659 Banbury, G. A. Lethbridge. Sierra Leone; or the White Man's
Grave. B. Quaritch, 1888.

2660 Butt-Thompson, Frederick William. The first generation of Sierra
Leoneans. [Freetown.] Govt. Printer, Sierra Leone [1952.]
65p. (M966.4B98)

2661 Fenton, J. S. Outline of native law in Sierra Leone. Freetown,
Sierra Leone, Government Printer, 1951. 40p. (AM966.4F36o)

2662 Gervis, Pearce. Sierra Leone story. London, Cassell, [1952.]
240p. (M966.4G32)

2663 Goddard, Thomas Nelson. The handbook of Sierra Leone. London,
G. Richards, limited, 1925. 335p. (AM966.4G54h)

2664 Gorvie, Max. Old and new in Sierra Leone. London and Redhill, United Society for Christian Literature, [1945.] 79p.
(M966.4G680)

2665 Gorvie, Max. Our people of the Sierra Leone protectorate. London,
and Redhill, United Society for Christian literature, 1944.
64p. (AM9664G68)

2666 Great Britain. Colonial Office. Reports on Sierra Leone. London,
H. M. Stationery Office, 1949-1951, 1954. Previously issued

in the numbered series of Colonial reports—annual which was suspended in 1949. (M966.4G79a)

2667   Great Britain. Colonial Social Science Research Council. Report for 1951. (M966.4G79c)

2668   Hall, Henry Usher. The Sherbro of Sierra Leone. Philadelphia, The University Press, University of Pennsylvania, 1938. 51p. (AM572.6642H14)

2669   Hargrave, Carrie Guerphan. African primitive life, as I saw it in Sierra Leone, British West Africa. Wilmington, N. C., Wilmington Printing Company, 1944. 115p. (AM916.64-H22a)

2670   Horton, James Africanus Beale. Physical and medical climate and meteorology of the west coast of Africa with valuable hints to Europeans for the preservation of health in the tropics. London, J. Churchill & Sons, 1867. 321p. (M966.4H78p)

2671   Horton, James Africanus Beale. West African Countries and peoples, British and native. With the requirements necessary for establishing that self-government recommended by the Committee of the House of Commons, 1865, and a vindication of the African race. London, W. J. Johnson, 1868. 287p. (M966.-4H78w)

2672   Johnson, Thomas Sylvester. The story of a mission; the Sierra Leone Church, first daughter of C. M. S. with a foreword by Archbishop of Canterbury. London, S. P. C. K., 1953. 148p. (M966.4J627)

2673   Kilham, Hannah. The claims of West Africa to Christian instruction, through the native languages. London, Harvey and Darton, 1830. 28p. (AM370K55)

2674   Kilham, Hannah. Present state of the Colony of Sierra Leone, being extracts of recent letters . . . Lindfield. Printed at the Schools of Industry, by C. Greene, 1831. 16p. (M966.4K55)

2675   Labor, A. B. C. Merriam. Britons through Negro spectacles, or a Negro on Britons, with a description of London (Illustrated). London, The Imperial and Foreign Company, 1909. 238p. (M966.4L11)

2676   Lewis, Roy. Ten years of Colonial development and welfare, 1946-1955. Washington, D. C., British Information Services, 1956. 39p. (M966.4L58)

2677   Little, Kenneth Lindsay. The Mende of Sierra Leone; a West African people in transition. London, Routledge & K. Paul, [1951.] 307p. (AM966.4L72m)

2678 Luke, Harry Charles Joseph. A bibliography of Sierra Leone, preceded by an essay on the origin, character and peoples of the colony and protectorate. London, H. Milford, Oxford University Press, 1925. 230p. (AM01L96)

2679 Lunn, Kathryn (Fowler). The gold missus. New York, W. W. Norton and Co., Inc., 1938. 303p. (AM916.64L97)

2680 McCulloch, Merran. Peoples of Sierra Leone Protectorate. London, International African Institute, 1950. 120p. (AM966.-4M13p)

2681 Migeod, Frederick William Hugh. A view of Sierra Leone . . . London, Kegan Paul, Trench, Trubner & Co., Ltd., 1926. 351p. (M966.4M58)

2682 Norton, Hon. Caroline (Sheridan). A residence at Sierra Leone. London, John Murray, 1849. 335p. (AM916.64N82r)

2683 Peacock, Amjogollo E. Missionary work in Sierra Leone. Washington, D. C., Howard University, (type written thesis) 1940. 75p. (M378.24ReP31)

2684 Sharp, Granville. A short sketch of temporary regulations (Until better shall be proposed) for the intended settlement on the grain coast of Africa, near Sierra Leone. 3d. ed. London, Printed by H. Baldwin, 1788. 184p. (AM966.41Sh2)

2685 Sierra Leone. Administration of the Provinces. Annual report for the year 1953. Freetown, The Government Printing Dept., 1955. (M966.40Si1Ad6a)

2686 Sierra Leone. Audit Department. Report for the year 1950. Freetown, The Government Printer, 1950. (M966.40Si1Au2r)

2687 Sierra Leone. Education Department. Reports for the years 1948-1950. Freetown, The Government Printer, 1952. (M966.40Si1Ed8a)

2688 Sierra Leone. Legislative Council. Debates. Freetown, Government Printer, 1950-1954. (M966.40Si1L52d)

2689 Sierra Leone. Proposals for the reconstitution of the legislative council in Sierra Leone. Freetown, Government Printer, 1948. 8p. (M966.4Si1p1)

2690 Sierra Leone, Protectorate Assembly. Proceedings of the Seventh Meeting at Bo, 26th, 27th, 29th, 30th September, 2nd and 3rd October, 1950. Freetown, The Government Printer, 1950. 110p. (M966.40Si1P94p)

2691 Sierra Leone. Protectorate Assembly. Proceedings of the Eighth Meeting at Bo, 17th, 19th, 20th, 22nd and 23rd October, 1951.

Freetown, The Government Printer, 1952. 90p. (M966.40-Si1P94p)

2692 Sierra Leone. Protectorate Assembly. Proceedings of the Ninth Meeting at Bo on 22nd, 23rd and 24th October, 1952. Freetown, The Government Printer, 1952. 54p. (M966.40Si1P-94p)

2693 Sierra Leone. Public Relations Dept. Report. 1949. Freetown, Government Printer. v. (M966.40Si1P96a)

2694 Sierra Leone. Report of the Committee appointed to examine the working of the tribal administration (Colony) ordinance, Cap. 244. Freetown, The Government Printing Dept., 1955. 21p. (M966.4Si1R1)

2695 Sierra Leone. Reports of the Director-General of Colonial Audit on the accounts of Sierra Leone for the year ended the 31st of December, 1947 and 1948 and the Governor's comments thereon to the Secretary of State for the Colonies. Freetown, The Government Printer, 1950. 3p.

2696 Sierra Leone. Reports on the Sierra Leone Protectorate for the years 1948-1951. Freetown. Government Printer, 1953. (M-966.40Si1a)

2697 Sierra Leone. Soil conservation and land utilization team. Soil conservation in Sierra Leone . . . Freetown, Sierra Leone Government Printer, 1951. 124p. (M966.40Si1So3s)

2698 Sierra Leone Company. An account of the colony of Sierra Leone, for its first establishment in 1793, being the substance of a report delivered to the proprietors. London, Printed and sold by James Philips, 1795. 242p. (AM966.4Ac2)

2699 Sierra Leone Company. Substance of the report of the court of directors of the Sierra Leone company, delivered to the general court of proprietors, on Thursday the 26th Feb. 1795. London, Printed by James Phillips, 1795. 31p. (M966.4Ac2)

2700 Statements illustrative of the nature of the slave-trade. To which are subjoined, some particulars respecting the colony at Sierra Leone. London, Printed by Harvey, Darton, and Co., 1824. 40p. (M326.9A)

2701 Thompson, T. J. The jubilee and century volume of Fourah Bay College, Freetown, Sierra Leone. Sierra Leone, The Elsiemay Printine Works, 1930. 173p. (M966.4T37j)

2702 Thompson, T. J. The people's appeal for an intermediate court of appeal and an efficient system for the administration of justice in the colony and protectorate of Sierra Leone. London, The Caxton Press, 1911. 34p. (M966.4T37p)

2703 Thorpe, Robert. A letter to William Wilberforce, containing remarks on the reports of the Sierra Leone Company, and African
institution: with hints respecting the means by which an uni-
versal abolition of the slave trade might be carried into effect.
London. F. C. and J. Rivington, 1815. 84p. (M326.9T39)

2704 U. S. Dept. of Commerce. Office of International Trade. Sierra
Leone and Gambia (Summary of current economic information.) Prepared by Bernard Blakenheimer, British Commonwealth branch. Washington, D. C., Government Printing Office, 1948. 7p. (M973Un31)

2705 Utting, Francis Arthur James. The story of Sierra Leone. London, New York, Longmans, Green & Co., 1931. 178p. (M966.-
4Ut8)

GAMBIA

2706 Gambia. Information Office. News Bulletin. Bathurst, Gambia,
1950. (M966.51 G14in)

2707 Gray, John Milner. . . . A history of Gambia. Cambridge, The
University Press, 1940. 508p. (M966.51 G79)

2708 Great Britain. Colonial Office. Annual Report on the Gambia.
London, H. M. Stationery Office, 1938. (M966.51 G79g)

2709 Haswell, Margaret Rosary. Economics of agriculture in a Savan-
nah village. . . . Gambia. London, published by H. M. Stationery Office for the Colonial Office, 1953. 143p. (AM966.-
51 H27)

2710 Jobson, Richard. The golden trade; or, a discovery of the river
Gambra, and the golden trade of the Aethiopians. Teignmouth, Devonshire, E. E. Speight & H. R. Walpole, [1904.]
209p. (M966J57g)

2711 Reeve, Henry Fenwick. The Gambia; its history, ancient, medieval
and modern. . . . London, Smith, Eder and Co., 1912. 287p.
(AM966.51 R25g)

2712 Southorn, Bella Sidney (Woolf) Lady. The Gambia. London,
Allen and Unwin, 1952. 283p. (AM966.51 So8g)

2713 U. S. Dept. of Commerce. Office of International Trade. Sierra
Leone and Gambia (Summary of current economic information). Washington, D. C., Government Printing Office, 1948.
7p. (M973Un31)

LIBERIA

2714 African Methodist Episcopal Church. Minutes of the seventeenth session of the Liberia Annual Conference of the African Methodist Episcopal Church, Jan. 2-4, 1907. Liberia, 1907. 20p.

2715 Allen, Gardner W. The trustees of donations for education in Liberia, a story of Philanthropic endeavor 1850-1923. Boston, [Thomas Todd Co., Printers] 1923. 132p. (M966.6A15t)

2716 Allen, Van Nes. I found Africa. Indianapolis, New York, The Bobbs-Merrill Co., [1939] 306p. (M916.66AL5)

2717 American Colonization Society. Information about going to Liberia. . . . Published by the American Colonization Society, Washington, D. Alexander, 1852. 24p. (M966.6Am3i)

2718 Anderson, Benjamin J. K. Appendix to Benjamin Anderson's Journey to Musadu. An exact fac-simile of a letter from the king of Musadu to the president of Liberia, written by a young Mandingo, at Musadu, in Arabic, in the latter part of 1868. Printed from photographic relief plates. With a translation by Rev. Edward Blyden. New York, Lithographing, engraving and printing Co., 1870. 14p. (M966.6An19a)

2719 Anderson, Benjamin J. K. Narrative of the expedition despatched to Musahdu by the Liberian government under Benjamin J. K. Anderson, Sr., esquire in 1874. Ed. by Frederick Starr. Monrovia, College of West Africa Press, 1912. 43p. (M966.An19)

2720 Anderson, Robert Earle. Liberia, America's African friend. Chapel Hill, University of North Carolina Press, [1952.] 305p. (M-966.6An2)

2721 [Armistead, Wilson.] Calumny refuted by facts from Liberia; with extracts from the inaugural address of the coloured President Roberts; an eloquent speech of Hilary Teage, a coloured senator; and extracts from a discourse by H. H. Garnett, a fugitive slave, on the past and present condition, and destiny of the coloured race. London, C. Gilpin; New York, W. Harned, Anti-slavery Office, 1948. 46p. (M326.5Ar5)

2722 Azikiwe, Nnamdi. Liberia in world politics. London, A. H. Stockwell, 1934. 406p. (M966.9Az21)

2723 Bane, Martin J. The Catholic story of Liberia. New York, D. X. McMullen Co., 1950. 163p. (M966.6B22c)

2724 Barclay, Arthur. Message of the President of Liberia communicated to the first session for the thirty-first legislature. Monrovia, R. A. Phillips, Government Printing office, 1907. 20p. (M966.6B23m)

2725 Barclay, Arthur. Message of the President of Liberia communicated to the second session of the thirty-first legislature. Monrovia, Government Printing Office, 1908. 34p.

2726 Barclay, Edwin. Annual message of His Excellency Edwin Barclay, President of Liberia, delivered before the first session of the thirty-seventh legislature, December 22, 1931. Monrovia, Liberia, Government Printing Office [1931.] 47p. (M966.-6B23a)

2727 Barclay, Edwin. Inaugural address of His Excellency, Edwin Barclay, President of the Republic of Liberia. Delivered January 4, 1932. Monrovia, C. C. Dennis, Printer [1932.] 16p. (M966.6B23)

2728 Benard, Pierre. Malikoko, président de la republic. Paris, Les Editions de France, 1931. 244p. (M966.6B45m)

2729 Benson, Stephen Allen. Fourth annual message of Stephen A. Benson, president of Liberia, delivered to the legislature, December 1858. 23p. (M966.6B44f)

2730 Blooah, Charles G. Jabo proverbs from Liberia; maxims in the life of a native tribe, by George Herzog . . . with the assistance of Charles G. Blooah. London, published for the International Institute of African Languages and Cultures by Oxford University Press, H. Milford, 1936. 272p. (M398B62)

2731 Blyden, Edward Wilmot. African colonization. Rev. E. W. Blyden's address at the annual meeting of the Maine Colonization Society. June 1932. [Lacks imprint.]

2732 Blyden, Edward Wilmot. The African society and Miss Mary H. Kingsley. Articles reprinted from "The Sierra Leone Weekly News", (March, April, May and June, 1901.) London, Printed and Published at the Office of "West Africa", 1901. 47p. (M966.6B62afr)

2733 Blyden, Edward Wilmot. The aims and methods of a liberal education for Africans. Inaugural address, delivered by Edward Wilmot Blyden, January 5, 1881. Cambridge, John Wilson, 1882. 30p. (M966.6B62ai)

2734 Blyden, Edward Wilmot. Christianity, Islam and the Negro race. With an introduction by the Hon. Samuel Lewis. London, W. B. Whittingham & Co., 1887. 432p (M966.6B62c)

2735 Blyden, Edward Wilmot. Our origin, dangers and duties. The annual address before the mayor and common council of the city of Monrovia, July 26, 1865, the day of national independence; and repeated on Tuesday, August 1, 1865, at Caldwell, St. Paul's River. New York, J. A. Gray & Green, Printers, 1865. 42p. (M966.6B62)

2736 Blyden, Edward Wilmot. The three needs of Liberia. A lecture delivered at Lower Buchanan, Grand County, Liberia, January 26, 1908. London, C. M. Phillips, Printer, 1908. 36p. (M966.-6B62t)

2737 Blyden, Edward Wilmot. A voice from bleeding Africa, on behalf of her exiled children. Liberia, G. Killian, Printer, 1856. 33p. (M966.6B62r)

2738 Blyden, Edward Wilmot. West Africa before Europe, and other addresses, delivered in England in 1901 and 1903. With an introduction by Casely Hayford. London, C. M. Phillips, 1905. 158p. (M966.6B62w)

2739 Boone, Clinton C. Liberia as I know it. Richmond, Va., n.p. 1929. 152p. (M916.66 B64)

2740 Boutilly, V. Le caféier de Libéria, sa culture et sa manipulation. Paris, A. Challamel, 1900. 137p. (M966.6B66c)

2741 Brawley, Benjamin Griffith. A social history of the American Negro, being a history of the Negro problem in the United States, including a history and study of the republic of Liberia. New York, The Macmillan Co., 1921. 420p. (M973B73so)

2742 Brittan, Harriete G. Scenes and incidents of every-day life in Africa. . . . New York, Pudney & Russell, 1860. 353p. (M-916.66B77)

2743 Brown, George William. The economic history of Liberia. Washington, D. C., The Associated Publishers, Inc., [1941.] 366p. (M966.6B81)

2744 Buell, Raymond Leslie. Liberia: a century of survival, 1847-1947. Philadelphia, University of Pennsylvania Press, the University Museum, 1947. 140p. (M966.6B86)

2745 Cassel, Nathaniel H. B. The baccalaureate, a discourse delivered to the graduating class of 1914 in Trinity Memorial Church, Monrovia, Liberia, College of West Africa Press, 1915. 29p. (M966.6C271)

2746 Cassel, Nathaniel H. B. The Liberian scholar, being the annual address delivered on the occasion of the commencement exercises of the College of West Africa at the Hall of Representatives, Monrovia, Liberia, The Government Printing Press, 1915. 18p. (M966.6C271)

2747 Ceston, Jean Marie. Le "Gree-Gree Bush" (Initiation de la Jeu-

nesse) chez les Nègres-Golah, Liberia. pp. 729-54. (M966.-
6C33)

2748   Christy, David. Ethiopia: her gloom and glory, as illustrated in
        the history of the slave trade and slavery, the rise of the re-
        public of Liberia, and the progress of African missions. With
        an introduction by W. P. Strickland. Cincinnati, Rickey,
        Mallory & Webb, 1857. 255 p. (M326.5C46)

2749   Christy, David. A lecture on African colonization. Including a
        brief outline of the slave trade, emancipation, the relation of
        the republic of Liberia to England. Delivered in the hall of
        the House of representatives of the state of Ohio. Cincinnati,
        J. A. & U. P. James, 1849. 56p. (M325.3AC461)

2750   Cole, Henry Benoni. The Liberian year book, 1956. Compiled
        and edited by Henry B. Cole. London, The Diplomatic Press
        and Publishing Co., 1956. 312 p. (M966.6C67)

2751   The College of West Africa. Annual report, 1913 (M966.6C68)

2752   [Cooper, Charles E.] Men make a nation. An address to his ex-
        cellency Daniel Edward Howard, president of the Republic
        of Liberia on the eve of his retirement from the government.
        Liverpool, W. W. Lea and Co., 1929. 47p. (M966.6C78)

2753   Cooper, Charles E. Love in ebony; a West African romance, by
        Varfelli Karlee (pseud.) With a foreword by Vernon Bart-
        lett. London, John Murray, 1932. 316p. (M896.3C78e)

2754   Coppinger, William. The new Africa. Hampton, Va., Normal
        School Press, 1887. 27p. (AM960C79n)

2755   Crummell, Alexander. The English language, in Liberia. The an-
        nual address before the citizens of Maryland county, Cape
        Palmas, Liberia—July 26, 1860. Being the day of national
        independence. New York, Bruce & Co., 1861. 32p. (M966.-
        6C88e)

2756   Crummell, Alexander. The future of Africa: being addresses, ser-
        mons, etc., delivered in the republic of Liberia. New York,
        C. Scribner, 1862. 354p. (M960C88f)

2757   Crummell, Alexander. The relations and duties of free colored
        men in America to Africa. A letter to Charles B. Dunbar.
        Hartford, Press of Case, Lockwood and Co., 1861. 50p.
        (M966.6C88)

2758   Curtis, L. C. Liberia and the Gold Coast. Orlando, Florida, Sen-
        tine-Reporter Print, 1904. 36p. (M966.6C94)

2759   Davis, Stanley A. This is Liberia; a brief history of this land of
        contradtions, with biographies of its founders and builders.

New York, William-Frederick Press, 1953.   151p.   (M966.-
6D29t)

2760   Delafosse, Maurice.   Les vai.   Leur langue et leur système d'-
écriture.   (Reprinted from L'Anthropologie, v. 10, p. 129-151,
249-314.) Paris, Masson et Cie, 1899.   (M966.6D37)

2761   Donations for Education in Liberia.   Annual report of the trustees
of donations for educations in Liberia.   Presented at the an-
ual meeting, 1851-18.   (AM966.6D71a)

2762   Donner, Etta.   Hinterland Liberia.   Translated by Winifred M.
Deans.   London, and Glasgow, Blackie and son, Ltd., [1939.]
302p.   (M966.6D71h)

2763   Downing, Henry Francis.   Liberia and her people.   [New York,
1925.] 26p.   (M966.6D751)

2764   Downing, Henry Francis.   A short history of Liberia (1816-1908)
with descriptive addenda in four parts, for schools and general reading.   New York, Amos M. Gailliard Co., n.d.   27p.
(M966.6D75)

2765   Durrant, Robert Ernest.   Liberia: a report.   London, African International Corporation, 1924.   71p.   (AM916.66D93)

2766   Ferguson, S. D.   Liberia's crisis; a national sermon preached in
Trinity Church, Monrovia, July, 1908.   Liverpool, W. H.
Lloyd and sons, 1908.   19p.

2767   Firestone Plantations Company.   Views in Liberia.   Chicago, R.
R. Donelley & Sons Co., [c1937.]   111p.   (M916.66F51v)

2768   Foote, Andrew Hull.   Africa and the American flag.   New York,
D. Appleton & Co. 1854.   390p.   (M966.6F73)

2769   Furbay, Elizabeth Jane (Dearmin).   Top hats and tom-toms.
Chicago, New York, Ziff-Davis Publishing Co., [1943.] 307p.
(M916.66F96)

2770   Genevray, J.   Eléments d'Une monographie d'une division administrative Liberieenne (Grand Bassa County).   Dakar, IFAN,
1952.   135p.   (M966.6G28)

2771   Gooch, Daniel Wheelwright.   Recognition of Hayti and Liberia.
Speech of Hon. D. W. Gooch of Mass., delivered in the House
of representatives, June 2, 1862.   [Washington, McGill, With-
erow & Co., 1862.]   8p.   (M972.94G59)

2772   Greene, Graham.   Journey without maps.   Garden City, N. Y.
Doubleday, Doran & Co., Inc., 1936.   (AM916.66G83)

2773   Grimes, L. A.   Report and opinions of L. A. Grimes.   Third annual series with appendices 1, 2, and 3.   Submitted to the 2nd

session of the 35th legislative body of the Republic of Liberia.
Monrovia, 1934.   84p.   (M966.6G88)

2774   Grimes, L. A.   Report of L. A. Grimes, Attorney General of Liberia, submitted to the 4th session of the 34th legislature of
the Republic of Liberia, and opinions filed by the Attorney
General during the year of 1922 with index.   98p.   (M966.-
6G88)

2775   Grimes, L. A.   Republic of Liberia, 1922, 1923, 1924.   Reports
and opinions.   (AM966.6G88)

2776   Gurley, Ralph Randolph.   Life of Jehudi Ashmun, late colonial
agent in Liberia.   With an appendix, containing extracts from
his journal and other writings; with a brief sketch of the life
of the Rev. Lott Cary.   Washington, J. C. Dunn, 1835. 160p.
(MC9As3g)

2777   Gurley, Ralph Randolph.   Report of the Secretary of State communicating the report of the Rev. R. R. Gurley, who was sent
out by the government to obtain information in respect to Liberia, 1850.   112p.   (M966.6G96)

2778   Hale, Sarah Josepha. (Buell)   Liberia; or, Mr. Peyton's experiments.   Edited by Mrs. Sarah J. Hale.   New York, Harper
& Bros., 1853.   304p.   (M966.6H13l)

2779   Hall, Anna E.   Hymn in the Kroo dialect.   Liberia, College of
West Africa Press, 1907.   27p.

2780   Handbook of Liberia. [No imprint] 1940. 62p. (M966.6H19)

2781   Harley, George Way.   Native African medicine; with special reference to its practice in the Mano tribe of Liberia.   Cambridge, Mass., Harvard University Press, 1941.   294p.   (AM-
610H22)

2782   Harley, George Way.   Notes on the Poro in Liberia.   Cambridge,
Mass., Harvard University Press, 1941.   36p.

2783   Harris, William Edward. "Plenty How-do" from Africa; letters
and stories from the Liberian Bush.   New York, Holy Cross
Press, 1941.   179p.   (M966.6H24p)

2784   Hartzell, Joseph C.   Diamond investments in Africa.   New York,
Africa Diamond Jubilee Commission Board of Foreign Missions
of the Methodist Episcopal Church, 1909.   16p.

2785   Harvard African Expedition, 1926-1927.   The African republic of
Liberia and the Belgian Congo.   Cambridge, Harvard University Press, 1930.   (AM916.66H25)

2786   Hayman, Arthur Ingram.   Lighting up Liberia, by Arthur I. Hayman and Harold Preece. [New York,] Creative Age Press, [1943.] 279p. (M966.6H331)

2787   Henries, A. D. Banks. Civics for Liberian schools. [London, John Corah & Sons,] 1954. 120p. (M966.6H39)

2788   Herzog, George. Jabo proverbs from Liberia; maxims in the life of a native tribe. London, published for the International Institute of African Languages & Cultures by Oxford University Press, 1936. 272p. (AM398H44)

2789   Holas, B. Mission dans l'Est Libérien. Dakar, IFAN, 1952. 566p. (M966.6H69)

2790   Howard University. Founders Library. Moorland Foundation. Liberia. Howard University, Founders Library, Moorland Foundation, 1951. 12p. (MO16.966H831)

2791   Huberich, Charles Henry. The political and legislative history of Liberia; a documentary history of the constitutions laws and treaties of Liberia from the earliest settlements to the establishment of the Republic, a sketch of the activities of the American colonization societies, a commentary on the constitution of the Republic and a survey of the political and social legislation from 1847 to 1944; with appendices containing the laws of the colony of Liberia, 1820-1839, and Acts of the Governor and Council, 1839-1847. Foreword by Roscoe Pound. New York, Central Book Co., 1947. 2v. (M966.6H86p)

2792   Innes, William. Liberia; or, The early history and signal preservation of the American colony of free Negroes on the coast of Africa. Edinburgh, Waugh and Innes, 1831. 152p. (AM-966.6In6)

2793   International Commission of Inquiry into the Existence of Slavery and Forced Labor in the Republic of Liberia. Communication by the government of Liberia dated Dec. 15, 1930, transmitting the commission's report. [Geneva, 1930.] 130p. (M966.61n8)

2794   Johnston, Harry Hamilton. Liberia, with an appendix on the Flora by Dr. O. Stapf. New York, Dodd, 1906. 2vols. (M966.6J62)

2795   Jordan, Lewis Garnett. Pebbles from an African beach. [Philadelphia, The Lisle-Carey Press, c1918.] 73p. (M966.6J76)

2796   Junge, Werner. African jungle doctor; ten years in Liberia. London, George G. Harrap and Co., 1952. 208p. (M966.-6J95a)

2797   Junge, Werner. Bolahun: an African adventure. New York, G. P.

Puttman's Sons, 1952. 248p. (M966.6J95b)

2798 Karnga, Abayomi. Liberia official postal guide. Monrovia, The Montserrado Printing and Publishing Co., 1923. 28p. (M-966.6K14)

2799 Kimble, David. The machinery of self-government. London, Penguin Books, 1953. 124p. (M966.7K56m)

2800 King, Charles Dunbar Burgess. The annual message of his excellency . . . president of the Republic of Liberia, delivered Oct. 18, 1928. Monrovia, Liberia, n.p. 1928. 65p. (M966.6K58)

2801 Kittrell, Flemmie P. A preliminary food and nutrition survey of Liberia. West Africa . . . December 1946. June 1947. Lacks imprint. 21p. (AM966.6K65p)

2802 Koelle, S. W. Narrative of an expedition into the Vy country of West Africa, and the discovery of a system of syllabic writing recently invented by the natives of the Vy tribe. London, Suleys, 1859. 34p. (M966K81n)

2803 Ladies' Liberia School Association. Philadelphia . . . Annual report . . . 1st 1833: 3rd Annual report, 1835. (M966.6L12a)

2804 La Rue, Sidney de. The land of the Pepper bird. Liberia, London, G. P. Putnam's Sons, 1930. 330p.

2805 Lelong, Maurice Hyacinthe. Le Libéria intime. Alger Baconnier, 351p. 1946. (M966.6L53a)

2806 Lelong, Maurice Hyacinthe. Monrovia, capitale pour rire. Alger Baconnier, 1946. 354p. (AM966.6L53av2)

2807 LeRoy, Marcel. Land of the Niamoo . . . London, Arthur Barker, Ltd., [1954.] 175p. (M966.6L56)

2808 Liberia. Acts passed by the legislature of the Republic of Liberia, during the session, 1901-1902. Published by authority. Monrovia, Government Printing Office, 1902. 41p. (M966.6L61)

2809 Liberia. Acts passed by the legislature of the Republic of Liberia during the session 1907-1908. Monrovia, Government Printing Office Monrovia, 1908. 38p.

2810 Liberia. Acts passed by the Legislature of the Republic of Liberia during the session 1907-1908. Monrovia, Government Printing Office Monrovia, 1908. 41p.

2811 Liberia. The annual message of William V. S. Tubman, President of Liberia delivered before the fourth session of the forty-second legislature, January 21, 1955. Monrovia, Government Printing Office, 1955. 42p. (M966.6L61a)

2812 Liberia. Booklet issued by the Ambassador of Liberia on the occasion of the official visit of the President of Liberia to the United States. 1954.

2813 Liberia. Centennial and victory exposition. Monrovia, Liberia, 1947-1949. [c1946.] 32p. (AM966.6L61c)

2814 Liberia. Code for the Justices of the Peace. Liberia, College of West Africa Press, 1907. 65p.

2815 Liberia. . . . Copy of an original agreement between the Government of the Republic of Liberia of the first part, Messrs. Emile Erlanger and Co., of the second part and the Liberian development Company chartered and limited of the third part. 1907. 14p.

2816 Liberia. Digest of the laws in force in the colony of Liberia, August 19th, 1824. 11p. (M966.6D56)

2817 Liberia. A diplomatic press survey. Special edition of the "Diplomatic Bulletin." London, No. 33, February, 1956. 31p. M966.6L61r)

2818 Liberia. Emigration to Liberia. [Report of the Standing Committee on Emigration of the American Colonization Society.] Prepared by Rev. Dr. Thomas G. Addison, Washington, D. C., Government Printing Office, 1883. 3p. (M966.6L61e)

2819 Liberia. Estimates of receipts and expenditure of revenue for the year commencing 1st Oct., 1908, ending 30th Sept., 1909. Liberia, College of West Africa Press, 1909. 18p.

2820 Liberia. Handbook of Liberia. [New York, Minden Press,] 1940. 3p. (M966.6H19)

2821 Liberia. Liberian Press directory and Who's Who, 1955. London, Arthur H. Thrower, 1955. 7p. (M966.6L615)

2822 Liberia Annual Conference. Official journal of the Liberia Annual Conference held at Clay-Ashland, Feb. 3-8, 1909. Liberia, College of West Africa Press, 1909. 61p.

2823 Liberia Baptist Missionary and Educational Convention. Minutes of the twelfth biennial session of the Liberia Baptist Missionary and Educational Convention; held with Providence Baptist Church, Monrovia, April 6-10, 1904. Liberia, A. B. Stubblefield, 1904. 33p.

2824 Liberia Bureau of Information. Department of State. Liberia, Monrovia, Bureau of Information, Department of State, 195? 48p. (M966.6L611)

2825 Liberia Bureau of Information. Department of State. The national unification program of Liberia; hands across the country.

Monrovia, Bureau of Information, Department of State, 195? 31p. (M966.6L61n)

2826 Liberia College, Monrovia. The report of Liberia College for the year 1907. Monrovia, Liberia College Press, 1907. 33p.

2827 Liberia College, Monrovia. The report of the Liberia College for the year 1908. Monrovia, Liberia College Press, 1908. 46p.

2828 Liberia College, Monrovia. Proceedings and addresses on the occasion of the inauguration of the Rev. Garretson Warner Gibson, D.D. as president of Liberia College, Wednesday, February 21, 1900. 67p. (AM378L61)

2829 Liberia College, Monrovia. Catalogue and register, 1925-1927. London, Churchman Publishing Co., 1928. (AM966.6L61ca)

2830 Liberia Constitution. Constitution, government and digest of the laws of Liberia, as confirmed and established by the board of managers of the American colonization society, May 23, 1825. Washington City, Printed by Way & Gideon, 1825. 11p. (M966.6L6.c)

2831 Liberia Customs Service. Laws and regulations with instructions to customs officers. London, Henry Good and Son, 1906. 70p.

2832 Liberia. Department of Agriculture and Commerce. Fourth annual progress report of the cooperative program in agriculture, forestry and fisheries under the joint Liberian-United States Commission for economic development. Monrovia, Department of Agriculture and Commerce, 1955. 143p. (M966.6L61f)

2833 Liberia. Department of State. Acts passed by the legislature of the Republic of Liberia during the session 1950-1951, Monrovia. Monrovia, Government Printing Office, 1951. 84p. (M966.6L6.ac)

2834 Liberia Grand Lodge, F. A. & A. M. Souvenir programme for the observance of the semi-centennial anniversary of the grand lodge. Monrovia, Liberia, College of West Africa Press, 1917. (M966.6L61s)

2835 Liberia Supreme Court. Opinions delivered by the honourable the Supreme Court of the Republic of Liberia in cases decided during its November term 1933 and its April term 1934. New annual series No. 1. Monrovia, Liberia, Printed by authority at the Government Printing Office, 1934. (M966.6L610)

2836 Liberia Supreme Court. Two of the opinions and judgments of the Honourable the Supreme Court of Liberia. Delivered during the November term of Court, 1936, with a foreword by the Hon. Arthur Barclay. Monrovia, Methodist Mission Press, 1937. 31p. (M966.6L61t)

2837 Liberia Treaties. Treaties and conventions concluded between the Republic of Liberia and foreign powers, 1848-1892. Published by the Department of State, Monrovia, 1907. 64p. (M966.6L61t)

2838 Liberian National Bar Association. Inaugural meeting of the Liberian National Bar Association in the Senate Chamber, Monrovia, Jan. 2, 1907. Liberia, College of West Africa Press, 1907. 27p.

2839 Liberian National Bar Association. Second annual meeting of the Liberian National Bar Association in the Executive Mansion, Monrovia, Feb. 5, 1908. Liberia, College of West Africa Press, 1908. 51p.

2840 Libermann, Francis Mary Paul. Notes et documents, relatifs à la vie et à l'oeuvre. Paris, Maison-Mère, 1936. 707p. (AM-266L61)

2841 Lief, Alfred. The Firestone story. New York, Whittlesey House, 1951. 437p.

2842 Lugenbeel, James Washington. Sketches of Liberia. Washington, C. Alexander, 1850. 43p. (AM916.66L96)

2843 McAllister, Ages. A lone woman in Africa, six years on the kroo coast. New York, Hunt & Eaton, Cincinnati, Cranston & Curtis, [1896.] 295p. (M966.6M11)

2844 McPherson, John Hanson Thomas. History of Liberia. Baltimore, The Johns Hopkins Press, 1891. 63p. (Johns Hopkins University studies in historical and political science. . . . 9th ser., x) (M966.6M24)

2845 Massachusetts colonization society. American colonization society and the colony at Liberia. Boston, Perkins and Marvin, 1832. 16p. (M326.51M38a)

2846 Massaquoi, Momolu. Oration. Monrovia, Liberia, Government Printing Office, 1922. 23p.

2847 Maugham, Reginald C. The Republic of Liberia; being a general description of the Negro republic, with its history, commerce, agriculture, flora, fauna, and present methods of administration. London, George Allen & Unwin, Ltd., New York, Charles Scribner's Sons, 1920. 299p. (M966.6M44r)

2848 Mayer, Karl Rodney. Forest resources of Liberia. Washington, United States Government Printing Office, 1951. 69p. (M966.-6M45f)

2849 Miller, Armistead. Liberia described. Philadelphia, Joseph M. Wilson, 1859. 18p. (AM966.6M611)

2850 Mitchell, Francis. Grown up Liberia. [Philadelphia, West Philadelphia Multigraphing and Printing Co.,] [1946.] c1945. 144p. (AM916.66M69)

2851 Moore, "Bye Tamiah" Johnson. Golah boy in America; a story of my youth in Africa, description of customs and practices in my tribe, and of my coming to "Big" America; also translations of the Bible verses, together with songs and poems. Richmond, Va., Quality Printing Co., 1937. 27p. (MB9M78)

2852 Morris, Edward S. The golden day; an address delivered at Monrovia, in the Republic of Liberia, January 1, 1863. Philadelphia, W. S. Young, 1863. 16p. (M966.6M83g)

2853 Niger Valley exploring party. Official report of the Niger Valley exploring party. New York, T. Hamilton, 1861. 75p. (M916.66M56)

2854 Payne, James Spriggs. Inaugural address of His Excellency James S. Payne, fourth president of the Republic of Liberia, January 6, 1868. Monrovia, George H. Hanson, Printer, 1848. 15p. (AM966.6P29i)

2855 Phillips, Hilton Alonzo. Liberia's place in Africa's sun. New York, The Hobson Book Press, 1946. 156p. (M966.6P54)

2856 President of Liberia. Message of the President of Liberia, communicated to the first session of the thirty-first legislature. Monrovia, Government Printing Office, 1907. 20p.

2857 President of Liberia. Message of the President of Liberia communicated to the second session of the thirty-first legislature. Monrovia, Government Printing Office, 1908. 34p.

2858 Price, Frederick A. Liberian odyssey "by hammock and surfboat". The autobiography of F. A. Price. New York, Pageant Press, 1954. 260p. (M966.6P93)

2859 Rand, A. L. Birds from Liberia. Chicago, Natural History Museum, 1951. 653p. (AM966.6R15b)

2860 Reed, William E. Reconnaissance soil survey of Liberia. Washington, D. C., United States Department of State, Technical Cooperation Administration and United States Department of Agriculture, Office of Foreign Agricultural Relations, 1951. 107p. (M966.6R25r)

2861 Reeve, Henry Fanwick. The black republic; Liberia, its political and social conditions today. London, H. F. and G. Witherby, 1923. 207p. (M966.6R259)

2862   Roberts, Joseph Jenkins. African colonization. An address at the fifty-second annual meeting of the American Colonization Society held in Washington, D. C., Jan. 19, 1869. New York, American Colonization Society, 1869. 16p. (M966.6R54a)

2863   Sadler, Wesley. Untangled Loma; a course of study of the Loma language of the western province of Liberia, West Africa. Baltimore, Board of Foreign Missions of the United Lutheran Church of America for the Evangelical Lutheran Church in Liberia, 1951. 465p. (M496Sa1)

2864   Schwab, George. Tribes of the Liberian hinterland. Cambridge, Mass., The Museum, 1947. 526p. (AM572.966.Sc9t)

2865   Scott, Emmett Jay. Is Liberia worth saving? Reprinted from vol. 1, No. 3. Jan., 1911, of the Journal of Race Development. pp. 277-301. (M966.6Sc83)

2866   Sibley, James L. Education and missions in Liberia, a preliminary survey of the field for the American Advisory committee on education, 1926. 120p. (AM370.96Sil) (Mimeograph)

2867   Sibley, James L. Liberia—old and new; a study of its social and economic background with possibilities of development, by J. L. Sibley and D. Westermann. Garden City, New York, Doubleday, Doran and Co., 1928. 317p. (M966.6Si1)

2868   Smith, C. C. The life and work of Jacob Kenoly. Cincinnati, Methodist Book Co., c1912. 160p. (MB9K41s)

2869   Starr, Frederick. Liberia, description, history, problems. Chicago, 1913. 227p. (M966.6St2)

2870   Stewart, Thomas McCants. Liberia: the America-African republic. New York, E. O. Jenkins' Sons, 1886. 107p. (M966.-6St4)

2871   Stockwell, G. S. The republic of Liberia: its geography, climate, soil, and productions, with a history of its early settlement. New York, A. S. Barnes and Co., 1868. 299p. (M966.6St6r)

2872   Sumner, Charles. Independence of Hayti and Liberia. Speech of Hon. Charles Sumner, of Massachusetts, on the bill to authorize the appointment of diplomatic representatives to the Republic of Hayti and Liberia, with the debate thereon; in the senate of the United States, April 23 and 24, 1862. Washington, D. C., Congregational Globe Office, 1862. 14p. (M972.-94Su6)

2873   Taylor, Wayne Chatfield. The Firestone operations in Liberia. District of Columbia, National Planning Association, 1956. 115p. (M966.9T21)

2874   Thomas, W. H.   History of Liberia (revised and illustrated). Brewerville, Liberia, Lott Carey Mission Press, 1935. 61p. (M966.6T36)

2875   Tolson, Melvin Beaunorus.   Liberetto for the Republic of Liberia. of inquiry into the existence of slavery and forced labour in New York, Twayne Publishers, 1953. 53p. (M966.6T58)

2876   Trustees of donations for education in Liberia.   Report. [1850, 1851.]   Boston, 1851.   (AM966.6T77)

2877   Tyler, Oliver W.   Liberia—The League of Nations' plan of assistance.   Washington, D. C., Howard University (unpublished thesis), 1944.   99p.   (M378.242HT97)

2878   U. S. Department of State.   Report of the international commission the Republic of Liberia, Monrovia, Liberia, Sept. 8, 1930. Washington, U. S. Government Printing Office, 1931.   227p. (M966.6V88)

2979   U. S. 31st Congress.   1st session.   Senate.   Report of the Secretary of State, communicating the report of the Rev. R. R. Gurley, who was recently sent out by the government to obtain information in respect to Liberia.   Sept. 14, 1850.   Washington, D. C., Government Printer, 1850.   75p.   (M966.6Un3r)

2880   Volz, Walter.   Reise durch das hinterland von Liberia, im Winter 1906-1907.   Bern, Verlag von A. Francke, 1911. 167p. (M916.-6V88)

2881   Walker, Thomas Hamilton Beb.   History of Liberia.   Boston, Cornhill Publishing Co., c1921.   175p.   (M966.6W15h)

2882   Warner, Esther Sietmann.   New song in a strange land.   Boston, Houghton Mifflin Co., 1948.   302p.   (M966.6W24n)

2883   Wauwermans.   Les prémices de l'oeuvre d'emancipation Africaine. Liberia . . . Bruxelles, Institut national de geographie, 1885. 271p.   (M966.6W35)

2884   West, Henry Litchfield.   The Liberian crisis.   [Washington, D. C., American Colonization Society,] 1933.   33p.   (M966.6W52)

2885   West, John B.   United States health missions in Liberia.   Washington, D. C., Government Printing Office, 1948.   14p.   (AM-966.6W52u)

2886   Westermann, Diedrich.   Die Kpelle, ein negerstamm in Liberia. Gottingen, Vanderhoek & Ruprecht; Leipzig, J. C. Hinrichs, 1921.   552p.   (AM496.4W52k)

2887   Westermann, Diedrich.   The Kpelle language in Liberia; grammatical outline, colloquial sentences and vocabulary by D.

Westermann and H. J. Melzian, Berlin, Reimer, Vohsen, 1930. 85p. (AM496W52K)

2888 Wilkeson, Samuel. A concise history of the commencement, progress and present condition of the American colonies in Liberia. Washington, Printed at the Madisonian Office, 1839. 88p. (M966.6W65)

2889 Williams, Samuel. Four years in Liberia. A sketch of the life of the Rev. Samuel Williams. With remarks on the missions, manners and customs of the natives of western Africa. Together with an answer to Nesbit's book. Philadelphia, King & Baird, 1857. 66p. (MB9W676)

2890 Wilson, Charles Morrow. Liberia. New York, W. Sloane, 1947. 226p. (M916.66W691)

2891 Yancey, Ernest Jerome. Historical lights of Liberia's yesterday and today. [Xenia, O., The Aldine Publishing Co., 1934.] 323p. (M966.6Y15)

2892 Yancey, Ernest Jerome. The recent Liberian crisis and its causes; and address delivered at Buffalo, New York, August 12 and 14, 1934, under auspices of the Buffalo Liberian Research Society, n.p. 1934. 12p. (M966.6Y15r)

2893 Young, James Capers. Liberia rediscovered. Garden City, New York, Doubleday, Doran and Co., 1934. 212p. (M966.6Y85)

FRENCH WEST AFRICA
GENERAL

2894 Abbatucci, S. Médecins coloniaux. Paris Éditions Larose, 1928. 148p. (AM614A19)

2895 'Abd Al-Rahmán ibn 'Abd Alláh. Documents arabes relatifs à l'historie du Soudan; Tarikh-es-Soudan. Paris, E. Leroux, 1898-1900. 2v.

2896 Abensour, Léon. La France noir; ses peuples, son historie, ses richesses (par) Léon Abensour (et) René Thévenin. Paris, Société Parisienne D'Edition, 1933. 290p. (M966.1Ab3)

2897 Abou Digu'en. Notre empire African noir, ses problèmes politiques et militaries. Paris, Charles-Lavauzelle & cie, 1928. 150p. (M966.1ab7)

2898 L'Afrique Occidentale Française. Agence économique. L'Afrique Occidentale Française. Paris, Agénce économique de l'Afrique Occidentale Française, n.d. 31p. (M966Af83no.1)

2899 Anfreville de la Salle, Dr. d' Sur la côte d'Afrique, villes, brousses, fleuves et Problémes de l'ouest African. 36 reproductions photographiques et une carte. Paris, Emile Larose, 1912. 318p. (M966An3)

2900 Annuaire Noria de l'Afrique Occidentale Française 1948-49. Paris, Editions Larose, 1948-49. 239p.

2901 Ardant du Picq, Charles Jean Jacques Joseph. Une population Africaine; les Dyerma. Paris, Larose Editeurs, 1933. 76p. (M966.26Ar2)

2902 Baratier, Albert Ernest Augustin. . . . A travers l'Afrique; édition definitive ornée de huit portraits et de six cartes. Ouvrage couronné par l'Académie française (Prix vitet). Paris, Perrin et Cie, 1912. 345p. (M966B231912)

2903 Baratier, Albert Ernest Augustin. Epopées Africanes; Illustrations d'après les dessins de 1. Pouzargues. Paris, Fayard, 1912. 126p. (M966B23e)

2904 Barret, Paul Marie Victor. Sénégambie et Guinée—La région gabonaise. L'Afrique occidentale, la nature et l'homme noir. Paris Challamel et cie, 1888. 2v. (M966.1B27)

2905 Barrows, David Prescott. Berbers and blacks; impressions of Morocco, Timbuktu and the Western Sudan. New York, The Century Co., 1927. 251p. (M966.2B27b)

2906 Baston, Alfred. African intrigue. Garden City, N. Y., Garden City Publishing Company, Inc., 1933. 307p. (M916.61B32)

2907 Beaudza, Louis. La formation de l'armee coloniale. Paris, Librairie Militaire L'Fournier et Cie, 1939. 618p. (M960B38)

2908 Bedouin, Jean-Louis. Noir d'ivoire, photos de Michel Huet. Paris, Hoa-Qui, 1950. 96p. (M966B39)

2909 Bernard, Augustin. Afrique septentrionale et occidentale; Deuxieme partie: Sahara-Afrique Occidentale (Geographie Universelle, v. XI). Paris, Librairie Armand Colin, 1937-39. (M960B45)

2910 Berthelot, André. L'Afrique Sahárienne et Soudanaise, ce qu'en ont connu les anciens. Paris, Les Arts, et le Livre, 1927. 431p. (M966B46)

2911 Besson, Maurice. Historie des colonies françaises. Paris, Boiloin and cie, 1931. 402p. (M960B46)

2912 Bever, L. Van. Le cinéma pour Africans. Préface par L. Piron. Bruxelles, G. Van Campenhout, 1950. 59p. (AM791.4B46)

2913 Blache, Joseph. Vrais noirs et vrais blancs d'Afrique qu xxe siecle. Lettre de M. William Guynet . . . 2nd ed. Orleans, Maurice Caillette, 1922. 443p. (M966.1B56)

2914   Bonneau, Oscar. Pour bien vivre aux colonies; Recette pratiques de Cuisine et de Patisserie. Paris, A. Challamel, 1913. 104p.

2915   Bordeaux, Henry. . . . Nos Indes noires; voyage en Afrique occidentale. Avec une carte hors texte. Paris, Librairie Plon [1936.] 312p. (M966B64n)

2916   Cazes, Alfred. Le Niger sentimental. Oran, Editions Heintz Freres, n.d. 472p. (M966.1C25)

2917   Césaire, Aimé. Discours sur le colonialisme. 2d ed. Paris, Presence Africaine [1955.] 71p.

2918   Chazelas, Victor. Territories Africains sous mandat de la France. Paris, Société d'éditions geographiques, maritimes, et coloniales, 1931. 240p. (M916.711C39t)

2919   Conférence forestière interafricaine. 1st, Abidjan, 1951. Première Conference forestière interafricaine, Abidjan, 4-12 dècembre 1951. [Paris, 1952.] 562p. (AM634.9C76)

2920   Cousse, Gaston. Le probleme colonial français. Paris, Société Anonyme de Publications Periodiques, 1928. 36p.

2921   Cremer, Jean. Les Bobo (la vie sociale), documents recueillis et traduits do Bobo. Paris, Paul Geuthner, 1925. 177p. (M966.-2C86bv.3)

2922   Cremer, Jean. Materiaux d'ethnographie et de linguistique Soudanises . . . Tome iv. Les Bobo . . . Paris, Librairie orientaliste, 1927. 212p. (AM966.2C86)

2923   Davis, Shelby Cullom. Resevoirs of men: a history of the black troops in French West Africa. Geneva, Librairie Kundig, 1934. 205p. (M966.1D29)

2924   Deherme, Georges. L'Afrique Occidentale Française; action politique, action économique, action sociale. Paris, Bloud et cie., 1908. 528p. (M966.1D36a)

2925   Delafosse, Maurice. Les frontières de la Côte d'Ivoire de la Côte d'Or et du Soudan. Avec 94 figures dans le texte d'après de photographies de l'auteur et une carte. Paris, Masson et Cie, 1908. 256p. (M966.68D37)

2926   Delafosse, Maurice. La Gâna et le Mali et l'emplacement de leurs capitales. Extrait du Bulletin du comite d'etudes historiques et scientifiques de l'Afrique occidentale française (no. de fuillet-Septembre 1924). 64p. (M966D37g)

2927   Delafosse, Maurice. Historie de l'Afrique Occidentale Française d'après les travaux et les indications de Maurice Delafosse. Paris, Delagrave, 1926. 341p. (M966.1D368)

2928 Delavignette, Robert Louis. Afrique Occidentale Française. Paris, Société d'éditions géographiques, maritimes et coloniales, 1931. 244p. (M966.1D37)

2929 Delavignette, Robert Louis. Freedom and authority in French West Africa. London, New York, Published for the International African Institute by the Oxford University Press, 1950. 152p. (M966.1D37f)

2930 Delavignette, Robert Louis. Les paysans noirs, recit soudanais en douze mois. Paris, Stock (Delamain at Boutelleau) 1931. 221p. (AM966.2D37)

2931 Des prêtres noirs s'interrogent, par A. Abble [and others.] Paris, Les Éditions du Cerf, 1956. 281p.

2932 D'Olloné. . . . De la côte d'Ivoire au Soudan et a la Guinée. Paris, Librarie Hachette et cie, 1901. 313p. (M966D69d)

2933 Doutressoulle, G. L'élevage en Afrique Occidentale Française. Paris, Larose, 1947. 298p. (M966.1D74)

2934 Dubois, Felix. Timbuctoo the mysterious . . . New York, Longmans, Green and Co., 1896. 377p. (M916.624D85)

2935 Dubois, Felix. Tombouctou la mysterieuse. Paris, Librairie E. Flammarion, 1897. 420p. (AM916.624D851)

2936 DuGard, Maurice Martin. Courrier D'Afrique. Paris, Flammarion, 1931. 247p. (M916.6M36)

2937 Dupuis, Auguste Victor dit Yakouba. Industries et principales professions des habitants de la region de Tombouctou. Paris, Emile Larose, Libraire-editeur, 1921. 193p. (M966.24D92i)

2938 Éboué, Adolphe Félix Sylvestre. Discours en Conseil d'Administration. [Afrique Française Libre, 1941.] 26p.

2939 Éboué, Adolphe Félix Sylvestre. Langues Sango, Banda, Baya, Manjia, notes, grammaticales. Mots groupés d'apres le sens. Phrases usuelles. Vocabulaire. Paris, Emile Larose, 1918. 109p.

2940 Éboué, Adolph Félix Sylvestre. Les peuples de l'Oubangui Chai. Essai d'ethnographie, de linguistique et d'economic sociale. Paris, Publications du Comité de l'Afrique française, 1933. 104 (8) p. (M968.41Eb7)

2941 Éboué Adolphe Félix Sylvestre. Les Sociétés d'initiés en pays Banda. (extrait-Bulletin de la Société des recherches Congolaises. no. 13, 1931. 15p.

2942 L'Ecole, William-Ponty. Le theatre indigene et la culture Franco-Africaine, 1936-1937. [Dakar, 1937.] 115p. (M966.3Ec7t)

2943 L'empire colonial français, par baron d'Anthouard; Gen. Archenard; Gen. Aubier. Paris, Plon, 1929. 361p. (M960Ls4)

2944 Ferry, Edmond. La France en Afrique. Paris, Librairie Armand Colin, 1905. 301p. (M960F41f)

2945 France. Direction de la documentation. French West Africa. [Paris, La Documentation francaise, 1954.] 63p. (M966.1F84)

2946 France. Ministere de colonies. Annuaire du Ministere des colonies. 1932-1933. (AM325.344F84)

2947 Frison-Roche, Roger. L'appel du Hoggar. Nouv. ed. [Paris] Flammarion, 1942, c1936. 140p. (M966.11F91a)

2948 Gautier, Émile Félix. L'Afrique noir occidentale; esquisse des cadres géographiques. Paris, Librairie Larose, 1935. 188p. (M966O23)

2949 Gautier, Émile Félix. La Sahara. Paris, Payot, 1928. 232p. (M-966.1G23)

2950 Gouilly, Alphonse. L'Islam dans l'Afrique Occidentale Française. Paris, Editions Larose, 1952. 318p. (AM297G72)

2951 Guéhenno, Jean. La France et les noirs. Paris, Gallimard, [1954.] 141p. (M966.1G93)

2952 Guy, Camille. L'Afrique Occidentale française. Préface de M. E. Roume. Paris, Larose, 1929. 207p. (M966.1G98)

2953 Haardt, Georges Marie. . . . Le raid Citroen. Paris, Plon-Nourrit et cie [1923] 307p. (M966.11H11r)

2954 Haywood, Austin Hubert Wightwick. Through Timbuctu and across the great Sahara: an account of an adventurous journey. 349p. (M966H33t)

2955 Histoire des colonies Française et de l'expansion de la France dans le monde. Tome IV. Afrique Occidentale Française par Maurice Delafosse, Afrique Equatoriale Française par Alfred Martineau. Sanhaville, Paris, Librairie Plon, 1931. 611p. (M-966H62)

2956 Huet, Michall. Les Hommes de Danse; photographies de Michel Huet; preface de Keita Fodeba. Lausanne, Ed. Guide du livre, 1954. 134p. (AM394.3H87)

2957 L'Institut française d'Afrique noire. Dakar, IFAN, 1954. 127p. (M966.321n7i)

2958 Jackson, James Grey. An account of Timbuctoo and Housa, territories in the interior of Africa, by El Hage Abd Salam Shabeeny; with notes, critical and explanatory. Orme & Brown, 1820. 547p. (M966J13a)

2959 Kerharo, J. Sorciers, féticheurs et guérisseurs de la Côte D'Ivorie. . . . Paris, Vigot, 1950. 144p. (M966.25K45a)

2960 Làbouret, Henri. A la recherche d'une politique indigene dans l'ouest Africain. Paris, Editions du Comité de l'Afrique Française, 1931. 128p. (M966L11r)

2961 Làbouret, Henri. Les Manding et leur langue. Paris, Larose, 1934. 270p. (AM966L11m)   ....

2962 Laffitte. Le pays des nègres et la côte des esclaves. Tours, Alfred mame et fils, éditeurs, 1875. 238p. (M966L13)

2963 Lebel, Roland. L'Afrique occidentale dans la littérature française (Depuis 1870). Thèse pour le Doctorate ès-lettres présentée a la faculté des lettres de l'université de Paris. Paris, Librarie Emile Larose, 1925. 277p. (M966.1L49)

2964 Lebel, Roland. Études de littérature coloniale. Paris, J. Peyronnet et Cie, 1928. 221p.

2965 Lebel, Roland. Historie de la littérature coloniale en France. Paris, Librairie Larose, 1931. 236p.

2966 Lebel, Roland. Le livre du pays noir (Anthologie de littérature Africaine). Paris, Les Editions du Monde Modern, 1928. 248p. (M896.C8149)

2967 Leblond, Marius-Ary. Anthologie coloniale, moreaux choisis d' Ecrivains français. Paris, J. Peyronnet and Cie, 1946. 333p. (M960L49a)

2968 Leca, N. . . . Les Pecheurs de Guet N'dar avec une note sur les Wolof, leur parler, les languages secrets. Paris, Librairie Larose, 1935. 110p. (M966.2L49p)

2969 Le Coeur, Charles. Dictionaire ethnographique Téda; Précédé d'un lexique Français-Teda. Paris, Librarie Larose, 1950. 211p. (AM572L49d)

2970 Le Corvaisier, Lucienne. Au pays des Sorciers et des Criots. Paris, L'Union Francaise, 1954. 157p.

2971 Leiris, Michel. L'Afrique fantome (illustre de 32 planches photographiques) [Paris] Gallimard [1934] 525p. (M966L53)

2972 Lenz, Oskar, i.e. Heintich Oskar. Timbouctou; voyage au Maroc, au Sahara et au Soudan. Paris, Librairie Hachette, 1886. 2v. (AM966.1L54)

2973 Londres, Albert. Terre d'ébène (La traite des noirs). Paris, Albin Michel, 1929. 266p. (M966.1L84t)

2974 Londres, Albert. A very naked people. New York, H. Liveright, [c1929.] 276p. (M966L84)

2975 Lyautey, Pierre. L'empire colonial français. Paris, Les éditions de France, 1931. 540p. (M966.1L98)

2976 Marmichael, Harold Alfred. A history of the Arabs in the Sudan and some account of the people who preceded them and of the tribes inhabiting Darfur . . . Cambridge, The University Press, 1922. 2v. (M966.2M22)

2977 Mahmud Kati ibn al-Haj al-Mutawakkil Kati. Documents arabes relatifs a l'histoire du Soudan: Tarikh El-Fettach; ou chronique du chercheur pour servir a l'histoire des Villes, des Armees, et des principaus personages du Tekrour. Paris, Ernest Leroux, 1913. 2v. (M966.2M31d)

2978 Maire, René. Études sur la flore et la végétation du Tibesti [par] R. Maire et Th. Monod. Paris, Larose, 1950. 140p. (M966.-1M28)

2979 Mangin, Charles Marie Emmanuel. Regards sur la France d'Afrique. Paris, Librairie Plon, 1924. 308p. (M966M31r)

2980 Marie André du Sacré Coeur, Sueur. La condition humaine en Afrique noire. Paris, Grasset [1953.] 262p. (AM301M33)

2981 Marie André du Sacré Coeur, soeur. . . . La femme noire en Afrique occidentale. Paris, Payot, 1939. 278p. (M966M33)

2982 Marquis-Sebie, Daniel. Cieux Africains. Paris editions, Jean Crès, 1937. 242p. (M916M34)

2983 Marty, Paul. Études sur l'Islam et les tribus Maures. Les Brankna. Paris, Édition Ernest Leroux, 1921. 398p. (M966.-1M36et)

2984 Mathis, Constant Jean Baptiste Marie J. L'oeuvre des pastoriens en Afrique noire Afrique Occidentale Française. Paris, Presses Universitaires de France, 1946. 580p. (AM610M420)

2985 Maurice, Albert. Félix Eboué, sa vie et son oeuvre. Bruxelles, Memorial Institute Royal Colonial Belge, 1954. 54p. (MB9Eb7m)

2986 Mercier, P. . . . Les tâches de la sociologie. [Dakar, I.F.A.N., 1951.] 93p (AM301M53t)

2987 Mercier, René. Le travail obligatoire dans les colonies Africaines. Paris, Larose, 1933. 242p. (AM331M53)

2988 Meyneir, Octave Frédéric François. La pacification du Sahara et la pénétration Saharienne (1852-1930). Paris, Imp. A. Pigelet & Cie Orleans, Publications du Comité National Métropolitain du Centenaire de L'Algérie, 1930. 62p. (M966.1M57)

2989 Miner, Horace Mitchell. The primitive city of Timbuctoo. Princeton, Published for the American Philosophical Society by

Princeton University Press, 1953. 297p. (AM966.24M66)

2990 Mockler-Ferryman, Augustus Ferryman. Up the Niger. London, G. Philip & Son, 1892. 326p. (M966.96M71)

2991 Monmarson, Raoul. L'Afrique noire et son destin. Paris, Collection "Présence de l'Empire," Editions France, 1950. 362p.

2992 Monteil, Charles. . . . Les Bambara du Ségou et du Kaarta. (Etude Historique, Ethnographique et Litteraire d'une peuplade du Soudan Français). . . . Paris, Emile Larose . . . 1921. 403p. (M960M76)

2993 Morand, Paul. Magie noire. Paris, B. Grasset, 1928. 303p. (AM-916M79)

2994 Morand, Paul. Magie noire, roman. Bois originaux en coleurs. Paris, Le Livre Moderne Illustre, 1930. 219p. (M916M79)

2995 Morand, Paul. Méditerrannée, mer des surprises. Tours, maison Mame, 1938. 240p. (AM916M79m)

2996 Mounier, Emmanuel. L'éveil de l'Afrique noire. Paris, Éditions du Sueil [1948.] 169p. (M966.1M86)

2997 Mumford, William Bryant. Africans learn to be French; a review of educational activities in the seven federated colonies of French West Africa, based upon a tour of French West Africa and Algiers undertaken in 1935. London, Evans brothers, ltd., [1937?] 173p. (M966.1M91)

2998 Les negres rouges; texte et 53 photographies de Maurice et Jeannette Fievet. [Grenoble.] Arthaud, 1955. 99p. (M966.9F46)

2999 Les plus beaux écrits de l'Union Française et du Maghreb. Présentes par Mohamed el Kholti, Léopold Cedar Senghbor Pierre do Dinh . . . Paris, La Colombe, 1947. 452p.

3000 Piazzini, Guy. Horizons noir. Paris, Toison d'or, 1954. 217p. (M966.1P57)

3001 Présence Africaine. L'art Negre. Paris, Aux Éditions du Seuil, 1951. 254p. (M960P92no.10-11)

3002 Présence Africaine. Les etudiants noirs parlent. Paris, Présence Africaine, 1953. 311p. (M960P92no.14)

3003 Présence Africaine. Hommage à Jacques Richard-Molard, 1913-1951. Paris, Présence Africaine, 1953. 383p. (M960P92-no.15)

3004 Présence Africaine. Le monde noir. Paris, Présence Africaine, 1950. 443p. (M960P92no.8-9)

3005 Présence Africaine. Le travail en Afrique noire. Paris, Aux Éditions du Souil 1952.   427p.   (M960P92no.13)

3006   Prèsence Africaine.   Trois ecrivains noirs.   Paris, Présence Afri-
       caine, 1954.   426p.   (M960P92no.16)

3007   Seabrook, William Buehler.   Jungle ways.   New York, Harcourt,
       Brace and Company [c1931] 308p.   (AM572.67Sel)

3008   Seabrook, William Buehler.   Secrets de la jungle.   Paris, Editions,
       Bernard Grasset, n.d.   102p.   (M966Sels)

3009   Seche, Alphonse.   Les noirs (d'apres des documents officiels). Paris,
       Payot & Cie, 1919.   256p.

3010   Sloane, William Milligan.   Greater France in Africa.   New York,
       Charles Scribner's Sons, 1924.   293p.

3011   Sonolet, Louis.   Le parfum de la dame noire, physiologie humoristi-
       que de l'amour Africain.   Publiée d'après le manuscrit original
       de Paul Bourgette.   Paris, La Renaissance du Livre, 1911.
       254p.   (AM396So5)

3012   Soubrier, Jacques.   Savanes et forêts.   (A travers le Soudan et le
       Liberia).   Préface d'Andre Demaison.   Paris, Les Ecrivians
       Français, 1926.   239p.   (M966.1So8)

3013   Tauxier, Louis.   Le Noir du Soudan, pays Mossi et Gourounsi,
       documents et analyses.   Paris, Emile Larose, 1912.   796p.
       (M966.2T19no)

3014   Tauxier, Louis.   Le noir du Yatenga; mossis, Nioniossés, Samos,
       Yarses, Silmi-Mossis, Peuls.   Paris, Emile Larose, 1917.   790p.
       (M966.2T19no2)

3015   Tauxier, Louis. . . . Nouvelles notes sur le Mossi et le Gourounsi.
       Paris, Emile Larose, Libraire-editeur, 1924.   206p. (M966.-
       2T19m)

3016   Tessmann, Gunter.   Die Pangwe.   Berlin, E. Fasmuth, a.-g., 1913.
       (AM572.966T28)

3017   Thiriet, E.   Au Soudan Francais.   Souvenirs 1892-1894, Macina-
       Tombouctou.   Paris, Imprimerie Andre Lesot, 1932.   233p.
       (AM966.2T34)

3018   Tuaillon, Jean Louis Georges.   Bibliographie critique de l'Afrique
       Occidentale Française.   Paris [etc.] Charles Lavauzelle & Cie,
       1936.   49p.   (AM016T79b)

3019   UNESCO.   Experiments in fundamental education in French Afri-
       can territories; a study compiled by the French Information
       Centre on Fundamental Education.   New York, UNESCO,
       1955.   68p.   (M967Un3)

DAHOMEY

3020 L'Afrique Occidentale Française. Agence économique. La Guinee
Française. Paris, Agence économique de l'Afrique Occidentale
Française, 1929. 20p. (M966 Af83 no. 4)

3021 L'Afrique Occidentale Française. Le Dahomey. Paris, Société
d'Éditions Géographiques, Maritimes et Coloniales, 1931. 149p.
(M966.8 Af8d)

3022 Akindele, A. Contribution a l'etude de l'histoire de l'ancien royaume
de Porto-Novo. Dakar, IFAN, 1953. 168p. (M966.83 Ak52)

3023 Bouche, Pierre Bertrand. Sept ans en Afrique Occidentale. La
Côte des Esclaves et le Dahomey. Paris, E. Plon, Nourrit
et cie., 1885. 403p. (M960 B66s)

3024 Brunet, L. Dahomey et dépendances; historique général-organisa-
tion - administration - ethnographie - productions - agriculture -
commerce. Paris, Augustin Challamel, Editeur, 1900. 535p.
(M966.8 B83d)

3025 Celarié, Henriette. . . . Nos frères noirs; Cameroun-Dahomey.
Paris, Hachette, 1932. 251p. (M966 C33n)

3026 D'Albéca, Alexandre L. La France au Dahomey. Paris, Librairie
Hachette, 1895. 236p. (M966.8 D15f)

3027 Dalzel, Archibald. The history of Dahomey, an inland kingdom
of Africa, compiled from authentic memoirs. London, printed
for the author, by T. Spilsbury, 1793. 230p. (M966.8D17)

3028 Hazoumé, Paul. Le pacte de sang au Dahomey. Paris, Institut
d'ethnologie, 1937. 170p. (AM572.966 H33p)

3029 Herskovitz, Melville Jean. Dahomey, an ancient West African
kingdom. New York, J. J. Augustin, 1938. 2 vols. (AM-
966.8 H43)

3030 Herskovitz, Melville Jean, and Frances S. An outline of Dahomean
religious beliefs. Menasha Wisconsin, George Banta Co., 1933.
71p. (Memoirs of the American anthropological Association)

3031 Hubert, Henry. Mission scientifique au Dahomey; ouvrage honoré
d'une subvention de l'Association française pour l'avancement
des sciences et de souscriptions, officielles du Ministère des colonies et du gouvernment général de l'Afrique Occidentale
Française. Paris, E. Larose, libraire-editeur, 1908. 568p.
(M966.8 H86)

3032 Le Herrisé, A. L'ancien royaume du Dahomey, moeurs, religion,
histoire. Paris, Emile Larose, 1911. 384p. (M966.8 L52a)

3033 Marty, Paul. Études sur l'Islam au Dahomey. Le bas Dahomey-

Lehaut Dahomey. Paris, Éditions Ernest Leroux, 1926. 273p. (M966.1 M36e)

3034 Mattei, Mattéo. Bas-Niger, Benoue, Dahomey. Grenoble, E. Vallier et cie, 1890. 196p. (M966.2M43)

3035 Nicolas, Victor. L'expédition du Dahomey en 1890, avec un aperçu géographique et historique. Paris, Imprimerie et Librairie Militaires, Henri Charles, 1892. 152p. (M966.8 N54)

3036 Quénum, Maximilien. Au pays des fons (us et coutumes du Dahomey). Paris, Larose editeurs, 1938. (M966.8 Que3)

3037 Quénum, Maximilien. Légendes africaines, Côte d'Ivoire, Soudan, Dahomey. Rochefort sur-Mer, Thoyon Thèze, 1946. 102p. (AM398.2q31)

3038 Savarian, N. . . . L'agriculture au Dahomey. Paris, Augustin Challamel, 1906. 110p. (AM966.8 Sa9a)

FRENCH GUINEA

3039 L'Afrique Occidental Française. Agence économique. La Guinée française. Paris, Agence économique de l'Afrique occidentale française, [1929] 20p. (M966Af83no.4)

3040 L'Afrique Occidentale Française. La Guinée. Paris, Société d'Édition Géographiques, Maritimes et Coloniales, 1931. 146p. (M967.1Af8g)

3041 Arcin, André. La Guinée Française, races, religions, costumes, production, commerce. Paris, Augustin Challamel, 1907. (M-966.52Ar2)

3042 Damas, Leon G. Veillees noires. Paris, Editions Stock, 1943. 220p. (M841D18p)

3043 Davis, Hassoldt. The junge and the damned. New York, Duell, Sloan and Pearce, [1952.] 306p. (M968D29j)

3044 Famechon, M. Notice sur la Guinée Française . . . Paris, Alcan-Levy, 1900. 229p. (M966.52F21)

3045 Gaisseau, Pierre Dominique. The sacred Forest; the fetishist and magic rites of the Toma. London, Weidenfield & Nicolson, 1954. 199p. (M966.6G12s)

3046 Greene, Graham. Journey without maps. Garden City, N. Y., Doubleday, Doran and Company, Inc., 1936. 310p. (M916.-66G83)

3047 Holas, B. Le culte de Zié, eléments de la religion kono (Haute Guinée française) Dakar, IFAN, 1954. 275p. (M966.4H68)

3048 Holas, B. Les masques Kono (Haute-Guinée Française) Leur rôle

dans la vie religieuse et politique. Paris, Librairie Orientaliste
Paul Geuthner, 1952. 200p. (M966.52H69)

3049 Laye, Camara. The dark child. New York, Noonday Press, 1954.
188p. (MB9L45)

3050 Laye, Camara. Le regard du roi. Paris, Librairie Plon, 1954.
(M966.52L45r)

3051 Martin du Gard, Maurice. . . . Courrier d'Afrique: Sénégal-Soudan-
Guinée. Paris, Flammarion, [1931.] 247p. (M916.6M36)

3052 Nosti, Jaimie. Agricultura de Guinea, promesa para España. Madrid, Instituto de Estudios Africanos, Consejo Superior de Investigaciones Científicas, 1948. 90p. (M976.18N84)

3053 Smith, William. A new voyage to Guinea: describing the customs,
manners, soil, climate, habits, buildings, education, manual arts,
agriculture, trade, employments, languages, ranks of distinction,
habitations, diversions, marriages, and whatever else is memorable among the inhabitants. Likewise, an account of their
animals, minerals, etc. With great variety of entertaining incidents, worthy of observation, that happened during the author's travels in that large country. London, Printed for John
Nourse, 1744. 276p. (M966Sm5n)

IVORY COAST

3054 L'Afrique Occidental Française. Agence économique. La Côte
d'Ivoire. Paris, Agence économique de l'Afrique occidentale
française, n.d. 21p. (M966Af83no.3)

3055 L'Afrique Occidentale Française. La Côte d'Ivoire. Paris, Société d'Éditions, Geographiques, Maritimes et Coloniales, 1931.
134p. (M966.68Af8c)

3056 Amon d'Aby, F. J. La Côte d'Ivoire la cité Africaine. Paris, Larose, 1951. 206p. (M966.68Am6)

3057 Clozel, J. Dix ans à la Côte d'Ivoire. Paris, Augustin Challamel,
1906. 350p. (M966.68C62)

3058 Davis, Hassoldt. Sorcerers' Village. New York, Duell, Sloan and
Pearce, 1955. 334p. (M966.68D29s)

3059 Delafosse, Maurice. Les frontieres de la Côte d'Ivoire de la Côte
d'Or et du Soudan. Paris, Masson et cie, 1908. 256p. (M966.-
68D37)

3060 Horn, Alfred Aloysius. . . . The ivory coast in the earlies . . .
London, Jonathan Cape, 1927. 320p. (M916H78i)

3061 Kerharo, J. Sorciers, féticheurs et guérisseurs de la Côte d'Ivoire-

Haute Volta; Les hommes, les croyances, les pratiques pharma-
copée et thérapeutique. Paris, Vigot, 1950. 144p. (M966.-
25K45s)

3062 Menalque, Marc. Coutumes civiles des Baoules de la region de
Dimbokro. Paris, Larose editeurs, 1933. 74p. (M966.683M52c)

3063 Moore, Ernest D. Ivory, scourge of Africa. New York and London, Harper and Bros., 1931. 256p. (M967M78)

3064 Quénum, Maximilien. Légendes africaines, Côte d'Ivoire, Soudan,
Dahomey. Rochefort sur-mer, Thoyon Thèze, 1946. 102p.
(AM398.2Q31)

3065 Villamur, Roger. . . . Les coutumes agni, rédigées et codifiées d'après
les documents officiels les plus récents. Paris, A. Challamel,
1904. (M966.68V71c)

FRENCH SUDAN

3066 'Abd al-Rahman ibn 'Abd Allàh. Documents arabes relatifs à
l'histoire du Soudan: Tarikh es-Soudan, par Abderrahman ben
Abdallah ben 'Imran ben 'Amir es-Sa'di. Traduit de L'Arabe
par O. Houdas. Paris, E. Leroux, 1900. 537p. (M966.2Ab3d)

3067 L'Afrique Occidentale Française. Le Soudan. Paris, Société d'
Éditions Géographiques, Maritimes et Coloniales, 1931. 166p.
(M966.2Af8s)

3068 L'Afrique Occidentale Française. Agence économique. Le Soudan
française. Paris, Agence économique de l'Afrique occidentale
française, 1928. 19p. (M966Af83)

3069 Barrons, David Prescott. Berbers and blacks; impressions of Morocco, Timbuktu and the western Sudan. New York, The Century Co., 1927. 251p. (M966.2B27b)

3070 Berthelot, André. L'Afrique Sahárienne et Soudanaise ce qu'en ont
connu les anciens. Paris, Les Arts et le Livre, 1927. 431p.
(M966B46)

3071 Boville, E. W. Caravans of the old Sahara; an introduction to the
history of the western Sudan. London, Published for the International institute of African languages and cultures by Oxford University Press, H. Milford, 1933. 6p.-300p. (M966.-
2B66)

3072 Cremer, Jean. Materiaux d'ethnographie et de linguistique Soudanises. Les Bobe. Paris, Librairie Orientaliste, 1927. 212p.
(M966.2C86)

3073 Delavignette, Robert Louis. Les paysans noirs, recit soudanais en

douze mois. Paris, Stock (Delamain et Boutelleau) 1931. 221p.
(M966.2D37)

3074 Domville-Fife, Charles William. Savage life in the black Sudan.
London, Seeley, Service & Co., Limited, 1927. 284p. (M916.-
26D71)

3075 Dubois, Felix. Timbuctoo the mysterious. Translated from the
French by Diana White. New York, Longmans, Green and
Co., 1896. 377p. (M916.624D85)

3076 DuBois, Felix. Tombouctou la mysterieuse. Paris, Libairie E.
Flammarion, 1897. 420p. (M916.624D851)

3077 Duncan, J. S. R. The Sudan; a record of achievement. Edin-
burg, Blackwood, 1952. 283p. (AM962.4D91s)

3078 Dupuis, Auguste Victor dit Yakouba. Industries et principales
professions des habitants de la région de Tombouctou, avec
numbreuses illustrations. Paris, Emil Larose, Libraire-editeur, 1921. 193p. (M966.24D92i 190847)

3079 Gourard, Henri. Souvenirs d'un Africain; au Soudan. Paris, Éditions Pierre Tisné, 1939. 253p. (M916G74)

3080 Mahmud Kati ibn al-Háj al-Mutawakkil Káti. Documents arabes
relatifs à l'histoire du Soudan; Tarikh El-Fettach; ou chronique du chercheur pour servir a l'histoire des Villes, des Armées
et des principaux personages du Tekrour par Mahmoûd ben
El 'Hâdj El-Mataouakkel Kati. tr. Française par O. Houdas
et M. Delafosse. Paris, Ernest Leroux, 1913. 2v. (M966.-
2M31d)

3081 Maran, René. Asepsie noir. Paris, Les Laboratories Martinet,
1931. 45p. (AM614M32a)

3082 Méniaud, Jacques. Géographie économique du Haut-Sénégal Niger.
Préface de M. E. Roume. Paris, Larose, 1912. 2v. (M966.-
2M52h)

3083 Miner, Horace Mitchell. The primitive city of Timbuctoo. Princeton, Published for the American Philosophical Society by
Princeton University Press, 1953. 297p. (M966.24M66)

3084 Monteil, Charles Victor. Les Khassonke; Monographie d'une peuplade du Soudan Francais. Paris, Ernest Leroux, Editeur, 1915.
528p. (M966.2M76k)

3085 Monteil, Charles Victor. Soudan français. Contes soudanais, par
C. Monteil. Preface de M. Rene Bassett. Paris, Ernest
Laroux, Editeur, 1905. 205p. (AM398M76)

3086 Morand, Paul. A. O. F. de Paris a Tombouctou. Paris, Flammerion, 1928. 126p. (M916.61M79)

3087 Piazzini, Guy. Horizons noir. Paris, Torson d'or, 1954. 217p. (M966.1P57)

3088 Tauxier, Louis. Le Noir du Soudan, pays Mossi et Gourounsi, documents et analyses. Paris, Emile Larose, 1912. 796p. (M966.2T19no)

3089 Tauxier, Louis. Le noir du Yatenga; Mossis, Nioniossés, Samos, Yarses, Silmi-Mossis, Peuls. Paris, Emile Larose, 1917. 790p. (M966.2T19no2)

3090 Thiriet, E. Au Soudan Francaise. Souvenirs 1892-1894 Macina-Tombouctou, avec carte et croquis de L'auteur. Paris, Imprimerie Andre Lesot, 1932. 233p. (M966.2T34)

3091 Trautmann, René Frédéric Alexandre. Au pays de "Batouala"; noirs et blancs en Afrique, préface de Pierre Mille. Paris, Payot and Co., 1922. 254p. (M960T69a)

3092 United Nations. General Assembly. Trusteeship agreement for the territory of Togoland under French administration, as approved by the general assembly on 13 December 1948. Lake Success, 1947. 8p. (M966.81Un3t)

3093 Valriant, Mme. Jane. La randonnée Soudanaise de Suzanne Davenel. Paris, Editions de La Caravelle, 1931. 331p. (M966.-1V24)

3094 Westermann, Diedrich. Die Mossi-sprachengrauppe im westlichen Sudan. Reprinted from Anthropos, Revue International d' Ethnologie et de Linguistique. Tome VIII, 1913. 469-504, 810-930pp. (M496.3W52)

MAURITANIA

3095 L'Afrique Occidentale Française. Agence économique. La Mauritanie. Paris, Agence économique de l'Afrique occidentale francaise, 1929. 14p. (M966Af83)

3096 L'Afrique, Occidentale Française. La Mauritanie. Paris, Société d'Editions Géographiques, Maritime et Coloniales, 1931. 62p. (M966.12Af8m)

3097 Du Puikaudeau, Odette. Pieds nus à travers la Mauritanie. Paris, Plon, 1936. 286p. (AM916.612D92)

NIGER

3098 L'Afrique Occidental Française. Agence économique. La Colonie du Niger. Paris, Agence économique de l'Afrique Occidentale

Française, 1929. 20p. (M966Af83 no.2)

3099 L'Afrique Occidentale Française. Le Niger. Paris, Société d'Éditions Géographiques, Martimes et Coloniales, 1931. 88p. (M-
966.96Af8n)

3100 Ardent du Picq, Charles Jean Jacques Joseph. Une population
Africaine; les Dyerma. Paris, Larose Editeurs, 1933. 76p.
(M966.26Ar2)

3101 Cazes, Alfred. Le Niger sentimental. Oran, Editions Heintz
Freres, s.d. 472p. (M966.1C25)

3102 Dupuis, Auguste Victor dit Yakouba. Les Gow; ou, Chesseurs du
Niger. Legends songai de la region de Tombouctou, avec pré-
face de M. Delafosse. Paris, Ernest Lerous, 1911. 303p.
(M966.24D92g)

3103 Urvoy, Yves Françoise Marie Aimé. Histoire des populations du
Soudan central (colonie du Niger). Paris, Larose, 1936. 350p.
(M966.2Ur8)

SENEGAL

3104 Adanson, Michel. A voyage to Senegal, the isle of Goree and
the river Gambia. . . . London, printed for J. Nourse and W.
Johnston in Ludgate Street, 1759. 337p. (M916 Ad1)

3105 L'Afrique Occidentale Française. Agence économique. Le Sénégal.
Paris, Agence économique de l'Afrique Occidentale Française,
1931. (M966 Af83 no.8)

3106 L'Afrique Occidentale Francaise. La circonscription de Dakar et
dépendances. Paris Société d'Éditions Géographiques, Maritimes et Colonials, 1931. 170p. (M966.32 Af8c)

3107 L'Afrique Occidentale Française. Le Sénégal. Paris, Société d'
Éditions Géographiques, Martimes et Colonials, 1931. 274p.
(M966.3 Af8s)

3108 Backer, Desaix. Dans les brousses Africaines. Port-au-Prince,
Cheraquit, 1935. 120p. (AM966.3 B12d)

3109 Beslier, Mme. Geneviéve G. Le Sénégal: L'antiquité, les Arabes
et les empires noirs, la colonisation Européenne du XIV au
XVIIe siècle, lére Négrière, La France colonisatrice au Sénégal, l'oeuvre des missions, formation de l'Afrique Occidentale
Française. Paris, Payot, 1935. 225p. (M966.3 B46)

3110 Burthe, d'Annelet, André Joseph Victor de. . . A travers l'Afrique
française; du Sénégal au Cameroun par les confins libyens
(Mauritanie, Soudan français, Niger, . . . 1935; par les con-

fins sahariens, octobre 1932-juin 1935). Paris, Firmin-Didot
et cie., 1939. 2 vols. (AM966.3 B95)

3111 . . . Coutumiers juridiques de l'Afrique Occidentale Française . . .
Paris, Larose, 1939. 3 vols. (M966.1 C83)

3112 Delafosse, Maurice. Chroniques de Fouta Sénégalais, traduites de
deux manuscrits arabes inedits de Siré-Abbas-Soh et accom-
panees de notes, documents annexes et commentaires, d'un
glossaire et de cartes. Paris, Ernest Leroux, Editeur, 1913.
328p. (M966.3 D37c)

3113 Dia, Mamadou. Contribution to the study of the cooperative movement in black Africa. (in Le mouvement coopératif en territoires tropicaux arriérès . .) Leiden, Universitaire Pers Leiden, 1953. pp. 159-162. (M966.3 D54c)

3114 Diallo, Backary. Force-bonté. Paris, F. Rieder et cie., 1926. 208p.
(M966.3 D549)

3115 Doudou, Thiam. La portée de la citoyenneté française dans les territoires d'outremer. These pour le doctorate en droit . . . Paris
Société d'Éditions Africaines, 1953. 180p. (M966.3 D74p)

3116 Geismar, L. Recueil des coutumes civiles des races du Sénégal.
Saint-Louis, Imprimerie du Gouvernement, 1933. 222p.

3117 Golbery, Sylvain Meinrad Xavier de. Travels in Africa . . . in the
western parts of that vast continent . . . London, Printed for
Jones and Bumford, 1810. (M966.3 G56t)

3118 Institut Français d'Afrique Noire. Dakar, IFAN, 1954. 127p.
(M966.32 In7i)

3119 Institut Français d'Afrique Noire. L'agglomération dakaroise;
quelques aspects sociologique et démographiques. Saint-Louis
du Sénégal, Centre IFAN-Sénégal, 1954. 83p. (M966.32 In7)

3120 Labouret, Henri. Les Manding et leur langue. . . . Paris, Larose,
1934. 270p. (M966L11m)

3121 Leca, N. . . . Les Pecheurs de Guet N'dar avec une note sur les
Wolof, leur parler, les languages secrets. Paris, Librairie
Larose, 1935. 110p. (M966.2 L49p)

3122 Lengyel, Emil. Dakar, outpost of two heimspheres. New York,
Random House, 1941. 312p. (M966.32 L54)

3123 Mademba, Abd-el-Kader. Au Sénégal et au Soudan Française.
Paris, Librairie Larose, 1931. 116p. (M966.3 M26s)

3124 Martin du Gard, Maurice. . . . Courrier d'Afrique: Sénégal-Soudan-
Guinée. Paris, Flammarion, 1931. 247p. (M916.6 M36)

3125 Marty, Paul. Études Sénégalaises (1785-1826). Paris, Société
      de l'histoire des colonies Françaises, et Editions Leroux (n.d.)
      236p. (AM966.3 M36e)

3126 Maugham, Reginald Charles Fulke. Africa as I have known it:
      Nyasaland - East Africa - Liberia - Senegal. London, John
      Murray, 1929. 372p. (M960 M44a)

3127 Mollien, Gaspard Theodore, comte de. Travels in the interior of
      Africa, to the sources of the Senegal and Gambia in 1818.
      London, Printed for Sir Richard Phillips and Co., 1820. 128p.
      (M916 M73)

3128 Séche, Alphonse. Les noirs (d'apres des documents officiels). L'
      armée noirs—le loyalisme des Sénégalais, l'âme du Sénégalais
      —le camp de Fréjus Berry-au-Bac - Dixmud - La somme - Ver-
      dun l'aisne - Les noirs sur la Côte d'Azur. Paris, Payot et cie.,
      1919. 256p. (AM355 Se1)

3129 Travélé, Moussa. Proverbs et contes Bambara accompagnes d'une
      traduction française et précédes d'un abrégé de droit coutumier
      Bambara et Malinke. Paris, Librairie Orientaliste Pual Geu-
      thner, 1923. 240p. (M398T69p)

UPPER VOLTA

3130 L'Afrique Occidental Française. Agence économique. La Haute-
      Volta. Paris, Agence économique de l'Afrique occidentale fran-
      çaise, 1928. 15p. (M966Af83no.6)

3131 L'Afrique Occidentale Française. La Haute-Volta. Paris, Société
      d'Éditions Géographiques, Maritimes et Colonials, 1931. 170p.
      (M966.25Af8h)

3132 Dim Delobsom, A. A. L'empire du mogho-naba; coutumes des
      Mossi de la Haute-Volta. Paris, Les editions Domat-Mon-
      tchrestien, 1932. 303p. (M966.25D59)

3133 Dim Delobsom, A. A. Les secrets des sorciers noirs. Paris, Li-
      brairie Emile Nourry, 1934. 298p. (M960D59s)

TOGOLAND

(British and French)

3134 Armattoe, Raphael Ernest Grail. The golden age of West African
      civilization. [Londonderry?] Pub. for the Lomeshie research
      centre by "The Londonderry sentinel," 1946. 116p. (M966.-
      81Ar5g)

3135 Bourret, F. M. The Gold Coast and British Togoland, 1919-1946.

Stanford, Calif., Stanford University Press, 1949. 231p. (M-966B66g)

3136 Cardinall, Allan Wolsey. Tales told in Togoland. London, Oxford University Press, H. Milford, 1931. 290p. (AM398 C17)

3137 Chapman, D. A. The human geography of Eweland (Anlo district). Paris, Librairie d'Amerique et d'Orient, 1950. 101p. (M966.81C36h)

3138 Chazelas, Victor. Territoiries Africains sous mandat de la France, Cameron et Togo. Paris, Société d'éditions geographiques, maritimes, et coloniales, 1931. 240p. (M916.711C39t)

3139 Froelich, F. C. La tribu Konkomba du Nord Togo. Dakar, IFAN, 1954. 253p. (M966F92)

3140 Garnier, Christine. Le fétichisme en Afrique noire (Togo-Cameroun). Paris, Payot, 1951. 213p. (AM572.966G18f)

3141 Great Britain. Colonial Office. Annual reports on Togoland. 1949-1953. London, H. M. Stationery Office. (M966.81 G79t)

3142 Great Britain. Colonial Office. Report by His Majesty's Government in the United Kingdom of Great Britain and Northern Ireland, to the General Assembly of the U.N. on the administration of Togoland under United Kingdom trusteeship. 1920-21. London, H. M. S. O. (AM966.81 G79r)

3143 Harris, Joseph Earl. Constitutional development in British Togoland since 1945. Washington, D. C. Howard University, 1956. 97p. (Thesis, Howard University) (M378.242H 1956)

3144 Kuku, Aaron. The life of Aaron Kuku of Eweland, born 1860—died 1929, told by himself. London, The Sheldon Press, 1931. 24p. (MB9K951)

3145 Lavergne de Tressan, Georges A. Inventaire linguistique de l'Afrique occidentale française et du Togo. Dakar, IFAN, 1953. 240p. (M496L38)

3146 Metzger, O. F. Unsere alte kolonie Togo. Neudamm, Verlag J. Neumann, 1941.

3147 Schönharl, Josef. Volkstundliches aus Togo. Märchen und fabeln, spirchworter und Rätsel, lieder und spiele, sagen und tauschungs-spiele der Eweneger von Togo. Dresden und Leipzig, C. U. Kochs verlagshuchandlung, 1909. 240p. (M966.81 Sch6)

3148 Spieth, Jakob. Die Ewe-Stämme material zur kunde des Éwevolkes in Deutsch-Toga. Berlin, Dietrich Reimer, 1906. Pp.80, 962. (AM966.81 Sp4)

3149 Spieth, Jakob. Die religion der Eweer in Süd-Togo. Göttingen, Vandenhoeck & Ruprecht; Leipzig, J. C. Heinrichs, 1911. 316p. (M966.81 Sp4r)

3150 United Nations. General Assembly. Trusteeship agreement for the territory of Togoland under French administration, as approved by the General Assembly on 13 December 1946. Lake Success [1947.] 8p. (M966.81Un3t)

3151 Witte, Anton. Beitrage zir ethnographie von Togo, Westafrika. Reprinted from *Anthropos,* Revue Internationale d'Ethnologie et de Linguistique, 1920. 1001p. (M966.81W78)

3152 Witte, Anton. Sprichwörter der Ewhe-Neger, Ge-Dialekt (Togo, Westafrika) 1918. 58-83p. (M496W78s)

3153 Wolf, Franz. Grammatik der Kposo-Sprache (Nord-Togo, West Afrika. 1909. pp. 142-67, 630-59. Reprinted from Anthropos. Tomo IV, 1909. (M496.3W83)

CAMEROONS

(British and French)

3154 Aellen, Villy. Contribution à l'étude des Chiroptères du Cameroun. Neuchâtel, 1952. 121p. (AM599.4 Ae4c)

3155 Albert, André. Cameroun français. Au pays bamiléké. Bandjoun: croyances, coutumes, folklore. Paris, Dillen; Phalsbourg (Moselle) L'auteur, 1937. 173p. (AM572 A1 1)

3156 Aymérich, Joseph Gauderique. La conquête du Cameroun, ler aôut 1914-20 fevrier 1916. Paris, Payot, 1933. 213p. (AM967.-11 Ay5)

3157 Boto, Eza. Ville cruelle. Paris, Éditions Africaines, 1955. 219p. (M967.11 B65v)

3158 Bruneau de Laborie, Emile Louis Bruno. Du Cameroun au Caire par le désert de Libye, chasses au Tchad. Paris, E. Flammarion, [c1924.] 406p. (AM967.11 B83)

3159 Calvert, Albert Frederick. The Cameroons. London, T. Werner Laurie, 1917. [148]p. (M967.11 C13c)

3160 Carlin, John. Gulla the tramp; an ethnological indiscretion. London, J. Cape, [1937] 407p. (M916.711C19)

3161 Celarié, Henriette. Nos frères noirs. Cameroun—Dahomey. [Paris] Hachette, [1932.] 251p. M966 C33n)

3162 Chazelas, Victor. Territories Africains sous mandat de la France, Cameron et Togo. Paris, Société d'éditions geographiques, maritimes, et coloniales, 1931. 240p. (M916.711C39t)

3163   Cottes, Anthony. La mission Cottes au sud-cameroun, 1905-1908. Paris, Ernest Leroux, éditeur, 1911. 252p. (AM967.11 C82)

3164   Dika-Akwa nya Bonambela. Bible de ta Sagess Bantoue. Choix d'aphorismes, devinettes et mots d'esprit du Cameroun et du Gabon. Paris, Centre Artistique et Culturel Camerounais, 1955. 147p.

3165   Dugast, Idelette. Monographie de la tribu des Ndiki (Banen du Cameroun) Paris, Institut d'ethnologie, 1955. 823p. (M967.-11 D87)

3166   Egerton, F. Clement C. African Majesty; a record of refuge at the court of the King of Bangangté in the French Cameroons. New York, C. Scribner's Sons, 1939. 348p. (M967.11 Eg2)

3167   Egerton, F. Clement C. African majesty. London, G. Routledge and sons, 1939. 348p. (AM916.711Eg2a)

3168   Garnier, Christine. Le fétichisme en Afrique noire (Togo-Cameroun) Paris, Payot, 1951. 213p. (AM572.966 G18f)

3169   Great Britain. Colonial Office. Annual Report of the Cameroons. 1953, 1954. London, H.M.S.O. (M966.94 G79a)

3170   Great Britain. Colonial Office. Report by His Majesty's Government in the United Kingdom of Great Britain and Northern Ireland to the General Assembly of the United Nations on the administration of the Cameroons under United Kingdom trusteeship. 1920-21-London, H.M.S.O. (M966.94 G79r)

3171   Hutter, Franz Karl. Wanderungen und forschungen im nord-hinterland von Kamerun. Braunschweig, F. Vieweg und sohn, 1902. 578p. (AM967.11 H97)

3172   Kaberry, Phyllis M. Women of the grassfields; a study of the economic position of women in Bamenda, British Cameroons, London, H.M.S.O., 1952. (AM967.11 K11w) 220p.

3173   Labouret, Henri. Le Cameroun. Paris, Paul Hartmann, éditeur, [1937] 259p. (M967.11 L11c)

3174   Mackenzie, Jean Kenyon. African clearings. Boston, New York, Houghton Mifflin company, 1924. 270p. (M967.11 M19)

3175   Mackenzie, Jean Kenyon. Black sheep; adventures in West Africa. Boston and New York, Houghton Mifflin co., 1916. 313p. (AM967.11 M19b)

3176   Marqueissac, H. de. L'Effort medical Français en Afrique Equatoriale et au Cameroun, un film du Docteur H. De Marqueissac, images de Robert Carmet, une production de la Société d'Applications Cinemato-graphiques. Paris, Édition de La Société Parisienne d'Expansion Chimique, [1949] [16p.] (M967.2M34)

3177 Martin du Gard, Maurice. L'appel du Cameroun. Paris, Flammarion, [1939] 210p. (AM916.711 M36)

3178 Megglé, Armand. Collection des "Terres Francaises," publiée sous le patronage du Comité National des Conseillers du Commerce Extérieur de la France. Afrique Equatoriale Francaise. Paris, Société Francaise d'Editions. 1931. vol. 5 and 6. (M967.11-M47)

3179 Moumé-Etia, Isaac. Les fables de Douala (Cameroun) en deux langues: Français-Douala. Bergerac, Imprimerie (Générale du Sud-Quest, 1930. 98p. (M398M86)

3180 Moumé-Etia, Isaac. La Langue de Douala (Cameroun.) (Grammaire, exercices, conversations . . .) Clermont-Ferrand, Imprimerie Générale, 1929. (M966.11M86c)

3181 Moumé-Etia, Isaac. Quelques reseignements sur la coutume locale chez les Doualas (Cameroun). Brest, Imprimerie de "l'Union Republicaine du Finistére", 1928. 15p. (M966.11M86f)

3182 Moumé-Etia, Isaac. Quelques reseignements sur la coutume locale chez les Doualas (Cameroun). Premiere edition [1927] 16p. (typewritten copy) (M966.11M86f)

3183 Moumé-Etia, Isaac. Quelques reseignements sur la coutume locale chez les Doualas (Cameroun). Troisieme partie. Lodève, Imprimerie-Papeterie-Librairie Julian. 25p. (M966.11M86f)

3184 Moumé-Etia, Isaac. Quelques reseignements sur la coutume locale chez les Doualas (Cameroun). Quatriéme partie. Brest, Imprimerie de "l'Union Republicaine du Finistère," 1928. (M966-11M86f)

3185 Nicol, Yves. La tribu des Bakoko, etude non-graphique d'economie coloniale. Un stade de l'evolution d'une tribu noire au Cameroun. Paris, Librairie Coloniale and Orientaliste, Larose, 1929. 240p. (M967.11 N54t)

3186 O'Brien, Brian. Beating about the bush. New York, L. Furman, inc., [1938] 352p. (AM916.711Ob6)

3187 Reyher, Rebecca (Hourwich) The Fon and his hundred wives. Garden City, New York, Doubleday, 1952. 318p. (AM967.11-R33f)

3188 Rudin, Harry Rudolph. Germans in the Cameroons, 1884-1914; a case study in modern imperialism. New Haven, Yale university press, 1938. 456p. (AM325 R83)

3189 Schuster, Franz Konrad. Die sozialen Verhaltnisse de Banjange-

Stammes (Kamerun) 1924. pp. 948-55. Reprinted from *Anthropos,* Revue Internationale d'Ethnologie et de Linguistique. Tome IX, 1914. (M967.11 Sc8)

3190 Schwabe, D. Kurd and Leutwein Paul, editors. Die deutschen kolonien... Berlin National-ousgabe, n.d. 2 vols. (AM967.11-Sch9)

3191 Susset, Raymond. La vérité sur le Cameroun et l'Afrique équatoriale française. Paris, Éditions de la Nouvelle revue critique, [1934] 218p. (AM967.11 Su8)

3192 Togo-Cameroun. (Magazine-Trimestriel). Paris, Abonnements de ce Numéro Avril, 1932.

3193 United Nations. General Assembly. Trusteeship agreement for the territory of the Cameroons under British administration, as approved by the General Assembly on 13 December 1946. Lake Success, N.Y. [1947] 7p. (M966.9Un3t)

3194 Wilbois, Joseph. Le Cameroun; les indigénes, les colons, les missions, l'administration française. Paris, Payots, 1934. 256p. (AM967.11 W64)

3195 The work of France in the Cameroons. Paris, Centre d'informations documentaires, 1939. 21p. (AM967.11 W89)

PORTUGUESE GUINEA

3196 Bernatzik, Hugo Adolf. ... Athiopen des westens; forschungrsreisen in Portugiesisch-Guinea. Wien, L. W. Seidel und sohn, 1933. 2 vols. (AM572.9665 B45)

3197 Carreira, Antonio. Mandingas da Guiné Portuguesa. PublicaÇao commemorativa do v centenário da descoberta de Guiné. Lisboa, 1947. 324p. (M966.57 C23)

3198 Guinea. Portuguese. Anuário. 1946-Lisboa. (M966.57 G94)

3199 Lyall, Archibald. Black and white make brown; an account of a journey to the Cape Verde islands and Portuguese Guinea. London, etc., W. Heinemann, ltd., 1938. 303p. (M966.58L98)

SPANISH GUINEA

3200 Alvarez Garcia, Heriberto Ramón. Historia de la acción cultural en la Guinea Espanola, con notas sobre le enseñanza en el Africa negra. Madrid, Instituto de Estudios Africanos, Consejo Superior de Investigaciones Cientificas, 1948. 557p. (M967-18 A18)

3201 Báguena Corella, Luis. Guinea. Madrid, Instituto de Estudios Africanos, 1950. 160p. (M967.18 B14)

3202 Capdevielle, Juan Manuel. Tres estudios y un ensayo sobre temas forestales de la Guinea Continental Española. Madrid, Consejo Superior de Investigaciones Cientificas, Instituto de Estudios Africanos, 1949. 235p. (AM967.18 C17)

3203 Crespo y Gil Delgado, Carlos. Notas para un estudio antropologico y etnologico del Bubi de Fernando Poo. Madrid, Institut de Estudios Africanos, 1949. 290p.

3204 Guinea Lopez, Emilio. En el páis de los pámues (relato ilustrado de mi primer viaje a la Guinea Española). Madrid, Consejo Superior de Investigaciones Científicas, Instituto de Estudios Africanos, 1947. 156p. (AM967.18 G94)

3205 Nosti, Jaime. Agricultura de Guinea promesa para España. Madrid, Instituto de Estudios Africanos, Consejo Superior de Investigaciones Científicas, 1948. 90p. (M979.18 N84)

3206 Ramón Alvarez, Heriberto. Leyandas y mites de Guinea. Madrid Instituto de Estudios Africanos, 1951. 55p. (AM398 R14)

3207 Yglesias de la Riva, A. Politica indigena en Guinea. Madrid Consejo Superior de Investigaciones Cientificas, Instituto de Estudios Africanos, 1947. 366p. (AM967.18Y4)

CENTRAL AFRICA

GENERAL

3208 African Development Trust. Partnership in practice in Central Africa. Sussex, The African Development Trust, 1954. 16p.

3209 Alexander, Boyd. From the Niger to the Nile. London, E. Arnold, 1907. 2v. (M967AL2f)

3210 Anderson-Morshead, A.E.M. The history of the Universities' mission to Central Africa, 1859-1898. London, Office of the Universities' Mission to Central Africa, 1902. 494p. (M968An2h)

3211 Arnot, F. S. Garenganze; or, Seven years' pioneer mission work in Central Africa. Chicago, Revell, [1889] 276. (M966 Ar6)

3212 Baker, Samuel White. Ismailia; a narrative of the expedition to Central Africa for the suppression of the slave trade. New York, Harper, 1875. (M916 B17i)

3213 Barnes, James. Through Central Africa from coast to coast. New York, D. Appleton and co., 1915. 283p. (M916.66 B26)

3214 Becker, Jerome. La vie en Afrique ou trois ans dans l'Afrique centrale. Paris, Bruxelles, J. Lebègue et cie., 1887. 2 vols. (AM967 B38v)

3215 Bedouin, Jean-Louis. Noir d'Ivoire. Paris, Roa-Qui, 1950. 96p.
      (M966B39)

3216 Bertieaux, Raymond. Aspects de l'industrialisation en Afrique cen-
      trale. Bruxelles, Institut des relations internationales, 1953.
      318p. (M967 B46)

3217 Blixen Finecke, Bror. African hunter, translated from the Swedish
      by F. H. Lyon. New York, A. A. Knopf, 1938. 284p. (M916-
      7B61

3218 Bowen, Thomas J. Central Africa. Adventures and missionary
      labors in several countries in the interior of Africa from 1849 to
      1856. Charleston, Southern Baptist Publication Society, 1857.
      359p. (M966.2B67)

3219 Branson, William Henry. Pioneering in the lion country. Nash-
      ville, Tenn., Southern publishing association [1938] 155p.
      (276.7B73)

3220 Busoni, Rafaello. Stanley's Africa. New York, The Viking Press,
      1944. 288p. (M916.7B96)

3221 Caddick, Helen. A white woman in central Africa. London, T. F.
      Unwin; New York, Cassell Company, ltd.; 1900. 242p. (M916-
      66 C11)

3222 Caillié, René. Journal d'un voyage à Temboctou et à Jenné dans
      l'Afrique centrale, précédé d'observations faites chez les Maures
      Braknas, les Nalous et d'autres peuples; pendant les années
      1824-1828. Paris, Impr. par autorisation du roi a l'Imprimerie
      royale, 1830. 3 vols. (M916 C12)

3223 Campbell, Dugald. Wanderings in Central Africa, the experiences
      and adventures of a lifetime of pioneering and exploration. Lon-
      don, Seeley, Service and co., ltd. 1929. 284p. (M916.7 C15)

3224 Campbell, Robert. A pilgrimage to my motherland. An account of
      a journey among the Egbas and Yorubas of Central Africa, in
      1859-1860. New York, T. Hamilton; Philadelphia; The Author
      1861. 145p. (M966.92 C15)

3225 Casati, Gaetano. Ten years in Equatoria and the return with Emin
      Pasha. London and New York, F. Warne and Co., 1891. 2 vols.
      (M967C26)

3226 Chaillé-Long, Charles. Central Africa: Naked truths of naked
      people. New York, Harper and bros. 1877. 330p. (M916.-
      7 C34)

3227 Chambliss, J. E. The life and labors of David Livingstone ... cov-
      ering his entire career in Southern and Central Africa. Care-
      fully prepared from the most authentic sources ... The whole

rendered clear and plain by a most accurate map of the whole
region explored and the routes clearly indicated. Philadelphia,
Boston and Cincinnati, Hubbard bros.; [etc., etc., 1875] 805p.
(M968C35)

3228   Colson, E.   Seven tribes of British Central Africa.   London, N.Y.,
       Oxford University Press, 1951.   409p.   (A572.967 C71s)

3229   Conference on Closer Association in Central Africa, London, 1951.
       Central African territories; report of Conference on Closer As-
       sociation, March, 1951.   London, H.M.S.O., 1951.   43p.   (M354-
       689 C76)

3230   Coupland, Reginald.   Kirk on the Zambesi, a chapter of African
       history.   Oxford, Clarendon press, 1928.   286p.   (M960C83)

3231   Crawford, Daniel.   Thinking black: 22 years without a break in
       the long grass of Central Africa.   New York, George H. Doran
       Co., [1913] 485p.   (M966 C85)

3232   Cross, D. Kerr.   Health in Africa.   A medical handbook for Euro-
       pean travellers and residents, embracing a study of malarial
       fever as it is found in British Central Africa.   London, James
       Nisbet & co., 1897.   222p.   (AM616 C88)

3233   Cureau, Adolphe Louis.   Savage man in central Africa.   London,
       T. F. Unwin, 1915.   351p.   (AM572 C92)

3234   Currie, Jessie Monteath.   The Hill of good-bye, the story of a soli-
       tary white woman's life in Central Africa.   London, G. Rout-
       ledge & sons, ltd., 1920.   249p.   (M916C93)

3235   Dean, Christopher.   The African traveler; or, Prospective missions
       in Central Africa.   2d ed.   Boston, Massachusetts Sabbath
       School Society, 1838.   159p.   (AM266D34)

3236   Debenham, Frank.   The Bangwelu swamps of Central Africa.   351-
       68p.   Reprinted from Vol. XXXVII, no. 3 of the Geographical
       Review published by the American Geographical Society of
       New York, July, 1947.   (M966 D35b)

3237   Decle, Lionel.   Three years in savage Africa.   New York, M. F.
       Mansfield, 1898.   594p.   (M966D35)

3238   Denham, Dixon.   Narrative of travels and discoveries in Northern
       and Central Africa, in the years 1822, 1823, and 1824.   Ex-
       tending across the Great Desert to the tenth degree of northern
       latitude, and from Kouka in Bornou, to Sackatoo, the capital
       of the Felatah empire.   Boston, Cummings, Hilliard & co.; Phil-
       adelphia, Carey and Lea, 1826.   112p.   (M916D41)

3239   Deutsche Zentral-Afrika-expedition, 1907-1908.   Wissenchaftliche
       ergebnisse der Deutschen Zentral-Africa-expedition 1907-8.

Leipzig, Klinkhardt, & Biermann, 1910. (M966 D48)

3240　Drummond, Henry. Tropical Africa. 10th ed. New York, C. Scribner's sons, 1903. 228p. (M916D84)

3241　Eulich, Margaret Sally. White mother in Africa. New York, R. R. Smith, 1939. 220p. (M916.73Eu5)

3242　Feather, A. G. Stanley's story; or, Through the wilds of Africa; a thrilling narrative of his remarkable adventures, terrible experiences, wonderful discoveries and amazing achievements in the Dark Continent. Philadelphia, J. E. Potter and Co., [1890.] 533p. (M916F31)

3243　Flandrau, Grace C. (Hodgson). Then I saw the Congo. New York, Harcourt, Brace and Company [c1929.] 308p. (M967-F61)

3244　Fraser, Donald. Winning a primitive people; sixteen years work among the warlike tribe of the Ngoni and the Senga and Tumbuka peoples of Cen. Africa. New York, E. P. Dutton & Co., 1914. 320p. (M968F86)

3245　Great Britain. Colonial Office. Central African territories: Comparative Survey of Native Policy, presented by the Secretaries of State for the Colonies and for Commonwealth Relations. London, H. M. S. O. 1951. 91p. (M325.342 G97ce)

3246　Great Britain. Colonial Office. Central African territories; geographical, historical and economic survey. London, H. M. S. O., 1951. 47p. (M968.9G79)

3247　Haardt, Georges Marie. La croisière noire, expédition citroen centre-Afrique, avec soixant-trois photographies hors texte, deux cartes et quatre portraits de Iacovleff. Paris, Librairie Plon, 1927. 327p. (M960H11)

3248　Hailey, William Malcolm Hailey. Central Africa: Zanzibar, Nyasaland, Northern Rhodesia. London, H. M. Stationery Office, 1950. 168p. (AM354 H12n)

3249　Headley, Joel Tyler. Stanley's wonderful adventures in Africa. Comprising accurate and graphic accounts of the exploration of equatorial Africa; the finding of Livingstone by Stanley; the expedition to the great lakes by Sir Samuel Baker; the discoveries of Lieutenant Cameron in his overland journey across the continent; the exploration of the Congo by Stanley. . . . The story of these wonderful adventures and brilliant achievements down to the present day is fully set forth by the Hon. J. T. Headley . . . and Willis Fletcher Johnson. [Philadelphia.] Edgewood publishing co. [1889] 687p. (M916H34)

3250   Headley, Joel Tyler. Stanley's adventures in the wilds of Africa. Philadelphia, Edgewood pub. co., 1882. 539p. (AM916H38)

3251   Hore, Edward Coode. Tanganyika, eleven years in Central Africa. London, Edward Stanford, 1892. 306p. (M967.82H78)

3252   Human problems in British Central Africa. Cape Town, London, Published for the Rhodes-Livingstone Institute by Oxford University Press, 1944. (M967 H88)

3253   . . . International Missionary Council, Dept. of Social and Industrial research. Modern industry and the African; an enquiry into the effect of the Copper Mines of Central Africa upon native society and the work of Christian missions made under the auspices of the Department of social and industrial research of the International missionary council. J. Merle Davis, Chairman of the Commission of enquiry and editor of the report. . . . London, Macmillan and Co., Limited, 1933. 425p. (M916. 894In8)

3254   Jephson, Arthur Jermy Mounteney. Emin Pasha and the rebellion at the equator; a story of nine months' experiences in the last of the Soudan provinces. 2d ed. London, Sampson Low, Marston, Searle & Rivington, 1890. 490p. (M967J46)

3255   Johnston, Sir Harry H. British Central Africa; an attempt to give some account of a portion of the territories under British influence north of the Zambesi. London, Methuen, 1898. 544p. (M916.7 J63b)

3256   Junker, Wilhelm Johann. Dr. Wilh. Junkers reisen in Africa, 1875-1886. Wien, U. Olmütz, E. Hölzel, 1889-91. 3v. (M-916.6J96)

3257   Knox, Thomas Wallace. The boy travellers in the Far East, Adventures of two youths in a journey through Africa. New York, Harper & Bros., 1884. 473p. (M916K77)

3258   Livingstone, David. The last journals of David Livingstone, in Central Africa, from 1865 to his death. With a narrative of his last moments and sufferings, obtained from his faithful servants Chumah and Susi. Hartford, Conn., R. W. Bliss & Company; Newark, N. J., F. C. Bliss Co.; [etc., etc.] 1875. 448p. (M967L76)

3259   Livingstone, David. Narrative of an expedition to the Zambesi and its tributaries; and of the discovery of the lakes Shirwa and Nyassa. 1858-1864. New York, Harper & Brothers, 1866. 638p. (M916.67L74)

3260   Livingstone, David. The Zambezi expedition of David Livingstone,

1858-1863.   London, Chatto and Windus, 1956.   462p. (M967.-
96 L76)

3261   Lumb, Sybil Victoria.   Central and Southern Africa; a short history.   Cambridge [Eng.]   University Press, 1954.   119p.
(M968L97)

3262   MacLeod, Olive.   Chiefs and cities of Central Africa, across Lake
Chad by way of British, French and German territories.   Edin-
burgh and London, W. Blackwood and Sons, 1912.   322p.
(M967 M13c)

3263   Manning, Olivia.   The reluctant rescue; the story of Stanley's
rescue of Emin Pasha from Equatorial Africa. [1st ed.] Garden
City, N. Y., Doubleday, 1947.   304p. (M967.5M31r)

3264   Moore, Ernest D.   Ivory, scourge of Africa.   New York and London, Harper and Bros., 1931.   256p. (M967 M78)

3265   Nigmann, E.   Die Waheh ihre geschichte, kult, Rechts, Kriegs, und
jagd-gebrauche.   Berlin, Ernst Siefried Mittler und Sohn,
1908.   131p. (AM967 N56)

3266   Nyabongo, Akiki K.   The story of an African chief.   New York, C.
Scribner's Sons, 1935.   312p. (M896N98)

3267   Oldham, Joseph Houldsworth.   New Hope in Africa; the aims of the
Capricorn Africa Society.   London, New York, Longmans,
Green [1955]   102p. (M968011n)

3268   Partnership in practice in Central Africa.   London, African Development Trust, 1955.   16p. (M966 P25)

3269   Pim, Alan William.   The financial and economic history of the African tropical territories.   Oxford, The Clarendon Press, 1940.
234p. (M966P64)

3270   Puleston, Fred.   African drums.   New York, Farrar & Rinehart,
Inc. [c1930.]   318p. (M966P96)

3271   Rehse, Hermann.   Kiziba, land und leute.   Stuttgart, Verlag von
Strecker und Schroder, 1910.   394. (AM967 R26)

3272   Rennell, Francis James Rennell Rodd, baron.   People of the veil;
being an account of the habits, organisation and history of the
wandering Tuareg tribes which inhabit the mountains of Air or
Asben in the central Sahara.   London, Macmillan and Co., Ltd.,
1926.   504p. (AM966.28 R29)

3273   Schlippe, Pierre de.   Shifting cultivation in Africa; the Zande
system of agriculture.   London, Routledge & Paul, 1956.   304p.
(AM630 Sc3)

3274   [Schnitzer, Eduard (known as Emin Pasha)].   Emin Pasha in Central Africa, being a collection of his letters and journals. London, G. Philip & Son, 1888. 547p. (M967 Sch5e)

3275 Schweinfurth, Georg August. The heart of Africa. Three years' travels and adventures in the unexplored regions of Central Africa, from 1868 to 1871. New York, Harper & Brothers, 1874. 2v. (M960Sch9)

3276 Scott, H. L. The truth of Africa, agricultural-mineral; a short history of the present conditions of Central and South Africa. Oakland, California, Wm. H. Day, 1901. (AM967 Sco8)

3277 Simmons, Jack. Livingstone and Africa. London, English Universities Press, Ltd., 1955. 180p. (M860Si4)

3278 Stanley, Sir Henry Morton. How I found Livingstone; travels, adventures, and discoveries in Central Africa, including an account of four months' residence with Dr. Livingstone. New York, C. Scribner's Sons, 1891. 736p. (M916.67 St25h)

3279 Stanley, Henry Morton. Im dunkelsten Afrika. New York, C. Scribner's Sons, 1890. 2v. (M916St2im)

3280 Stanley, Henry Morton. In darkest Africa; or The quest, rescue, and retreat of Emin governor of Equatorie. New York, Charles Scribner's sons, 1890. 548p. (M916St25i)

3281 Stanley, Henry Morton. Through the Dark continent; or, The sources of the Nile, around the great lakes of equatorial Africa, and down the Livingstone River to the Atlantic Ocean. New York, Harper and Bros., 1878. 2v. (M916St25t)

3282 Swayne, George Carless. Lake Victoria; a narrative of explorations in search of the source of the Nile. Edinburgh and London, W. Blackwood and Sons, 1868. 342p. (M916.76Sw2)

3283 Taylor, Bayard. Journey to Central Africa; or, Life and landscapes from Egypt to the Negro Kingdoms of the white Nile. New York, Putnam, 1854. 522p. (M962T21j)

3284 Tegnaeus, Harry. Bloodbrothers, an ethno-sociological study of the institutions of blood-brotherhood with special reference to Africa. Stockholm, Ethnographical Museum of Sweden, 1952. 181p. (AM572.7T23b)

3285 Tew, Mary. Peoples of the Lake Nyasa region. London, Pub. for the International African Institute by the Oxford Univ. Press, 1950. 131p. (M967.9T31p)

3286 Torday, Emil. On the trail of the Bushongo; an account of a remarkable and hitherto unknown African people, their origin, art, high, social and political organization and culture, derived from the author's personal experience amongst them. London, Seeley, Service & Co., Ltd., 1925. 286p. (M967.5T63o)

3287 Tyndale, Walter. Below the cataracts. Philadelphia, J. B. Lippincott Co.; London, W. Heinemann, 1907. 270p. (AM967.Ab2f)

3288 Verner, Samuel Phillips. Pioneering in Central Africa. Richmond, Presbyterian Committee of Publication, 1903. 500p. (M916.7 V59)

3289 Wauters, Alphonse Jules. Stanley's Emin Pasha expedition. London, J. C. Nimmo, 1890. 378p. (M966W35)

3290 West Central Africa regional conference. Abundant life in changing Africa. Report of the West Central Africa regional conference held at Leopoldville, Congo Belge, July 13-24, 1946. N. Y., Africa committee of the Foreign Missions Conference of North America, 1946. 202p. (AM967 W52a)

3291 Weule, Karl. Wissenschaftliche ergebnisse meiner ethnographischen forschungereise in den Susosten Deutsch-Ostafrikas. . . . Berlin, Ernst Siegfried Mittler und Sohn, 1908. 150p. (AM967 W54)

3292 Wilhelm, prince of Sweden. Among pygmies and gorillas with the Swedish zoological expedition to Central Africa 1921. London [etc.] Gyldendal, 1923. 296p. (M916.76W64)

3293 Wilhelm, prince of Sweden. Among pygmies and gorillas with the Swedish zoological expedition to Central Africa 1921. N. Y., Dutton, [n.d.] 296p. (M967.6W64a)

3294 Wilson, Godfrey. The analysis of social change, based on observations in Central Africa. Cambridge, The University Press, 1945. 177p. (M966 W69a)

3295 Wissmann, Herman von. My second journey through equatorial Africa, from the Congo to the Zambesi, in the years 1886 and 1887. London, Chatto & Windus, 1891. 326p. (M967W76b)

FRENCH EQUATORIAL AFRICA

3296 Anderson. Efraim. Contributions à l'ethnographie des Kuta I. Uppsala, Almquist & Wiksells, 1953. 363p. (M967.2 An2)

3297 Ballif, Noél. Dancers of God; translated from the French by James Cameron. London, Sidgwick and Jackson, 1955. 213p. (M-967.2B21)

3298 Bittremieux, Léo. La Société secréte des Bakhimba au Mayombe. Bruxelles. Lib. Falk fils, 1936. 327p. (M967.2 B54s)

3299 Briault, R. P. Dans la forêt du Gabon etudes et scenes Africaines. Paris, Bernard Grasset, 1930. (AM916.721)

3000   Brom, John L.   The pitiless jungle.   New York, D. McKay, [1955.]
        309p.   (M967.2 B78)

3301   Bruel, Georges. . . . L'Afrique Equatoriale Française (A.E.F.; pré-
        face de m.   Lucien Hubert.   Paris, Larose, 1930.   256p.   (M-
        967.2 B83)

3302   Bruel, Georges. . . . Bibliographie de l'Afrique Equatoriale Française.
        Paris, E. Larose, 1914.   326p.   (M967.B83b)

3303   Bruel, Georges. . . . La France équatoriale africaine. le pays. Les
        habitats.   La colonisation.   Les pouvoirs publics.   Paris, La-
        rose, 1935.   558p.   (M967.2 B83)

3304   Bruyns, L.   De social (i.e. sociaal) economische ontwikkeling van
        de Bakongo. (gewest Inkisi) (Leuven) 1951.   343p.   (M967.-
        26 B83)

3305   Challaye, Felicien.   Le Congo française, la question internationale
        du Congo.   Paris, F. Alcan, 1909.   311p.   (M967.2C35)

3306   Cureau, Adolphe Louis.   Les Sociétes primitives de L'Afrique, Equa-
        toriale.   Paris, A. Colin, 1912.   420p.   (AM572C92s)

3307   Eboué Adolphe Félix Sylvestre. . . . Les peuples de l'Oubangui-
        Chari.   Essai d'ethnographie, de linguistique et d'economie
        sociale.   Paris, Publications du comite de l'Afrique française,
        1933.   104p.   (M967.41 Eb7)

3308   L'Encyclopedie Coloniale et Maritime.   Encyclopedie of Tunisie,
        Afrique Occidentale Française, Afrique Equatoriale Française,
        Algérie et Sahara, Cameroun Togo, et Marco.   Paris, Editions
        de l'Union Française, 1948-1951. 7v. (M960En19)

3309   Fourneau, Alfred.   Au vieux Congo; notes de route.   Paris, Éditions
        du Comité de l'Afrique Française, 1932.   323p.   (M916F82)

3310   France.   Direction de la documentation.   French Equatorial Africa.
        [Paris, La Documentation Française, 1954.]   47p.   (M967.2
        F84)

3311   Frey, Roger.   Brazzaville; capitale de l'Afrique Équatoriale Fran-
        caise.   Paris, Encyclopédia Mensuelle d'Outre Mer, 1954. 154p.

3312   Gaud, Fernand.   Les Mandja (Congo Français).   Bruxelles, A.
        de Wit, etc., 1911.   574p.   (M967.41G23)

3313   Gide, André Paul Guillaume.   Travels in the Congo.   New York,
        London, A. A. Knopf, 1929.   375p.   (M967.2G36)

3314   Gide, André Paul Guillaume.   Voyage au Congo, carnets de route.
        32. éd.   Paris, Gallimard [1928]   249p.   (M967G36)

3315   Guthrie, Malcolm.   The Bantu languages of Western Equatorial
        Africa.   London, New York, etc., Published for the International

African Institute by the Oxford University Press, 1953. 94p.
(M496.3G98b)

3316 Jephson, Arthur Jermy Mountenay. Emin Pasha and the rebellion
at the equator. London, Sampson Low, Marston, Searle and
Rivington, 1890. 490p. (AM967 J46)

3317 Joy, Charles Rhind. The Africa of Albert Schweitzer; with a con-
cluding essay by Albert Schweitzer. London, Black, 1949. 159p.
(M960J84a)

3318 Junod, Henri A. Les Ba-ronga. Etude ethnographique sur les indigenes de la baie de Delagoa. Moeurs, Droit coutumier, vie
nationale, industrie, traditions, superstitions et religion. Neu-
chatel, Imprimerie Paul Attinger, 1899. 517p. (AM967.99 J96)

3319 Laguerre, Andre. Free French Africa. London, New York, Oxford
University Press, 1942. 38p. (AM967.2 L13)

3320 Lauraint, André. Les próblèms de transport de l'Afrique Equatoriale Française. Brazzaville, [Institut d'Etudes,] 1945. 31p.
(M355.6 L37p)

3321 Londres, Albert. Terre d'ébène (La traite des noirs). Paris, Albin
Michel, 1929. 266p. (M966.1L84t)

3322 Londres, Albert. A very naked people. New York, H. Liveright
[c1929] 267p. (M966L84)

3323 Maigret, Julien. Afrique Equatoriale Française. Paris, Société
d'Éditions Geographiques, Maritimes et Coloniales, 1931. 220p.
(M967.2 M28)

3324 Maran, René. Le Tchad de sable et d'or. Documentation de Pierre
Deloncle, couverture en coulerus de Charles Fouqueray. Paris,
Libraire de la Revue Francaise Alexis Redier, Editeur, 1931.
(AM967.2M32)

3325 Marie André du Sacré Coeur, soeur. La condition humaine en
Afrique noire. Paris, Grasset [1953] 262p. (AM301M33)

3326 Marqueissac, H. de. L'Effort medical Français en Afrique Equatoriale et au Cameroun, un film du Docteur H. de Marqueissac,
images de Robert Carmet, une production de la Société d'Applications Cinematographiques . . . Paris, Edition de la Société
Parisienne d'Expansion Chimique, [1949] [16]p. (M967.-
2 M34)

3327 Nassau, Robert Hamill. My Ogowe; being a narrative of daily
incidents during sixteen years in equatorial West Africa. New
York, The Neale Publishing Company, 1914. 708p. (M966N18)

3328 Proyart, Liévain Bonaventure. Histoire de Loango, Kakongo, et autres royaumes d'Afrique. Paris, Chez Mequignon-Junion, 1819. 295p. (AM967.2 P94)

3329   Schweitzer, Albert. African notebook. New York, H. Holt and Co., 1939. 144p. (AM916.721 Sch9)

3330   Schweitzer, Albert. On the edge of the primeval forest; Experiences and observations of a doctor in equatorial Africa. New York, Macmillan Co., 1948. 222p. (M967.21 Sch9)

3331   Sinda, Marital. Premier chant du depart. Paris, Pierre Seghers, 1955. 60p. (M967.2 Si6p)

3332   Susset, Raymond. La vérité sur le Cameroun et l'Afrique Équatoriale Française. [Paris] Éditions de la Nouvelle revue critique [c1934] 218p. (M967.11Su8)

3333   Trilles, R. P. Les pygmées de la forêt équatoriale; cours professé à l'Institut catholque de Paris. Paris, Libraire Bloud et Gay, 1932. 530p. (M572.9672 T73)

3334   Valdi, Francois. Le Gabon: l'homme contre la foret. Paris, Librairie de la Reve Francaise, Alexis Redier, Editeur, 1931. 159p. (M916.721 V23)

3335   Vergiat, Antonin Marius. Moeurs et coutumes des Manjas. Paris, Payot, 1937. 323p. (AM967.41 V58m)

3336   Vergiat, Antonin Marius. Les rites secrets des primitifs de l'Oubangi; preface du general Bouscat. Paris, Payot, 1936. 210p. (AM967.41 V58r)

3337   Wissman, Hermann von. My second journey through equatorial Africa, from the Congo to the Zambesi, in the years 1886 and 1887. London, Chatto and Windus, 1891. 326p. (AM967 W76b)

BELGIAN CONGO and RUANDA-URUNDI

3338   Académie royale des sciences coloniales, Brussels. Biographie coloniale belge. Bruxelles, Librairie Falk fils, 1948-1956. 4v. (M967.5Ac1)

3339   L'Action sociale du Congo Belge et au Ruanda-Urundi. Bruxelles, Centre d'information et de Documentation du Congo Belge et du Ruanda-Urundi. 1954.

3340   Adriaens, Léon. Contribution à l'étude chimique des sols salins et de leur végétation au Ruanda-Urundi, par L. Adriaens et G. Waegemans. [Bruxelles, G. Van Campenhout, 1943.] 186p. (AM581.526Ad8)

3341   Adriaens, Léon. Le ricin au Congo belge; étude chimique des graines, des huiles et des sous-produits. Bruxelles, G. Van Campenhout, 1938. 206p. (AM583Ad8r)

3342 Afrika Institut Leiden. Land tenure symposium, Amsterdam, 1950. Tropical Africa—Netherlands East Indies before the Second World War; organized by the Afrika Instituut Leiden, 26-28 Oct., 1950. Leiden, Universitaire Per Leiden, 1951. 151p. (M967.5Af8)

3343 Akeley, Mary L. (Jobe). Congo Eden; a comprehensive portrayal of the historical background and scientific aspects of the great game sanctuaries of the Belgin Congo with the story of a six months' pilgrimage throughout that most primitive region in the heart of the African Continent. London, Gollancz, 1951. 356p. (M967.5AK3c)

3344 Baumer, Guy. Les centres indigènes extra coutumiers au Congo Belge. Paris, F. Leviton, 1939. 239p. (AM354.675B32)

3345 Baxter, Paul Trevor William. The Azande, and related peoples of the Anglo-Egyptian Sudan and Belgian Congo. London, International Africa Institute, 1953. 152p. (AM967.5B33)

3346 Beaucorps, Remi de. Les Basongo de la Luniungu et de la Gobari. Bruxelles, Falk fils, 1941. 172p. (M967.5B38b)

3347 Beaucorps, Remi de. Les Bayansi du Bas-Kwilu. Louvain, Editions de l'Aucam, 1933. 135p. (M967.5B38ba)

3348 Beaucorps, Remi de. L'évolution économique chez les Basongo de la Luniungu et de la gobari. Bruxelles, n.p. 1951. 68p. (M-967.5B38b2)

3349 Bedinger, Robert Dabney. Triumphs of the Gospel in the Belgian Congo. Richmond, Va. Presbyterian Committee of Publication, 1920. 218p. (AM266B39t)

3350 Belgian Congo-American survey, a publication devoted to the promotion of trade relations between Belgium, The Belgian Congo and the United States of America. New York, Belgian Chamber of Commerce in the United States of America, 19? 168p. (M967.5B39)

3351 Belgian Congo appraised; a selection of articles on the Belgian Congo recently published in the American daily and weekly press. New York, Belgian Government Information Center, 1952. 63p. (M967.5B41)

3352 The Belgian Congo from the wilderness to civilization. Brussels, Belgium, Les Beaux Arts, n.d. 38p. (M967.5B41c)

3353 Belgium. Belgium Government Information Centre, New York. The sacred mission of civilization; to which peoples should the

benefits be extended? The Belgian thesis. New York, 1953.
64p. (M967.5B415)

3354 Belgium. Ministère des colonies. Report soumis par le gouvernement belge à l'Assemblée générale des Nations Unies au sujet
de l'administration du Ruanda-Urundi. Bruxelles, Établisse-
ments généraux d'impr. 1954. (M967.57B41r)

3355 Belgium. Ministère des colonies. A ten year plan for the economic
and social development of the Belgian Trust Territory of
Ruanda-Urundi. New York, Belgian Govt. Information Center,
1952. 83p. (M967.57B41t)

3356 Belgium. Office du tourisme du Congo et Ruanda-Urundi: Trav-
erler's guide to the Belgian Congo and Ruanda-Urundi. Brussels, 1951. 757p. (M967.5B41t)

3357 Bellotti, Felice. Fabulous Congo; translated from the Italian by
Mervyn Savill. London, A. Dakers, 1954. 222p. (M967.5B42)

3358 Bolamba, Antoine Roger. Les problems de l'évolution de la femme
noire. Préface de M. Robert Godding. Elisabethville, Editions de l'Essor du Congo, 1949. 167p. (M967.5B63p)

3359 Boone, Clinton C. Congo as I saw it, by C. C. Boone . . .who repre-
sented in Congo the Lott Carey Baptist foreign missionary convention of the U. S. A. and the American Baptist foreign missionary society of Boston, Mass., from 1901 to 1906. [New
York, Printed by L. J. Little and Ives Company, c1927]
96p. (M910B64c)

3360 Bourne, Henry Richard Fox. Civilization in Congoland. London,
P. S. King & Son, 1903. 311p. (M967.5B66)

3361 Bradley, Mary (Hastings). Caravans and cannibals. New York,
London, D. Appleton and Co., 1926. 319p. (M916.75B72)

3362 Briey, Renaud, comte de. Le sphinx noir, essai sur les problèmes
de colonisation Africaine. Paris, Berger-Lerault, 1926. 260p.
M967.5B76s)

3363 Burrows, Guy. The land of pigmies. New York, Crowell, 1898.
299p. (M916.73B94)

3364 Burton, William F. P. Missionary pioneering in Congo forests.
Preston R. Seed and Sons, 1922. 216p. (AM266B95)

3365 Castagne E. Contribution a l'êtude chimîque des légumineuses in-
secticides du Congo Belge. Bruxelles, Georges Van Campenhout, 1938. 102p. (M967.5C27)

3366 Centre d'information et de documentation du Congo Belge et du
Ruanda-Urandi. L'action sociale au Congo Belge et au Ruanda-

Urundi. Bruxelles, Imprimé en Belgique, 1954. 132p. (M-967.5C33a)

3367 Centre d'Information et de Documentation du Congo Belge et du Ruanda-Urundi. Social action in the Belgian Congo and Ruanda-Urundi. New York, Belgian Government Information Center, 1954. 128p. (M967.5C33s)

3368 Challaye, Felicien. Le Congo Français. Paris, Cahiers de la Quinzaine. 119p. (M967.2C35)

3369 Cleene, N. de. Le clan matrilinéal dans la société indigene; hier, aujourd'hui, demain. Bruxelles, Georges Van Campenhout, 1946. 99p. (AM572C58c)

3370 Clouzot, Henri. Sculptures Africaines et Oceaniennes; Colonies françaises et Congo Belge. Paris, Librairie de France, n.d. 24p. (AM730C62)

3371 Congo-Nil. Guide du Congo-Belge et du Ruanda-Urundi, 1948-49. Bruxelles, Van Assche. 639p. (M967.5C75)

3372 Congres International d'agronomie tropicale 19 au 23 mai 1910. Bruxelles, 1910.

3373 Cooper, Reginald Davey. Hunting and hunted in the Belgian Congo. London, Smith, Elder and Co., 1914. 262p. (M967.5C78h)

3374 Courtney Roger. Footloose in the Congo. London, H. Jenkins, [1948.] 222p. (M967.5C83f)

3375 Crowe, S. E. The Berlin West African conference, 1884-1885. London, New York, Longmans, Green and Co., 1942. 249p. (M967.5C88)

3376 Davis, Richard Harding. The Congo and coasts of Africa. New York, C. Scribner's Sons, 1907. 220p. (M916.75D29c)

3377 Davis, William Ellsworth. Ten years in the Congo. New York, Reynal & Hitchcock, [1940.] 301p. (M916.75D29)

3378 Daye, Pierre. Problèmes Congolais. Bruxelles, Les Ecrits, 1943. 295p. (M967.5D33)

3379 Decker, J. M. de. Les clans Ambuun (Bambunda) d'après leur littérature orale. Bruxelles, 1950. 146p. (M967.51D35c)

3380 Delhaise, Charles Godefroid Félix François. Les Warega (Congo belge). Bruxelles, A. de Wit, 1909. 376p. (M967.5D37w)

3381 Denuit, Désiré. Le Congo d'aujourd'hui. Bruxelles, Office de Publicité, J. Lebêgue and Cie, éditeurs, 1948. 93p. (M967.5D43c)

3382 Dessart, Charles. Katanga. Introduction de M. A. Lefevre. Bruxelles, Charles Dessart, ed., 1954. 147p. (M967.58D47)

3383 Dieu, Léon. Dans le brousse Congolaise (Les origines des missions de Scheut au Congo). [Leige] Marcéchal, 1946. 279p. (M-967.5D56d)

3384 Domont, Jean-Maire. Élite noire, préface de M. Gustave Sand. Léopoldville, Belgian Congo, Courrier d'Afrique, 1948. 206p. (M967.5D71e)

3385 Doucy, Arthur. Problems du travail et politique sociale au Congo belge par Arthur Doucy et Pierre Feldheim. Bruxelles, Librairie Encyclopedique, 1952. 156p. (M967.5D74p)

3386 Doyle, Arthur Conan. The crime of the Congo. New York, Doubleday, Page and Co., 1909. 128p. (M967.5D77)

3387 Dye, Royal J. Bolenge: a story of Gospel triumphs on the Congo. Cincinnati, O., Foreign Christian Missionary Society, 1909. 225p. (M967D98)

3388 Edmiston, Althea Brown. Grammar and dictionary of the Bushonga; or, Bukuba language as spoken by the Bushonga or Bukuba tribe who dwell in the Upper Kasai District, Belgian Congo, Central Africa. Luebo, J. Leighton Wilson Press, n.d. 619p. (M496Ed5)

3389 Edmond, Verhulpen. Baluba et balibaisés du Katanga. Anvers, les Editions de L'Avenir Belge, 1935. 534p. (M967.58Ed5)

3390 Encyclopédie du Congo Belge. Bruxelles, Bieleveld, 1950. (M967.-5En1)

3391 Etat Independant du Congo. Department de l'Interieur. Recueil Administratif. Bruxelles, F. Van Buggennourt, 1904. 670p.

3392 Flandrau, Grace C. (Hodgson). Then I saw the Congo. New York, Harcourt, Brace and Co., 1929. 308p. (M967F61)

3393 Flavin, Martin. Black and white, from the Cape to the Congo. 1st ed. New York, Harper [1950] 332p. (M968F61b)

3394 Fouarge, Joseph. Bois du Congo. Bruxelles, G. Gerard and E. Sacre, 1953. 424p. (M967.5F82b)

3395 Fourneau, Alfred. Au vieux Congo; notes de route. Paris, Editions du Comite de l'Afrique francaise, 1932. 323p. (M916F82)

3396 Franssen, J. Dioramas Congolais (Vie matérièlle du noir) avec 10 illustrations photographiques. Liége, Éditions Soledi, 1943. 1943. (M967.5F85)

3397 Frobenius, Leo. Im Schatten des Kongostaates. Berlin Druck und Verlag von Georg Reimer, 1907. 468p. (M967.5F92)

3398 Gaffé, René. Le sculpture au Congo Belge. Paris, Éditions du Cercle d'art, [1945.] 65p. (AM703G12s)

3399 Gatti, Attilio. Great mother forest. New York, C. Scribner's Sons, 1937. 355p. (M916.75G22)

3400 Gaud, Fernand. Les Mandj, Congo française. Bruxelles, Albert de Wit, 1911. 573p. (M967.41G23)

3401 Gheerbrant, Alain. Congo noir and blanc. Dixième edition. [Paris.] Guillimard, [1955.] 230p. (M967.5G34)

3402 Gide, André Paul Guillaume. Travels in the Congo; translated from the French by Dorothy Bussy. New York, London, A. A. Knopf, c1927. 375p. (M967.2G36)

3403 Gide, André Paul Gillaume. Voyage au Congo, carnets de route. Paris, Gallimard, 1928. 249p. (M967G36)

3404 Glave, E. J. In savage Africa; or six years of adventure in Congoland. New York, R. H. Russell and Sons, [1892.] 247p. (M967G46)

3405 Gochet, Jean Baptiste. La Barbarie Africaine et l'action civilisatrice des missions Catholiques au Congo et dans l'Afrique Equatoriale, contenant. Liege, H. Dessain, 1889. 206p. (AM-967G53)

3406 Hahn, Emily. Congo solo, misadventures two degrees north. Indianapolis, The Bobbs-Merrill Co., [c1933] 335p. (M916.-75H12)

3407 Harris, J. S. Education in the Belgian Congo. Reprinted from vol. XV, No. 3, summer, 1946 of the Journal of Negro Education. 410-426pp. (M967.5H24)

3408 Harroy, Jean-Paul. Afrique, terre qui meurt. Marcel Hayez, Bruxelles, 1949. 557p.

3409 Hendecourt, Roger d'. N'Gombe; contes et croquis des ranches du Katanga. Bruxelles, Librairie Vanderlinden, 1940. 134p. M967.5H38g)

3410 Heyse, Théodore. Bibliographie du Congo Belge et du Ruanda-Urundi (1939-1951). Documentation général: bibliographies et centres d'études, expositions, Presse et propagande. Bruxelles, G. Van Campenhout, 1952. 57p. (MO16.967H51b)

3411 Heyse, Théodore. Bibliographie du Congo Belge et du Ruanda-Urundi (1939-1951) Documentation générale: folklore philatélie, sports, tourisme. Bruxelles, G. Van Campenhout, 1952. 40p. (MO16.967H1f)

3412 Heyse, Théodore. Bibliographie du Congo Belge et du Ruanda-Urundi (1939-1951) Sciences Coloniales. Repertoire suivi d'un complement a la "Politique indigene" periode anteriure à

1940. Bruxelles, G. Van Campenhout, 1952. 71p. (MO16.-967H512s)

3413   Hilton-Simpson, Melville William.   Land and peoples of the Kasai. London, Constable and Co., 1911.   356p.   (M967.5H561)

3414   Hinde, Sidney Langford.   The fall of the Congo Arabs.   New York, Thomas Whittaker, 1897.   308p.   (M967.5H58)

3415   Hoefer, Ferdinand.   Afrique Australe; Afrique Orientale; Afrique Centrale; Empire de Maroc.   Paris, Firmin Didot Freres, Editeurs, 1848.   498p.   (M967H67)

3416   Hurel, Eugene.   La poésie chez les primitifs ou contes, fables, récits et proverbes du Rwanda (Lac Kivu).   Bruxelles, Goemaere, Imprimeur du Roi, Editeur, 1922.   260p.   (AM398H93)

3417   Institut National pour l'Etude Agronomiaue du Congo belge, Brussels.   Flore du Congo Belge et du Ruanda-Urundi; spermatophytes.   Bruxelles, I.N.E.A.C., 1952. 3v. (M967.51n7p)

3418   International Congress of tropical agriculture.   Brussells, J. Goemaere, 1910.   2v.   (AM630In8)

3419   Jameson, James Sligo.   The story of the rear column of the Emin Pasha relief expedition.   New York, United States Book Co., [1891.]   455p.   (AM967.5J23)

3420   Jentgen, Pierre.   Genèse de l'hypothèque conventionnelle en droit congolais.   [Bruxelles, 1950.]   133p.   (AM658J45)

3421   Johnston, Harry Hamilton.   George Grenfell and the Congo; a history and description of the Congo Independent State and adjoining districts of Congo and.   London, Hutchinson and Co., 1908.   2v.   (M967.5J64)

3422   Kagame, Alexis.   Le code des institutions politiques du Rwanda précolonial.   Bruxelles, Institut Royal Colonial Belge, 1952. 136p.   (M967.5K10c)

3423   Kagame, Alexis.   La divine pastorale, traduction français, par l'auteur, de la première Veillée d'une épopée écrite en langue Ruandaise.   Bruxelles, Editions du Marais, 1952.   108p.   (M-967.5K10d)

3424   Kagame, Alexis. Iyo Wiliwe nta rungu. Kabgayi, Les Editions Royales, 1949.   232p.

3425   Kagame, Alexis.   La naissance de l'univers.   Illustrations par Ant. de Vinck.   Bruxelles, Editions du Marais, 1955.   85p. (M967.-5K10n)

3426   Kagame, Alexis.   Les organisations socio-familia-les de l'ancien

Rwanda. Bruxelles, Académie royale des Sciences Coloniales, 1954. 355p. (M967.5K10o)

3427   Kagame, Alexis. La poésie dynastique au Rwanda. Bruxelles, Institut Royal Colonial Belge, 1951. 240p. (M967.5K10p)

3428   Kanza, Thomas. Congo pays de deux evolues, Editions Actualities Africaines, 1956. 29p.

3429   Kellersberger, Julia Lake (Skinner). Congo Crosses; a study of Congo womanhood. Boston, The Central Committee on the United study of Foreign Missions, 1936. 222p. (M266K28c)

3430   Kitambala, Jerome. Contes Africains by Jerome Kitambala, Paul Malulu Simon Mundiangu and Robert Musungaie. Leverville, Biliotheque de L'Etoile, 1955. 32p. (M967.5K64c)

3431   Kligny, Dierre. A ten year plan for the economic and social development of the Belgian Congo. New York, Belgian Government Information Center, 1950. 72p.

3432   Knox, Thomas Wallace. The boy travellers on the Congo; adventures of two youth in a journey. New York, Harper and Bros., 1888. 463p. (M967.5K77b)

3433   Kochnitzky, Leon. Negro art in Belgian Congo. New York, Belgian Government Information Center, 1948. 80p. (AM709.-6K81n)

3434   Lagae, C. R. Les Azande; ou, Niam-Niam, l'organisation Zande familiales. Bruxelles, Vromant and Co., 1926. 224p. (AM-967.4L13)

3435   Lamal, François. Essai d'étude démographique d'une population du Kwango. Les Basuku du territoire de feshi. Bruxelles, Librairie Falk fils, 1949. 189p.

3436   Laman, Karl. The Kongo, I. Stockholm, 1953. 155p. (M967.-5L16k)

3437   Latouche, John. Congo. [New York,] Willow, White and Co., [1945.] 192p. (M916.75L35c)

3438   Lepersonne, J. Les terrasses du fleuve Congo au Stanley-Pool, et leurs relations avec celles d'autres régions de la cuvette congolaise. Bruxelles, G. van Campenhout, 1937. 67p. (AM-551L55)

3439   Leplae, Edmond. Le palmier a huile en Afrique; son exploitation su Congo Belge et en extrème-orient. Bruxelles, Georges van Campenhout, 1939. 108p. (M967.5L55)

3440   Lotar, P. L. La grande chronique de l'Uele. Bruxelles, Georges Van Campenhout, 1946. 363p. (M967.55L91)

3441 Mabie, Catherine Louise Roe. Congo cameos. [1st ed.] Philadelphia, Judson Press, [1952.] 191p. (M967.5M11e)

3442 Maes, Joseph. Aniota-kifwebe; les masques des populations du Congo Belge et le materiel des rites de circoncision. Avers, Editions "de Sikkel", 1924. 63p. (M967.5M26a)

3443 Maes, Joseph. Sculpture; decorative; ou, symbolique des instruments et musique du Congo Belge. Bruxelles, Imprimerie Typ' Art, 1937. 44p. (AM730M26)

3444 Malula, Joseph. Foyer heureux. Leverville, Bibliotheque de L' Etoile, 1951. 96p. (M967.5M29f)

3445 Manning, Olivia. The reluctant rescue; the story of Stanley's rescue of Emin Pasha from Equatorial Africa. [1st ed.] Garden City, New York, Doubleday, 1947. 304p. (M967.5M31r)

3446 Marvel, Tom. The new Congo. New York, Duell, Sloan and Pearce, 1948. 395p. (M916.75M36n)

3447 Maurice, Albert. Stanley lettre inédites. Bruxelles, Office de Publicité, 1955. 219p. (MB9st2m)

3448 Mbaya, Pierre. Contes d'aujourd'hui. Leverville, Bibliothque de L'Etoile, n.d. 24p. (M967.5M45c)

3449 Mertens, Joseph. Les Ba dzing de la Kamtsha. Bruxelles, Georges Van Campenhout, Librairie Falk fils, 1935. 381p. (M967.-5M55b)

3450 Miller, Janet. Jungles preferred. Boston and New York, Houghton Mifflin Co., 1931. 320p. (M916.75M61j)

3451 Moeller, A. Les grandes lignes des migrations des Bantous de la Province Orientale du Congo Belge. Bruxelles, Librairie Falk fils, 1936. 578p. (M967.5M72)

3452 Monheim, Christian. Le Congo et les livres. Anthologie coloniale. Bruxelles, Librarie Albert Dewit, 1928. 368p. (M967.5M74c)

3453 Mopila, Francisco José. Memorias du un congolés; ensayo de autobiografiá. Madrid, Consejo Superior de Investigaciones Científicas Instituto de Estudios Africanos, 1940. (M967.579)

3454 Morel, Edmund Dene. Red rubber; the story of the rubber slave trade flourishing on the Congo in the year of grace 1906. London, T. F. Unwin, 1906. 213p. (M967.5M81)

3455 Mottoulle, L. Politique sociale de l'Union Minière du Haut-Katanga pour sa main-d'oeuvre indigène et ses résultats au cours de vingt anées d'application. Bruxelles, Librairie Falk fils, 1946. 67p. (M967.58M85)

3456 Mutombo, Dieudonne. Hygiene de l'alimentation. Leverville, Bibliotheque de L'Etoile, 1954. 39p. (M967.5M98h)

3457 Mutombo, Dieudonne. Victoire de l'amour. [novel] Leverville, Bibliotheque de L'Etoile, 1953. 127p. (M967.5M98v)

3458 McCaw, Grace Anna (Main). "Mrs. Alexander MaCaw". Congo, the first alliance mission field. Harrisburg, Penna, Christian Publications, Inc., 1937. 168p. (AM276.75M12)

3459 Naigisiki, Joseph Saverio. Escapade Ruandaise. Journal d'un clerc en sa trentieme année. Bruxelles, G. A. Deny, [1950.] 208p. (MB9N14e)

3460 Ngwete, Martin. Les maladies vénériennes. Congo Belge, Bibliotheque de L'Etoile, 1951. 71p. (M967.5N51m)

3461 Overbergh, Cyrille Van. Les Bangala (Estat Ind. Du Congo) Par Cyrill Van Overbergh over la collaboration de ed. de Jonghe. Bruxelles, Albert DeWit, 1907. 458p. (M967.50v3)

3462 Paul, Austin. Trumpet notes in Congo. Brooklyn, Africa Inland Mission, 1949. 95p. (M967.5P28t)

3463 Perier, Gaston-Denys. Les arts populaires du Congo Belge. Bruxelles, Office de Publicite, J. Lebegue and cie, editeurs, 1948. 77p. (AM967.5P41a)

3464 Perier, Gaston-Denys. Moukanda. Choix de lectures sur le Congo et quelques régions voisines. Bruxelles, J. Lebègue and cie., 1914. 379p. (M967.5P41m)

3465 Perier, Gaston-Denys. Nègreries et curiosités congolaises. Bruxelles, L'Eglantine, 1930. 122p. (M967.2P41n)

3466 Pétillon, Leon. Speech by the Governor General Leon Pétillon. [Brussels, 1955.] 54p. (M967.5P44)

3467 Polinard, Edmond. La bordure nord du socle granitique dans la région de la Lubi et de la Bushimaie, Congo belge. Bruxelles, G. van Campenhout, 1939. 48p. (AM533.52P75)

3468 Poulaine, Mme. Madeleine. Une blanche chez les noirs. Paris, J. Tallandier, [1931.] 188p. (M916P86w)

3469 Probert, Herbert. Life and scenes in Congo. Philadelphia, American Baptist pub. soc., [1889.] 192p. (916.75P94)

3470 Proyart, Liévain Bonaventure. Histoire de Loango, Kakongo, et autres royaunes d'Afrique. Paris, Chez Mequignon-Junior, 1819. 295p. (M967.2P94)

3471 Rinchon, Dieudonné. La traité et l'esclavage des Congolais par les Européens; histoire de la déportation de 13 millions 250,-

000 noirs en Amérique. Préface de son excellence m. Engels. [Bruxelles,] 1929. 306p. (M967.5R47)

3472 Robert, Maurice. Contribution à la morphologie du Katanga, les cycles géographiques et les pénéplaines. [Bruxelles,] G. van Campenhout, 1939. 59p. (AM551R54)

3473 Ruanda Urundi. Introduction de Georges Sandrart; Photographies de J. Cayet et Ch. Dessart. Bruxelles, Charles Dessart, Editeur, 1953. (M967.57R82)

3474 Ruanda Urundi. Notule préparée à l'intention de tous ceux qui auront la bonne fortune de suivre sa Majesté le Roi dans ses déplacements a travers le territoire sous Tutelle, 30 Mai t Juin, 1955. 59p. (M967.57R82r)

3475 Ruhe, Robert V. Erosion surfaces of central African interior high plateaus. Bruxelles, I.N.E.A.C., 1954. 38p. (M967.5R85e)

3476 Schebesta, Paul. Bambuti, die zwerge vom Kongo. Leipzig, F. A. Brockhaus, 1932. 270p. (AM572.67Sch2)

3477 Schebesta, Paul. Revisiting my pygmy hosts. London, Hutchinson and Co., Ltd., 1936. 288p. (AM572.67Sch2r)

3478 Schouteden, H. Le Congo Belge, n.p. n.d. (M967.5Sch6)

3479 Schumacher, Peter. Die Ehe in Ruanda. Reprinted from Anthropos, Revue Internationale d'Ethnologie et de Linguistique, 1910. (M967.57Sc8)

3480 Schumacher, Peter. Die tracht in Ruanda (Deutsch-Ostafrika). Reprinted from Anthropos, Revue Internationale d'Ethnologie et de Linguistique, 1916. (M967.57Sc8d)

3481 Severn, Merlyn. Congo Pilgrim. London, Museum Press, [1952.] 221p. (M967.5Se8)

3482 Sheppard, William Henry. Presbyterian pioneers in Congo. Richmond, Va., Presbyterian committee of publication [1917.] 157p. (M285Sh4p)

3483 Sion, Georges. Kivu, introduction et legendes de Georges Sion. Bruxelles, Charles Dessart, 1952. 150p. (M967.5Si7)

3484 Smith, H. Suton. "Yakusu" the very heart of Africa, being some account of the Protestant mission at Stanley Falls, Upper Congo. London, Marshall, n.d. 288p. (M960Sm5y)

3485 Société Belge d'Etudes et d'Expansion. Oeuvre de collaboration internationale, de documentation, et de vulgarisation économique et coloniale. Bruxelles, Société Belge d'Etudes et d'Expansion, 1955. 192p. (M967.5So1)

3486   Sohier, A. Le mariage en droit coutumier Congolais. Bruxelles, Librairie Falk fils, 1943. 248p. (M967.5So2)

3487   Stanley, Henry Morton. The Congo and the founding of its free state; a story of work and exploration. New York, Harper and Bros., 1885. 2v. (M967.5St2)

3488   Starr, Frederick. Congo natives; an ethnographic album. Chicago, [Lakeside Press,] 1912. 38p. (M572.67St28)

3489   Starr, Frederick. The truth about the Congo: the Chicago tribune articles. Chicago, Forbes & Co., 1907. 129p. (M967.5St2t)

3490   Steenackers. Le Congo Belge; cours de géographie physique, politique économique et historique. Destine a l'enseignement moyen. Bruxelles, Librairie Albert DeWit, 1909. (M967.5St3c)

3491   Stonelake, Alfred R. Congo, past and present. London, New York, World Dominion Press, 1937. 202p. (M967.5St7)

3492   Strang, Herbert. Fighting on the Congo; the story of an American boy among the rubber slaves. Indianapolis, The Bobbs-Merrill Co., [1906.] 382p. (AM967St82)

3493   Tervueren, Belgium. Musée du Congo Belge. Bureau de documentation ethnographique. Les peuplades du Congo belge nom et situation géographique, par J. Maes et O. Boone. Bruxelles, Imprimerie veuve monnom, 1935. (M967.5T27)

3494   Torday, Emil. Causeries congolaises. Bruxelles, Librairie Albert DeWit, 1925. 235p. (AM572.9675T65)

3495   Torday, Emil and T. A. Joyce. Notes ethnographiques sur les peuples communetment appeles Bakuba, ainsique sur les peuplades apparentees. Les Bushongo. Bruxelles Annales du Musee du Congo Belge, 291p.

3496   Torday, Emil. On the trail of the Bushongo; an account of a remarkable and hitherto unknown African people. London, Seeley, Service and Co., 1925. 286p. (AM967.5T630)

3497   Tuckey, James Kingston. Narrative of an expedition to explore the river Zaire; usually called the Congo. London, J. Murray, 1818. 498p. (M916.75T75)

3498   United Nations. General Assembly. Trusteeship agreement for the Territory of Ruanda-Urundi, as approved by the General Assembly on December 13, 1946. Lake Success, 1947. 7p. (M-967.57Un3t)

3499   United Nations. United Nations visiting mission to trust territories in East Africa, 1951. Report on the trust territory of Ruanda-Urundi, together with the relevant resolution of the trusteeship council. New York, United Nations, 1952. 39p. (M-967.57Un3u)

3500 Van Bulck, G. Les recherches linguistiques au Congo Belge. Résultats acquis nouvelles enquêtes a entreprendre. Bruxelles, Librairie Falk fils, 1948. 767p. (M967.5V27r)

3501 Verger, Pierre. Congo belge et Ruanda-Urundi. Deux cent vingt deux photos. Introd. de Charles d'Ydewalle. Bruxelles, Librairie générale, 1952. (M967.5V58d)

3502 Verhoeven, Joseph Ch. M. Jacques de Dismude l'Africain; Contribution à l'histoire de la Société antiesclavagiste belge 1888-1894. Bruxelles, Libraire Coloniale, R. Weverbergh [1929] 159p. (M967V58)

3503 Viaene, Ernest. Contribution à l'ethnologie Congolaise, by Ernest Viaene et Fernand Bernard. Reprinted from Anthropos, Revue Internationale d'Ethnologie et de Linguistique, 1910. (M-967.5V65)

3504 Wack, Henry Wellington. The story of the Congo Free State; social, political, and economic aspects of the Belgian system of government in Central Africa. New York and London, G. P. Putnam's Sons, 1905. 634p. (M967.5W11)

3505 Ward, Herbert. Five years with the Congo cannibals. London, Chatto and Windus, 1890. 308p. (M916.75W21)

3506 Ward, Herbert. My life with Stanley's rear guard. New York, C. L. Webster & Co., 1891. 151p. (M967.5W21m)

3507 Ward, Herbert. A voice from the Congo; comprising stories, anecdotes, and descriptive notes, with illustrations from photographs, sculpture, and drawings by the author. New York, C. Scribner's Sons, 1910. 330p. (M967.5W21)

3508 Weeks, John H. Among the primitive Bakongo. London, Seeley, Service and Co., ltd., 1914. 318p. (M967.5W41a)

3509 Weeks, John H. Congo life and folklore. London, The Religious Tract Society, 1911. 468p. (M967.5W41c)

3510 Werbrouck, R. La campagne des Troupes coloniales belges en Abyssinie. [Léopoldville, Congo Belge, 194-.] 153p. (M967.-5W49)

3511 Wigny, Pierre Louis. A ten year plan for the economic and social development of the Belgian Congo. 2nd ed. New York, Belgian Government Information Center, 1951. 72p. (M967.5W63t)

3512 Wildeman, Émile de. Le Congo belge possède-t-il des ressources en matiéres premières pour la pâte à papier? [Bruxelles, G.

van Campenhout, 1942.] 156p. (AM580W64)

3513   Wissmann, Hermann von. My second journey through Equatorial Africa, from the Congo to the Zambesi, in the years 1886 and 1887. London, Chatto & Windus, 1891. 326p. (M967W76b)

EASTERN AFRICA

GENERAL

3514   Abubakr, Abdulla M. The life of Khalifa Abubakr Siddik. Nairobi, The Eagle Press, 1925. 31p.

3515   Adimola, A. B. Lobo Acoli. (A geographical survey of Acoli district.) Nairobi, East African Literature Bureau, 1956. 37p. (Written in Lwo)

3516   African Education Commission. Education in East Africa, New York, Phelps-Stokes Fund, 1925. 416p. (AM370.96Af8e)

3517   Aggrey Memorial School. Bulletin. Registered at the Government Department of Education, Makerere, Kampala . . . Akatabo Akanyonyola Aggrey Memorial School, Esomero lyawandikibwa Mu Kitongole kya Masomero, Makerere, Kampala . . . Buganda, Aggrey Memorial School, n.d. 19p. (M967.611Ag3)

3518   Agriculture and Veterinary Services. Nyasi ni mali [Grass is wealth.] Nairobi, The Eagle Press, 1950. 34p.

3519   Appleby, L. L. Amatala amasamgafu [Village life and how to improve it.] Nairobi, The Eagle Press, 1949. 12p.

3520   Ashall, C. Nzige: The desert locust. Nairobi, The Eagle Press, 1952. 15p.

3521   Baker, E. C. Mwarabu na binti wake na hadithi nyingine [The Arab and his daughter, and other stories.] Nairobi, The Eagle Press, 1950. 59p.

3522   Baker, Richard St. B. Africa drums. London, Lindsay Drummond, Ltd.m 1943. 159p. (AM916.76B17a)

3523   Baker, Richard St. B. Men of the trees. New York, L. MacVeagh, The Dial Press, 1931. 283p. (AM916.76B17)

3524   Baker, Richard St. B. Tambours Africains. Paris, Stock, Delmain et Boutelleau, 1949. 234p. (AM916.76B17t)

3525   Barbosa, Duarte. The book of Duarte Barbosa. An account of the countries bordering on the Indian Ocean and their inhabitants. Completed about the year 1518 A. D. Translated from the Portuguese text. London, Printed for the Hakluyt Society, 1918-21. 2v. (AM967B23b)

3526 Bigland, Eileen. Pattern in black and white. London, Lindsay Drummond, 1940. 159p. (AM967.6B48)

3527 Burton, Richard Francis. First footsteps in East Africa; or an exploration of Harar. London, Longman, Brown, Green and Longmans, 1856. 648p. (AM967.7B95f)

3528 Capon, Mary. Habari za bendera iitwayo Union Jack Kitabu hiki kimetungwa kwa ajili ya Scouts na Girl Guides wa Afrika ya mashariki [A book on the history and formation of the Union Jack for scouts and girl guides in East Africa.] Nairobi, The Eagle Press, 1950. 8p.

3529 Carnegie Corporation of New York. Report of Rev. Anson Phelps Stokes on education; native welfare and race relations in East and South Africa. 59p. (AM370 C21)

3530 Carpenter, Frank George. Uganda to the Cape. Garden City, New York, Doubleday, Page and Co., 1924. 263p. (M916 C22u)

3531 Carson, J. B. The preliminary survey for the Kenya and Uganda railway 1891-1892. Nairobi, The Eagle Press, 1950. 16p. (M967.6C23p)

3532 Church, Archibald George. East Africa, a new dominion; a crucial experiment in tropical development and its significance to the British Empire. London, H. F. & G. Witherby, 1927. 315p. (M967.6C47e)

3533 Churchill, Winston Leonard Spencer. My African journey. London, Hodder and Stoughton, 1908. 226p. (M916 C47m)

3534 Cory, H. Sikikizeni mashairi. Nairobi, The Eagle Press, 1950. 34p.

3535 Coupland, Reginald. East Africa and its invaders, from the earliest times to the death of Serrid Said in 1856. Oxford, The Clarendon Press, 1938. 584p. (M967.6C83)

3536 Coupland, Reginald. The exploitation of East Africa. London, Faber and Faber, Ltd., 1939. 507p. (AM967.6C83e)

3537 Culwick, G. M. Turiria ki? [What shall we eat?] Nairobi, The Eagle Press, 1950. 24p.

3538 Davies, D. A. East Africa's weather service. Nairobi, The Eagle Press, 1952. 32p. (M967.6D29)

3539 Dawson, F. C. James Hannington, first bishop of Eastern Equatorial Africa. A history of his life and work 1847-1885. New York, Anson D. F. Randolph and Co., 1886. 442p. (M967-D32j)

3540 Deuber, A. G. C. British East Africa; economic and commercial conditions in British East Africa during the immediate post-war period. London, H. M. Stationery Office, 1948. 93p. (AM967.6D48b)

3541 Diva, D. E. Sungura Mjanja [Here is a rascal.] Nairobi, The Eagle Press, 1953. 29p.

3542 Diva, David E. Ujiongezee maarika kitabu cha kwanza. Nairobi, The Eagle Press, 1950. 7p.

3543 Diva, David E. Ujiongezee maarifa. Nairobi, The Eagle Press, 1950. 7p.

3544 Diva, David E. Ujiongezee maarifa; Kitabu cha tatu. Nairobi, The Eagle Press, 1950. 8p.

3545 Diva, David E. Ujiongezee maarifa; Kitabu cha nne. Nairobi, The Eagle Press, 1950. 8p.

3546 Diva, David E. Ujiongezee maarifa; Kitabu cha tano. Nairobi, The Eagle Press, 1953. 8p.

3547 Diva, David E. Ujiongezee maarifa; Kitabu cha sita. Nairobi, The Eagle Press, 1953. 8p.

3548 Diva, David E. Ujiongezee maarifa; Kitabu cha saba. Nairobi, The Eagle Press, 1953. 8p.

3549 Diva, David E. Ujiongezee maarifa; Kitabu cha nane. Nairobi, The Eagle Press, 1953. 8p.

3550 Drummond, Henry. Tropical Africa. New York, C. Scribner's Sons, 1903. 228p. (AM916 D84)

3551 Duff, Hector Livingstone. African small chop. London, Hodder and Stoughton, Ltd., 1932. 222p. (AM916.76D87a)

3552 Dundas, Charles. African crossroads. London, Macmillan, St. Martin's Press, 1955. 242p. (M967.6D91)

3553 East Africa High Commission. East African Leprosy Research Centre (John Lowe Memorial) Nairobi, Government Printer, 1956. (M967.6 Ea71)

3554 East Africa High Commission. East African medical survey. Department report. Mwanza, East Africa High Commission, 1952. (M614.1Ea7)

3555 East Africa High Commission. East African veterinary research organization, Annual report, 1950. Nairobi, The Government Printer, 1951. 37p. (M967.6Ea7)

3556 East Africa Royal Commission. The future of East Africa; a summary of the report of the Royal Commission with an index to the report. London, The Africa Bureau, 1955. 48p. (M-967.6Ea7f)

3557 Elkin, W. An African labor force; two case studies in East African factory employment. Kampala, East African Institute of Social Research, 1956. 59p. (M967.61EL5)

3558 Elphinstone, Howard. Africans and the law. Nairobi, The Eagle Press, 1951. 75p.

3559 Elphinstone, Howard. The standard Swahili examination. Nairobi, The Eagle Press, 1950. 70p.

3560 Farson, Negley. Last chance in Africa. New York, Harcourt, Brace, 1950. 381p. (M916.76F251)

3561 Faucett, L. W. and M. G. M. Awaragasia akanykaonwon [Nine fables.] Nairobi, The Eagle Press, 1950. 20p.

3562 Field, Henry. Contributions to the anthropology of the Faiyum, Sinai, Sudan and Kenya. Berkeley, University of California Press, 1952. 352p. (AM572F45c)

3563 Fisher, Ruth B. On the borders of Pigmy land. London, Marshall Bros., n.d. 215p. (M967.6F53o)

3564 Forbes-Watson, R. Charles New. London, Nelson, 1951. 78p. (MB9N42f)

3565 Frank, W. and C. G. Richards. Kisa cha yohana njinga na utiivu wake. Dar-es-salaam, The Eagle Press, 1951. 14p.

3566 French, H. M. Ngozi ni mali [Hides are wealth.] Nairobi, The Eagle Press, 1950. 32p.

3567 Garriock, L. H. Omulimu gw'omukazi mu maka. Nairobi, The Eagle Press, 1952. 34p.

3568 Great Britain. Colonial Office. The British territories in East and Central Africa, 1945-1950. London, H. M. Stationery Office, 1950. 165p. (M967.6G79b)

3569 Great Britain. Colonial Office. Despatches from the governors of Kenya, Uganda and Tanganyika and from the administrator, East Africa High Commission commenting on the East Africa Royal Commission, 1953-55. London, Her Majesty's Stationery Office, 1956. 196p.

3570 Great Britain. Colonial Office. Introducing East Africa. London, H. M. Stationery Office, 1950. 91p. (M967.6G81i)

3571 Great Britain. Colonial Office. Report on the East Africa High Commission, 1954. London, H. M. Stationery Office, n.d. (M-354.676G79)

3572　Great Britain.　Colonial Office.　East Africa Royal Commission Report.　London, H. M. Stationery Office, 1955.　482p.　(M967.-6G79r)

3573　Gulliver, Pamela H.　The central Nilo-Hamites.　London, International African Institute, 1953.　106p.　(AM967.6G95)

3574　Gulliver, Pamela H.　The family herds; a study of two pastoral tribes in East Africa, the Jie and Turkana.　London, Routledge & K. Paul, 1955.　271p.　(M967.6G94)

3575　Hailey, William Malcolm.　East Africa; Uganda, Kenya, Tanganyika.　London, H. M. Stationery Office, 1950.　358p.　(AM354-H12n)

3576　Head, M. E.　Ensi mwe tuli n'abantu nga bagyeyambisa [The land and how men use it.]　Nairobi, The Eagle Press, 1953. 8p.

3577　Hemingway, Ernest.　Green hills of Africa.　New York, C. Scribner's Sons, 1935.　294p.　(AM799.2 H37)

3578　Hertslet, Jessie.　Mpala, awaragan naka esapat loka Afrika: Mpala, the story of an African boy.　Nairobi, The Eagle Press, 1951. 81p.

3579　Hertslet, Jessie.　Nyithindo e dala kendo e skul: Children at home and at school.　Nairobi, The Eagle Press, 1950.　70p.

3580　Hobley, Charles William.　Bantu beliefs and magic, with particular reference to the Kikuyu and Kamba tribes of Kenya Colony, together with some reflections on East Africa after the war.　London, H. F. and G. Witherby, 1922.　312p.　(M967.6H65)

3581　Hobley, Charles William.　Ethnology of a Kamba and other African tribes.　Cambridge, The University Press, 1910.　172p.　(AM-572H65)

3582　Holding, Mary E.　Kamincuria metho [Meru reading primer for adults.]　Nairobi, The Eagle Press, n.d.　26p.

3583　Holding, Mary E.　Mucii jumwega [The good home.]　Nairobi, The Eagle Press, 1950.　23p.

3584　Holding, Mary E.　Tunkunyua ki? [What shall we drink?] Nairobi, The Eagle Press, 1950.　15p.

3585　Holding, Mary E.　Usafi was nyumbani [Cleanliness in the home.] Nairobi, The Eagle Press, 1951.　23p.

3586　Holding, Mary E.　Utheru bwa mucii [Cleanliness in the home.] Nairobi, The Eagle Press, 1950.　14p.

3587　Holgate, Alice M.　Ngono cia afya [Hygiene games and stories.] Nairobi, The Eagle Press, 1950.　6p.

3588 Holmes, Olive, Peoples, politics and peanuts in Eastern Africa. New York, Foreign Policy Association, 1950. 163p. (AM-967.6H73p)

3589 Hoyt, Elizabeth E. An old man and his children: Mzee na wanawe. Kampala, The Eagle Press, 1953. 65p.

3590 Hubbard, Mrs. Margaret (Carson). No one to blame; an African adventure. New York, Minton, Balch and Co., 1934. 276p. (AM916 H86)

3591 Humphrey, N. Ensolo zirina ebyetaago bimu nga ffe [Animals have the same needs as we do.] Translated by S. K. Mulindwa. Kampala, East African Literature Bureau, 1950. 10p.

3592 Huntingford, George Wynn Brereton. The northern Nilo-Hamites. London, International African Institute, 1953. 108p. (M967.-6H92n)

3593 Huntingford, George Wynn Brereton. The southern Nilo-Hamites. London, International Institute (African), 1953. 152p. (AM-967.6H92s)

3594 Hussey, E. R. Higher education in East Africa. Report of the Commission for the colonies. Supplement to the Journal of the Royal African Society, 1937. 19p. (AM370H96)

3595 Huxley, Elsepth. Race and politics in Kenya, a correspondence between Elspeth Huxley and Margary Perham with an introduction by Lord Lugard. London, Faber and Faber, 1944. 247p. (M967.6H98r)

3596 Huxley, Elsepth. The sorcerer's apprentice; a journey through East Africa. London, Chatte and Windus, 1948. 265p. (M-916.7H98)

3597 Huxley, Julian Sorrell. Africa view. New York and London, Harper and Brothers, 1931. 478p. (M967.6H98)

3598 Isaacs, Nathaniel. Travels and adventures in Eastern Africa. Cape Town, The Van Riebeeck Society, n.d. 2v. (M916.831s7)

3599 Jackson, Frederick John. Early days in East Africa. With a foreword by Lord Cranworth. London, E. Arnold and Co., 1930. (M967.6J13)

3600 Johnson, Martin Elmer. Over African jungles. New York, Harcourt, Brace and Co., [c1935.] 263p. (M916.76J63)

3601 Johnson, Martin Elmer. Safari. New York, Putnam's Sons, 1928. 294p. (M916.76J63s)

3602 Johnson, Osa Helen (Leighty). Four years in paradise. New York, Halycon House, 1944. 192p. (M916.76J636f)

3603　Johnson, Victor Eugene. Pioneering for Christ in East Africa. Ill., Augustana Book Concern, 1948. 192p. (AM276.8J63p)

3604　Jury, S. J. Cash accounting for the African trader. Nairobi, Sir Isaac Pitman and Sons, Ltd., and The Eagle Press, 1951. 31p.

3605　Kakembo, Robert H. An African soldier speaks. London, Edinburgh House Press, 1947. 48p. (M967.6K12a)

3606　Kaleya, Stephen M. Kedo ni ngima [The fight for health.] Nairobi, The Eagle Press, 1949. 12p.

3607　Karanga, R. The adventures of Ngondo, Mungai and Wangari. London, Nelson and Sons, Ltd., 1951. 82p.

3608　Kawere, Edward K. N. Zinunula Omunaku. Nairobi, The Eagle Press, 1954. 109p.

3609　Kebaso, John K. Jinsi Afrika mashariki inavyowiwa deni kubwa na utawala wa sola ye kiingereza [East Africa owes much to British rule.] Nairobi, The Eagle Press, 1953. 45p.

3610　Koenig, Oskar. The Masai story. London, Michael Joseph, 1956. 189p. (M967.63K81)

3611　Koeune, Esther. The African housewife and her home. Nairobi, The Eagle Press, 1952. 186p.

3612　Koeune, Esther. How to teach hygiene, home nursing and first aid: A book for primary schools and welfare center in East Africa. Nairobi, The Eagle Press, 1950. 64p.

3613　Koeune, Esther. Mama wa Afrika na nyumba yake [The African housewife and her home.] Nairobi, East Africa Literature Bureau, 1955. 40p.

3614　Koeune, Esther. Mapambo [Decorating and furnishing.] Nairobi, The East Africa Literature Bureau, 1953. 25p.

3615　Koeune, Esther. Upishi. [Cookery.] Nairobi, East Africa Literature Bureau, 1955. 60p.

3616　Koeune, Esther. Utunzaji wa mtoto na uuguzaji wa nyumbani [Child welfare and home nursing.] Nairobi, East African Literature Bureau, 1955. 38p.

3617　Koeune, Esther. Utunzaji wa nyumba [cleaning and care of the home.] Nairobi, East African Literature Bureau, 1955. 34p.

3618　Koeune, Esther. Uwanja [The compound.] Nairobi, East African Literature Bureau, 1955. 12p.

3619　Krapt, Ludwig. Travels, researches and missionary labours, during an eighteen years' residence in Eastern Africa. Together with Journeys to Jogga, Usambara, Ukambani, Shoa, Abessinia, and

Khartum, and a coasting voyage from Mombay to Cape Delgado. With an appendix respecting the snow-capped mountains of Eastern Africa; the source of the Nile; the languages
and literature of Abessinia and Eastern Africa, etc., etc., and
a concise account of geographic researches in Eastern Africa
by Dr. Livingstone in September last, by E. G. Ravenstein,
F.R.S. London, Trubner and Fields, 1860. 566p. (M916 K86)

3620 Lambert, H. E. Ameru baria bakeeja nyumene. [The Meru yet to
come]. Nairobi, East African Literature Bureau, 1956. 32p.
(Written in Meru).

3621 Laubach, F. C. Enjigiriza y'okusoma [Alphabet book.] Nairobi,
The Eagle Press, 1952. 52p.

3622 Leclercq, Jules. Aux sources du Nil par le chemin de fer de l'
Ouganda. Paris, Plon-Nourrit et cie, 1913. 302p. (M916.-
76L49)

3623 Leigh, William Robinson. Frontiers of enchantment; an artist's
adventures in Africa. New York, Simon and Schuster, 1938.
299p. (AM591 L53)

3624 Lindblom, Gerhard. The Akamba in British East Africa, an ethnological monograph. Uppsala, 1920. 607p. (M967.6L64a)

3625 Lloyd, B. W. Men of Livingstone; a brief account of their part in
his major expeditions 1852-1873. London, Chas. J. Sawyer,
Ltd., 1955. 23p. (M967.96L74)

3626 Lloyd, T. E. African harvest. London, Lutterworth Press, 1953.
96p. (M967.6L77a)

3627 Loftus, E. A. Elton and the East African coast slave-trade. Being
extracts from the diary of Captain James Elton. London,
Macmillan and Co., 1952. 63p. (M967.6L82g)

3628 Loftus, E. A. Gregory; the Great Rift Valley. Nairobi, Thomas
Nelson and Sons, 1952. 63p. (M967.6L82g)

3629 Loftus, E. A. Johnston and Kilimanjaro. London, Thomas Nelson
and Sons, 1952. 79p. (M967.6L82j)

3630 Loftus, E. A. Speke and the Nile source. Nairobi, East African
Literature Bureau, 1954. 73p. (MB9Sp31)

3631 Loftus, E. A. Thomson; through Masai land. London, Thomas
Nelson and Sons, 1951. 72p. (M967.6L82t)

3632 Loveridge, Arthur. Tomorrow's a holiday (Kesho siku kuku).
New York and London, Harper and Bros., 1947. 278p. (M-
968.963L94t)

3633 Lowdermilk, Walter C. Riathana ria ikumi na rimwe [The eleventh commandment or care of the land.] Great Britain, W. & F. Mackay and Co., n.d. 16p.

3634 Lugard, Frederick John Dealtry. The rise of our East African empire; early efforts in Nyasaland and Uganda, with 130 illustrations from drawings and photographs under the personal superintendence of the author, also 14 specially prepared maps. Edinburgh and London, W. Blackwood and Sons, 1893. 2 vols. (M960L96r)

3635 Mackenzie, Jean Kenyon. Mwekuru mwaria [Talking women.] Nairobi, The Eagle Press, 1951. 52p.

3636 Macmillan, Mona. Introducing East Africa. London, Faber and Faber, 1952. 312p. (M967.6M22)

3637 Malo, S. Sigend luo ma duogo chuny [Merry stories.] Nairobi, The Eagle Press, 1951. 42p.

3638 Mane midwaro? Midenyo koso yieng'o? What do you want? [Starvation or nourishment.] Nairobi, The Eagle Press, 1950. 8p.

3639 Markham, Beryl (Clutterbuck). West with the night. Boston, Houghton Mifflin Co., 1942. 293p. (M916.76M34w)

3640 Masefield, G. B. Omulimi w'omu Uganda [The Uganda farmer.] Nairobi, The Eagle Press, 1951. 186p.

3641 Mason, Philip. A new deal in East Africa: [the basic arguments and certain implications of the Report of the Royal Commission on East Africa.] London, Royal Institute of International Affairs [1955.] 37p. (M967.6M38)

3642 Matheson, J. K. East African agriculture. A short survey of the agriculture of Kenya, Uganda, Tanganyika, and Zanzibar and of its principal products. London and New York, Oxford University Press, 1950. 332p. (M967M42e)

3643 Mathias, C. A. and Kenneford. Wangula akabi k'okufa mu makubo [Keep death off the road.] Nairobi, The Eagle Press, 1948. 25p.

3644 McCutcheon, John Tinney. In Africa: hunting adventures in the big game country. Indianapolis, The Bobbs Merrill Co., [c1910.] 402p. (M916M13)

3645 McDermott, P. L. British East Africa or Ibea; a history of the formation and work of the Imperial British East Africa Company. London, Chapman and Hall, 1893. 382p. (M967.6M14)

3646 McKilliam, K. R. Gavumenti kye ki? [What is government?] Nairobi, East African Literature Bureau, 1956. 18p.

3647 Medical Training Centre, King George VI Hospital. Elementary notes for nurses on nursing procedures hygiene anatomy and physiology. Nairobi, East African Literature Bureau, 1956. 143p.

3648 Mitchell, Philip Euen. African afterthoughts. London, Hutchinson, [1954.] 287p. (M967.6M69a)

3649 Morrill, Madge Haines. Fighting Africa's black magic. Mountain View, California, Pacific Press, 1938. 155p. (AM916.76M83)

3650 Mwikalile wa askali [Life of an Askari in the army.] Nairobi, The Eagle Press, 1950. 24p.

3651 Norden, H. White and black in East Africa. London, H. F. & G. Witherby, 1924. 304p. (AM916N75)

3652 Okukozesa accounts: Using accounts, a handbook to assist Africans in trade. Kampala, East African Literature Bureau, n.d. 39p.

3653 Oldham, Joseph Houldsworth. New hope in Africa; [the aims of the Capricorn Africa Society.] London, New York, Longmans, Green [1955.] 102p. (M968011n)

3654 Omar, C. A. Shariff. Hadithi ya Hazina binti sultani [The tale of Hazina, the sultan's daughter.] Nairobi, The Eagle Press, 1951. 33p.

3655 Omar, C. A. Shariff. Kisa cha Hasan-Li-Basir [The Adventures of Hasan-Li-basir.] Nairobi, The Eagle Press, 1951. 30p.

3656 Omar, C. A. Shariff. Kisiwa cha Pemba historia na masimuliza: History and traditions of the island of Pemba. 21p.

3657 Ominde, S. H. The Luo girl from infancy to marriage. London, Macmillan, 1952. 69p.

3658 Opwa, Antonio. An East African Chief in England. Nairobi, The Eagle Press, 1952. 38p. (MB90p8)

3659 Parry, E. Winifred. Red cross book of health and welfare for East Africa. Nairobi, The Eagle Press, 1953. 35p.

3660 Patterson, John Henry. In the grip of the nyika; further adventures in British East Africa. New York, The Macmillan Co., 1909. 389p. (M916P27)

3661 Patterson, John Henry. The man-eaters of Tsavo and other African adventures. New York, The Macmillan Co., 1927. 401p. (M916 P27m)

3662 Perham, Margery. East African future. A report to the Fabian Colonial Bureau. London, Victor Gollancz, 1952. 47p.

3663 Perren, G. Guide to teaching English in African primary and intermediate schools together with schemes of work. Nairobi, The Eagle Press, 1954. 49p.

3664   Perrott, D. V. Bagamoyo mpaka Uganda Speke na uvumbi wa Nile Bagamoyo to Uganda [Speke's discovery of the Nile source.] Kampala, The East African Literature Bureau, 1955. 23p.

3665   Perrott, D. V. Safari za watangulizi [Kroph and Rebmann in Uchaga, Vuga and Ukambani.] Kampala, The Eagle Press, 1955. 20p.

3666   Perrott, D. V. Thomson ukikuyuni, umassani na Katika nchi ya Nyanza [Thomson in the country of the Kikuyu and Masai in Nyanza.] Kampala, East African Literature Bureau, n.d. 20p.

3667   Perrott, D. V. Uvumbuzi wa ziwa Nyasa na mto Ruvuma na safari za Ugala na Umasali [Exploring Lake Nyasa and the Rovuma river. Journeys among the Galla and Masa.] Kampala, The Eagle Press, n.d. 22p.

3668   Powys, Llewlyn. Black laughter. New York, Harcourt, Brace and Co., [c1924.] 216p. (M916 P86)

3669   Price, William Salter. My third campaign in East Africa. London, W. Hunt and Co., 1891. 33p. (AM916.76P93)

3670   Reche, Otto. Zur ethnographie des abflusslosen gebietes Deutsch Ost Afrikas . . . Hamburg, L. Frederich and Co., 1914. 130p. (AM572 R24)

3671   Reflections on the report of the Royal Commission on East Africa. London, The Africa Bureau, n.d. 46p.

3672   Reusch, Richard. History of East Africa. Evang. Missionary G.M.B.H., 1954. 343p. (M967.6R31h)

3673   Richards, C. G. Krapf, missionary and explorer. London, Nelson, 1950. 85p. (MB9K86r)

3674   Ryan, C. W. W. Kwa nini tuna haja [Why do we have government.] Nairobi, The Eagle Press, 1954. 17p.

3675   Ryan, C. W. W. Maendeleo na jasho [Progress and perspiration.] Nairobi, The Eagle Press, 1954. 19p.

3676   Ryan, C. W. W. Mtu maskini mwenye sh. 1,000,000. [The poor man with a million shillings.] Nairobi, The Eagle Press, 1954. 16p

3677   Shackleton, Charles Walter. East African experiences, 1916, from the diary of a South African infantryman in the German East

African campaign. Durban, South Africa, The Knox Publishing Co., 1940. 123p. (M968Sh1)

3678   Sheldon, M. F. Sultan to Sultan. Boston, Mass., Arena Co., 1892. 435p. (AM916 Sh4)

3679   Slater, Isobel. Mafunzo katika kutunza wanyama wetu [Education in animal welfare; a series of 12 easy lessons for use in East Africa.] Kampala, The Eagle Press, 1955. 62p.

3680   Smith, J. Stephen. Aids to scoutmasters in East Africa. Nairobi, The Eagle Press, 1951. 49p.

3681   Soper, J. R. P. Instrakta ni mwalimu [An agricultural instructor is also a teacher.] Nairobi, The Eagle Press, n.d. 7p.

3682   Stoneham, Charles Thurley. Out of barbarism. London, Museum Press, 1955. 190p. (M967.6St71)

3683   Streeter, Daniel Willard. Denatured Africa. New York, London, Putnam's Sons, 1926. 338p. (M799.2 St8)

3684   Swayne, George Carless. Lake Victoria. Edinburgh and London, W. Blackwood and Sons, 1868. 342p. (M916.76Sw2)

3685   Synge, Patrick M. Mountains of the moon. London, L. Drummond, Ltd., 1937. 221p. (M916.76Sy7)

3686   Thornton, R. S. Maelezo ya mchezo wa mpira [A guide to the rules of football.] Nairobi, The Eagle Press, 1951. 39p.

3687   Thurnwald, Richard C. Black and white in East Africa; the fabric of a new civilization; a study of social contact and adoption of life in East Africa, . . . with a chapter on women. London, G. Routledge and Sons, 1935. 419p. (M960T42)

3688   Tjader, Richard. The big game of Africa . . . with many illustrations from photographs by the author. New York and London, D. Appleton and Co., 1910. 363p. (M960 T54)

3689   Torrance, Arthur. Junglemania. New York, The Macaulay Co., 1933. 310p. (AM960 T63j)

3690   Trowell, H. C. Mmere ki gye tusaanira okulya? [What food should we eat?] Nairobi, The Eagle Press, 1951. 23p.

3691   Twining, H. M. and Esther Koeune. Masomo ya afya msalaba mwekudu kwa nchi ya Tanganyika [The red cross health course for Tanganyika.] Kampala, The Eagle Press, 1955. 73p.

3692   Ukwenda ng'aragu kana buthi [Which do you want, starvation or nourishment?] Nairobi, The Eagle Press, 1949. 9p.

3693   Vanden Bergh, Leonard John. On the trail of the pigmies; an anthropological exploration under the cooperation of the American museum of natural history and American universities. New York, The James A. McCann Co., 1921. 264p. (M967.-6V28o)

3694   Weston, Frank. The black slaves of Prussia. Boston and New York, Houghton Mifflin Co., 1918. 23p. (AM960 W52b)

3695   Weule, Karl. Native life in East Africa; the results of an ethnological research expedition. London, I. Pitman and Sons, 1909. 431p. (M967.6W54)

3696   White, Stewart Edward. African camp fires. Garden City, New York, Doubleday, Page and Co., 1913. 378p. (M916.76 W58)

3697   Wilhelm, prince of Sweden. Among pygmies and gorillas with the Swedish zoological expedition to central Africa, 1921. New York, E. P. Dutton, n.d. 296p. (M967.6W64a)

3698   Wilhelm, prince of Sweden. Among pygmies and gorillas. London, Gyldendale, 1926. 296p. (M916.76W64)

3699   The Year book and guide to East Africa. London, S. Low, Marston, 1950. (M967.6Y32)

3700   Young, T. Cullen. African ways and wisdom; a contribution towards understanding. London, The United Society for Christian Literature, [1937.] 143p. (AM572 Y87)

UGANDA

3701   André Marie. Les martyrs noirs de L'Ouganda. Paris, Librairie Bloud et Gay, 1936. 203p. (M967.61An2)

3702   Ansorge, William John. Under the African sun; a description of native races in Uganda, sporting adventures and other experiences. London, William Heinemann, 1899. 355p. (M916An8)

3703   Anywar, Reuben Stephen. Acoli ki ker megi. Nairobi, The Eagle Press, 1954. 223p. (M967.61 An9)

3704   Ashe, Robert Pickering. Chronicles of Uganda. New York, A.D.F. Randolph and Co., 1895. 480p. (M967 As3)

3705   Bakaluba, E. Buganda n'ensimbi zaayo: [Buganda and its systems of currency.] Kampala, The Eagle Press, 1951. 20p. (M-967.61B17b)

3706   Bell, W. D. M. Karamojo safari. New York, Harcourt, Brace, 1949, 298p. (AM967.615 B41k)

3707   Butt, Audrey J. The Nilotes of the Anglo-Egyptian Sudan and Uganda. London, International African Institute, 1952. 198p. (M962.4B98n)

3708 Carpenter, Frank George. Uganda to the Cape; Uganda, Zanzibar, Tanganyika territory, Mozambique, Rhodesia, Union of South Africa. Garden City, N. Y., Doubleday, Page & Company, 1924. 263p. (M916C22u)

3709 Carson, J. B. The preliminary survey for the Kenya and Uganda railway 1891-1892. Nairobi, The Eagle Press, 1950. 16p. (M967.6 C23p)

3710 Churchill, Winston Leonard Spencer. My African journey. London, Hodder and Stoughton, 1908. 226p. (M916C47m)

3711 Cunningham, James Frederick. Uganda and its peoples; notes on the protectorate of Uganda, especially the anthropology and ethnology of its indigences. London, Hutchinson and Co., 1905. 370p. (M967.61 C91)

3712 East Africa High Commision. East African Leprosy Research Centre (John Lowe Memorial). Annual report. 1955-56. Nairobi, Government Printer, 1956. (M967.6Ea7L)

3713 East African Statistical Department. African population of Uganda Protectorate. Nairobi, 1950. 59p. (M967.61 Ea7a)

3714 Elkan, W. An African labour force; two case studies in East African factory employment. Kampala, East African Institute of Social Research, 1956. 59p (M967.61 EL5)

3715 Fahs, Sophia B. L., . . . Uganda's white man of work; a story of Alexander M. Mackay . . . Foreign Missionary Society United Brethren in Christ, 1907. 289p. (MC9 M19f)

3716 Fisher, nee Ruth Hurditch. Twilight tales of the Black Baganda. London, Marshal Bros., Ltd., n.d. 198p. (M967 F53)

3717 Ford, V.C.R. The trade of Lake Victoria; a geographical study. Kampala, East African Institute of Social Research, 1955. 65p.

3718 Gray, Sir John Milner. Ebyafaayo ebitonotono ku Uganda. [Short history of Uganda.] Nairobi, The East African Literature Bureau, 1956. 25p.

3719 Great Britain. Colonial Office. Annual report on Uganda, 1946, 1947, 1949. London, H. M. Stationery Office. (M967.61 G79a)

3720 Guillebaud, M. L. G. Aira a Uganda. Nairobi, The Eagle Press, 1951. 22p.

3721 Hailey, William Malcolm Hailey, baron. East Africa: Uganda, Kenya, Tanganyika. London, H. M. Stationery Office, 1950. 358p. (AM354H12n)

3722 Hattersley, Charles W. The Baganda at home, with one hundred pictures of life and work in Uganda. London, Religious Tract.

Soc., 1908, XVI, 227p.   (M967.61 H28b)

3723   Hayley, Thomas Theodore Steiger.   The anatomy of Lango religion and groups.   Cambridge, The University Press, 1947.
207p.   (AM572.9H13a)

3724   Hertslet, Jessie.   Abaana mu maka ne mu ssomero: [Children at
home and at school.]   1950.   61p.

3725   Johnston, Harry Hamilton.   The Uganda protectorate; an attempt
to give some description of the physical geography, botany,
zoology, anthropology, languages and history of the territories
under British protection in East Central Africa. . . . London,
Hutchinson and Co., 1902.   2 vols.   (M967.61 J64u)

3726   Kagwa, Apolo.   The customs of the Bakanda.   New York, Columbia
University Press, 1934.   199p.   (M967.61K11c)

3727   Kagwa, Apolo.   Ekitabo kya basekabaka bebuganda, Nabebunyoro,
Nakekoki, Nabetoro Nabenkole.   London, Luzac and Co., 1912.
340p.   (M967.61 K11ek)

3728   Kagwa, Apolo.   Ekitabo kye mpisa za Baganda (the customs of Baganda in the Luganda language) kyawandikibua Sir Appolo
Kagwa.   Kampala, Uganda Printing and Publishing Co., 1918.
319p.   (M967.16K11e)

3729   Kagwa, Apolo.   Engero za Baganda (Uganda folklore stories).
London, The Sheldon Press, 1927.   120p.   (M967.61 K11en)

3730   Kagwa, Apolo.   The tales of Sir Apolo, Uganda folklore and prov-
erb.   London, The Religious Tract Society, n.d.   95p.   (M967.-
61K11t)

3731   Kakoza, Polycarp K.   Omupiira [Football.]   Kampala, The Eagle
Press, 1953.   74p.

3732   Kalibala, Ernest Balintuma.   Wakaima and the clay man, and
other African folktales.   New York, Green and Co., 1946. 6p.
(M398K12)

3733   Kasirye, Joseph.   Stanislaus Mugwanya (a biography).   Nairobi,
The Eagle Press, 1953.   22p.

3734   Katate, Aloysius G.   Abagabe b'Ankole; Ekitabo I [History of the
Kings of Ankole.]   Kampala, The Eagle Press, 1955.   147p.
(M967.61 K15a vol. 1)

3735   Katate, Aloysius G.   Abagabe b'Ankole, E Kitabo II.   History of
the Kings of Ankole.   Kampala, the Eagle Press, 1955.   89p.
(M967.61 K15a vol. 2)

3736   Katiti C. B.   Ishe-Katabazi.   [Traditional stories of the Ankole
people of Uganda.]   Nairobi, The Eagle Press, 1947. 40p.

3737 Katyanku, Lucy O. Obwomezi by-omukama Duhaga II: [Life of Duhaga II.] Nairobi, The Eagle Press, 1950. 71p.

3738 Kirkland, Caroline. Some African highways; a journey of two American women to Uganda and the Transvaal. Boston, D. Estes & Company [c1908.] 345p. (M968.2K63)

3739 Kitching, Arthur Leonard. On the backwaters of the Nile; studies of some child races of Central Africa. New York, C. Scribner's Sons, 1912. 295p. (M967.61 K64)

3740 Kollmann, Karl Paul. The Victoria Nyanza the land, the races and their customs. . . .London, S. Sonnenschein and Co., Ltd., 1899. 254p. (M967.612 K83v)

3741 Latham, Clare L. The teaching of civics in East African primary schools with special reference to Uganda. Nairobi, The Eagle Press, 1950. 18p.

3742 Leclercq, Jules. Aux sources du Nil par le chemin de fer de l'Ouganda. Paris, Plon-Nourrit et cie, 1913. 302p. (M916.-76L49)

3743 Lloyd, Albert Bushnell. A life's thrills; brief records of my life, 1894-1946. London, Lutterworth Press, 1948. 142p. (M967.-61 L77)

3744 Lloyd, Albert Bushnell. Uganda to Khartoum; life and adventure on the Upper Nile. New York, E. P. Dutton & Co., 1906. 312p. (M916L77u)

3745 Lubambula, Y. B. Ennyimba ezimu: [Some Luganda songs.] Nairobi. The Eagle Press, 1953. 17p.

3746 Lugard, Frederick John Dealtry, baron. The rise of our East African empire; early efforts in Nyasaland and Uganda. Edinburgh and London, W. Blackwood and Sons, 1893. 2v. (M-960L96r)

3747 Lule, Julia M. Ssebato bazannya, by Julia M. Lule and E. N. Asaph. London, Longmans, Green and Co., 1950. 44p. (M-967.61 L97)

3748 Mair, Lucy P. An African people in the twentieth century. London, G. Routledge, 1934. 300p. (M967.611 M28a)

3749 Malandra, Alfred. A new Acholi grammar. Nairobi, The Eagle Press, 1952. 153p. (M967.61 M29n)

3750 Matheson, J. E., ed. East African agriculture. A short survey of the agriculture of Kenya, Uganda, Tanganyika, and Zanzibar, and of its principal products. London, New York, Oxford University Press, 1950. 332p. (M967M42e)

3751   Mubiru, Wilson. Ebyafa e Ssaayi [The story of Ssaayi.] Nairobi,
       The Eagle Press, 1952. 9p.

3752   Mubiru, Wilson. Paspalum [The value of Paspalum grass.] Nai-
       robi, The Eagle Press, n.d. 18p.

3753   Mukasa, Ham. Uganda's Katikiro in England, being the official
       account of his visit to the coronation of His Majesty King
       Edward VII. London, Hutchinson & Co., 1904. 278p. (M-
       914.2 M89)

3754   Mukwaya, A. B. Land tenure in Buganda; present day tendencies.
       Nairobi, The Eagle Press, 1953. 79p. (M967.61 M89L)

3755   Mulira, Enoch E. K. Olugero lwa Kintu. [Story of the first king
       of Buganda.] Nairobi, The Eagle Press, 1951. 31p. Part I.

3756   Mulira, Enoch E. K. Olugero lwa Kintu. [Story of the first king
       of Buganda.] Nairobi, The Eagle Press, 1951. 30p. Part II.

3757   Mulira, Enoch E. K. Troubled Uganda. London, Fabian Publica-
       tions and Victor Gollancz, [1950.] 44p. (M967.61M91t)

3758   Munger, Edwin S. Relational patterns of Kampala, Uganda. Chic-
       ago, 1951. 165p. (M967.61 M92r)

3759   Nganwa, Kesi K. Abakozire eby'okutangaza. Omuri Ankole. Pub-
       lished for the Ankole literature committee. Nairobi. The
       Eagle Press, 1949. 36p. (M967.61 N51a)

3760   Nganwa, Kesi K. Emi twarize ya wakami. [Traditional stories of
       the Ankole people of Uganda.] Nairobi, The Eagle Press,
       1951. 35p. (M967.61 N51e)

3761   Norden, Hermann. White and black in East Africa; a record of
       travel and observation in two African crown colonies. London
       H. F. ad G. Witherby, 1924. 304p. (M916N75)

3762   Nsimbi, M. B. Olulimi Oluganda [Correct Luganda.] Nairobi, The
       Eagle Press, 1955. 52p. (M967.61 N87o)

3763   Ntungwerisho, Yemima K. Ekirooto ky'omufuzi era ekimuli sekisu-
       muluzo [The ruler's dream and the key flower.] Nairobi,
       The Eagle Press, 1949. 14p.

3764   Ntungwerisho, Yemima K. Ensulo era n'ekitole ky'ebbuma [The
       source and a handful of clay.] Nairobi. The Eagle Press,
       1949. 10p.

3765   Nyabongo, Akiki K. Africa answers back. London, G. Routledge
       & Sons, 1936. 278p. (M967.61N98a)

3766   Nyabongo, Akiki K. The "Bisoro" stories, by Akiki K. Nyabongo.
       Oxford, Basil Blackwell, 1927. 111p. (M967.61 N98b)

3767 Nyabongo, Aiki K. The story of an African chief. New York, C. Scribner's Sons, 1935. 312p. (M967.61N98s)

3768 Nyabongo, Akiki K. Winds and lights; African fairy tales. New York, The Voice of Ethiopia, 1939. 45p. (M967.61N98w)

3769 O'Brien, Terence Patrick, The prehistory of Uganda protectorate. Cambridge, [Eng.], The University Press; [New York, Macmillan] 1939. 318p. (M967.61 Ob6)

3770 Okech, Lacito. Tekwaro ki ker lobo acholi. [History and chieftainship records of the land of the Acholi people of Uganda.] Nairobi, The Eagle Press, 1953. 90p. (M967.61 Ok2t)

3771 Olinga, Enoch. Kidar Aijarakon. [Look after your life.] Kampala, The Eagle Press, [1952.] 48p. (M967.61012k)

3772 Opwa, Antonio. An East African chief in England. Nairobi, The Eagle Press, 1952. 38p. (MB90p8)

3773 Patterson, John Henry. The man-eaters of Tsavo and other African adventures. New York, The Macmillan Company, 1927. 401p. (M916P27m)

3774 Purvis, John Bremner. Through Uganda to Mount Elgon. New York, American Tract Society, 1909. 371p. (M967.61 P97)

3775 Richards, Audrey Isabel. Economic development and tribal change; a study of immigrant labour in Buganda. Published for the East African Institute of Social Research by W. Heffer, Cambridge, England, 1952? 301p.

3776. Robertson, D. W. Etaka n'ebika mu bosoga [Busoga land tenure] Nairobi, The Eagle Press, 1955. 90p.

3777 Roscoe, John. The Bagesu and other tribes of the Uganda protectorate; the third part of the report of the Mackie ethnological expedition to Central Africa. Cambridge, Eng., The University Press, 1924. 205p. (M967.61 R71b2)

3778 Roscoe, John. The Bakitara, or Banyoro. 1st part of Mackie expedition to Central Africa. Cambridge, Engl., University Press 1923. 370p. (M967.61 R71b3)

3779 Roscoe, John. The Banyankole; the second part of the report of the Mackie ethnological expedition to Central Africa. Cambridge, Eng., The University Press, 1923. 176p. (M967.61-R71b4)

3780 Roscoe, John. The soul of Central Africa; a general account of the Mackie ethnological expedition. London, New York, Cassell and co., 1922. 336p. (M967.61 R71s)

3781 Saali, E. M. Abazungu nga bwe tubalaba: [Europeans as we see them.] Kampala, The Eagle Press, 1952. 28p.

3782   Savage, G. A. R. A short Acoli-English and English-Acoli vocabulary. Nairobi, The Eagle Press, 1955. 50p. (M967.61 Sa9s)

3783   Sempa, Kalule A. The Buganda government and its constitutional functions. [Gavumenti ya Buganda n'emirimu gyayo.] Kampala, The Eagle Press, 1953. 55p. (M967.61 Se5b)

3784   Sofer, Cyril and Rhona. Jinja transformed; a social survey of a multi-racial township. Kampala, East African Institute of Social Research, 1955. 120p. (M967.61 So8)

3785   Southall, Aidan W. and Peter C. W. Gutkind. Townsmen in the making: Kampala and its suburbs. Kampala, East African Institute of Social Research, 1956. 272p. (M967.61 So8)

3786   Staples, E. G. Pwonye me pur: [Lectures in elementary agriculture.] Nairobi, The Eagle Press, 1949. 25p.

3787   Streicher, H. The twenty-two martyrs of Uganda. New York, The Paulist press, n.d., n.p. (AM266 St8)

3788   Tarantino, Father A. Locaden remo ma komgi gum me Uganda: [The Uganda martyrs.] Nairobi, The Eagle Press, 1952. 53p.

3789   Thoonen, J. P. Black martyrs. London, Sheed & Ward, 1941. 302p. (M266 T38)

3790   Trowell, Margaret. Tribal crafts of Uganda. London, Oxford univ. press, 1953. 422p. (M967.61 T75t)

3791   Uganda. Agriculture department. Report, 1950 Entebbe. 1951. (M967.61 Ug1)

3792   Uganda. Department of Commerce. The bank and how it will help Africa's Kampala; The Eagle Press, 1955. 16p.

3793   Uganda. Department of Commerce. The grocer, A handbook to assist Africans in trade. Kampala, The Eagle Press, 1955. 16p.

3794   Uganda. Survey, Land and Mines Department. Report, 1951, 1952 (M967.61 Ug1s)

3795   Welbourn, Hebe. Endiisa ennungi ey'omwana; [How would you feed your child?] Nairobi, The Eagle Press, 1952 27p. (M967-61 W44)

3796   Wild, J. V. Early Travellers in Acholi. Edinburgh, Thomas Nelson and sons, ltd. 1954. 62p. (W967.61 W64e)

3797   Wild, J. V. The story of the Uganda agreement. Nairobi, The Eagle Press, 1950. 96p. (M967.61 W64s)

3798   Winter, E. H. Bwamba economy; the development of a primitive

subsistence economy in Uganda. Kampala, East African Institute of Social Research, 1955. 44p. (M967.61W73)

3799 Worthington, Edgar Barton. A development plan for Uganda. [En-
tebbe] Uganda Protectorate Government Press, 1947. 112p.
(M967.9P44e)

KENYA

3800 Aaronovitch, S. Crisis in Kenya. London, Lawrence & Wishart,
[1947] 211p. (M967.6 Aa1c)

3801 Adelphio, pseud. His kingdom in Kenya. London, Hodder and
Stoughton, [1953] 125p. (M967.62Ad3)

3802 Altrincham, Edward W. M. G., Kenya's opportunity; Memories,
hopes and ideas. London, Faber and Faber, ltd., 1955. 308p.
(M967.62 A17)

3803 Anywar, Reuben S. Acoli ki ker megi. Nairobi. The Eagle Press,
1954. 223p.

3804 Armstrong, Lilias Eveline. The phonetic and tonal structure of
Kikuyu. London, Pub. for the International Institute of
African Languages & Cultures by the Oxford University Press,
1940. 363p. (M496.3 Ar5)

3805 Askwith, T. G. The story of Kenya's progress. Nairobi, The Eagle
Press, 1953. 115p. (M967.62 As3s)

3806 Baker, Richard St. Barbe. Africa drums. London, L. Drummond,
ltd., [1942] 159p. (M916.76B17a)

3807 Baker, Richard St. Barbe. Men of the trees; in the mahogany forests
of Kenya and Nigeria. New York, L. MacVeagh, The Dial
press; Toronto, Longmans, Green & co., 1931 283p. (M916.-
76B17)

3808 Baker, Richard St. Barbe. Tambours africains. Traduit de l'Anglais par Suzanne Christoflour. Paris, Stock, Delamain et Boutelleau, 1949. 234p. (M916.76B17t)

3809 Benuzzi, Felice. No picnic on Mount Kenya. London, W. Kimber,
[1952] 230p. (M967.62 B43n)

3810 Bewes, T. F. C. Kikuyu conflict; Mau Mau and the Christian witness. London, Highway Press, 1953. 76p. (AM266 B46)

3811 [Blixen, Karen] Out of Africa. by Isak Dineson (pseud) New
York, Modern Library, 1952. 389p. (M960 B61)

3812 [Blixen, Karen] Out of Africa. New York, Random house [c1938]
389p. (M960B61)

3813 Bostock, P. G. The peoples of Kenya; the Taita. London, Macmillan and co., ltd. 1950. 42p. (M967.62 B65p)

3814 Brodhurst-Hill, Evelyn. So this is Kenya! London, and Glasgow, Blackie and son, ltd. [1936] 246p. (M967.64 B78s)

3815 Bunche, Ralph Johnson. The Irua ceremony among Kikuyu of Kiambu District, Kenya. Reprinted from The Journal of Negro History, 26:46-65, January 1941. (HM378MB88i)

3816 Carey, Walter. Crisis in Kenya: Christian common sense on Mau Mau and the colour-bar. London, A. R. Mowbray & Co., 1953. 39p. (M967.62 C18)

3817 Carpenter, Frank George. Cairo to Kisumu; Cairo-the Sudan-Kenya colony. Garden City, N.Y., Doubleday, Page & company, 1923. 313p. (M962C22c)

3818 Carson, J. B. The preliminary survey for the Kenya and Uganda railway, 1891-1892. Nairobi, The Eagle Press, 1950. 16p. (M967.6 C23p)

3819 Cayzac, Joseph. La religion des Kikuyu (Afrique Orientale). Reprinted from Anthropos. Revue Internationale d'Ethnologie et de Linguistique. Tome 5, 1910. pp. 309-319. (M967.65C31)

3820 Collister, P. Pioneers of East Africa, by P. Collister and E. Vere-Hodge. Nairobi, The Eagle Press, 1956. 131p. (M967.6 C69)

3821 Conseil scientifique pour l'Afrique au Sud du Sahara. [Brochure] Kikuyu, Kenya, C.S.A., 1951. 12p. (M967.6 C765)

3822 Conseil Scientifique pour l'Afrique au Sud du Sahara. Reports, 1950. Kikuyu, Kenya, 1950.

3823 Copley, Hugh. Wanyama wa porini wa porini wa Afrika ya mashariki. [Game animals of East Africa] Nairobi, The Eagle Press, 1953. 59p. (M967.62 C79w)

3824 Daniel, Roland. The Kenya tragedy. London, Wright & Brown, ltd., 1948. 223p. (M896D22k)

3825 Davies, D. A. East Africa's weather service. Nairobi, The Eagle Press, 1952. 32p.

3826 De Watteville, Vivienne. L'appel de l'Afrique; séjour et méditations parmi les éléphants et les montagnes du Kenya. Paris, Payot, 1936. (M967.6 D51a)

3827 Dilley, Marjorie Ruth. British Policy in Kenya Colony. New York, T. Nelson and sons, 1937. 296p. (M967.6 D58)

3829 East African Literature Bureau. Maji ni mali [Water is wealth.] Nairobi, The Eagle Press, 1950. 23p.

3830 East African Literature Bureau. Wia wa mundu muka e musyi,
      [The work of women in the home] Nairobi, The Eagle Press,
      1950. 16p.

3831 East African Statistical Department. African population of Kenya
      colony and protectorate. Nairobi, 1950. 58p. (M967.62 Ea7a)

3832 Elphinstone, Howard. Africans and the law. Nairobi, The Eagle
      Press, 1951. 75p. (M967.62EL6)

3833 Evans, Peter. Law and disorder; or, Scenes of life in Kenya. Lon-
      don, Secker and Warburg, 1956. 296p. (M967.6 Ev1)

3834 Farson, Negley. Last chance in Africa. [1st American ed.] New
      York, Harcourt, Brace [1950] 381p. (M916.76F251)

3835 Fontaine, S. H. La. Local government in Kenya. Nairobi, The
      Eagle Press, 1955. 52p. (M967.62 F73)

3836 Fontaine, S. H. Thirikari ya handu o handu Kenya [Local govern-
      ment in Kenya; its origins and developments.] Nairobi, The
      Eagle Press, 1955. 63p.

3837 Gakwa, S. N. Haria turi riu [Where are we now] Nairobi, The
      Eagle Press, 1949. 25p.

3838 Gathigira, Stanley Kiama. Ng'ano na thimo cia ugikuyu [Tradi-
      tional stories and proverbs.] Nairobi, The Eagle Press, 1950.
      52p.

3839 Gecaga, B. Mareka. Gwata ndai [Riddles and stories] Nairobi. The
      Eagle Press, 1950. 39p.

3840 Gecaga, B. Mareka. Home life in Kikuyu-land; or, Kariuki and
      Muthoni. Nairobi, The Eagle Press, 1949. 17p. (M967.62-
      G26h)

3841 Gordon, Alastair. A slight touch of safari. London, M. Parrish,
      [1952] 135p. (M967.62 G653)

3842 Granville, Roberts. The Mau Mau in Kenya. London, Hutchinson,
      1954. 47p.

3843 Great Britain Colonial Office. Annual Report of Kenya. 1948, 1953
      London, H.M.S.O., 1948. (M967.6G79K)

3844 Great Britain. Commission on financial position and system of tax-
      ation of Kenya. Report of the Commission appointed to en-
      quire into and report on the financial position and system of
      taxation of Kenya. London, H.M. Stationery Office, 1936. 260p.
      (M967.62 G79)

3845 Hailey, William Malcolm Hailey, baron. East Africa: Uganda,
      Kenya, Tanganyika. London, H. M. Stationery Off., 1950.
      358p. (AM354H12n)

3846 Hennings, Richard Owen. African morning. London, Chatto & Windus, 1951. 240p. (M967.64 H39a)

3847 Hotchkiss, Willis Ray. Then and now in Kenya colony; forty adventurous years in East Africa. New York, Fleming H. Revell co., [1937] 160p. (M916.76 H79)

3848 Huntingford, George Wynn Brereton. The Nandi of Kenya; tribal control in a pastoral society. London, Routledge and Paul, 1953. 169p. (M967.62 H92n)

3849 Huxley, Elspeth J. Race and Politics in Kenya, a correspondence between Elspeth Huxley and Margery Perham. London, Faber and Faber, Ltd., [1956] 302p. (M967.62 H98)

3850 Inoti, F. M. Mwari uri muono uti nda. [Embodying moral and sex teaching for girls]. Nairobi, The Eagle Press, 1949. 17p.

3851 Johnson, Martin Elmer. Safari; a saga of the African blue. New York, London, G. P. Putnam's sons, 1928. 294p. (M916.-76J63s)

3852 Kenya (Colony and Protectorate). Agriculture Department. Annual reports—1951, 1952. Nairobi, Govt. Printer, 1953, 1954. (M-967.6K42)

3853 Kenya (Colony and Protectorate). Commerce and industry in Kenya 1955. Nairobi, Ministry of Commerce and Industry, 1955. 62p. (M967.6K42c)

3854 Kenya (Colony and Protectorate). Commerce and industry in Kenya, 1955-1956. Nairobi, Government Printer, 1956. 70p. (M-967.6K42c)

3855 Kenya (Colony and Protectorate). Education Department. Annual report, 1951. Nairobi, Government Printer, 1953. (M967.-6Govt. Doc.)

3856 Kenya (Colony and Protectorate). Education Department. Syllabus for African primary schools. Nairobi, The Eagle Press, 1953. 78p. (M967.62K42)

3857 Kenya (Colony and Protectorate). Education Department. Tentative syllabus for African Intermediate Schools, Kampala, The Eagle Press, 1953. 46p.

3858 Kenya (Colony and Protectorate). Notes on Commerce and Industry in Kenya. Nairobi, Office of the Member for Commerce and Industry, 1953. 51p. (M967.6K42n)

3859 Kenya (Colony and Protectorate). Report on Committee on educational expenditure. 1948. Nairobi, Government Printer, 1948. (M967.5 Govt. Doc.)

3860 Kenya (Colony and Protectorate). A ten-year plan for the development of African education. Nairobi, Printed by the government printer, 1948. 16p. (M967.6K42t)

3861 Kenya Committee for Democratic Rights for Kenya Africans. Kenya Report, ed. ed. London, 1954. 19p. (M967.62K42)

3862 Kenyatta, Jomo. Facing Mount Kenya; the tribal life of Gikuyu. An introduction by B. Malinowski ... London, Secker and Warburg, [1938] 339p. (M967.65K42f)

3863 Kenyatta, Jomo. Kenya: The land of conflict. London, Panaf service, ltd., [1944] 23p. (M967.76K42)

3864 Kenyatta, Jomo. My people of Kikuyu and the life of Chief Wangome., London, United Society for Christian Literature, 1942. [63] p. (M967.65K42)

3865 Kirkman, James. The Arab city of Gedi; excavations at the great mosque, architecture and finds. London, Oxford University Press, 1954. 197p. (M967.62K63)

3866 Koinage, Mbiyu. The people of Kenya speak for themselves. Detroit, Kenya Publication Fund, 1955. (M967.62K82)

3867 Lambert, H. E. Kikuyu Social and Political Institutions. London, Oxford University Press, 1956. 149p. (M967.65 L17)

3868 Lambert, H. E. The use of indigenous authorities in tribal administration: Studies of the Meru in Kenya Colony. Cape Town, Univ., of Capetown, School of African Studies, 1947. 44p. (M967.62 L17u)

3869 Leakey, Louis Seymour Bazett. Defeating Mau Mau. London, Methuen, 1954. 151p. (M967.62 L48d)

3870 Leakey, Louis Seymour Bazett. Mau Mau and the Kikuyu. London, Methuen, 1952. 114p. (M967.62 L47)

3871 Leakey, Louis Seymour Bazett. The stone age cultures of Kenya Colony. Cambridge [Eng.], The University Press, 1931. 278p. (M571.676 L47)

3872 Leakey, Louis Seymour Bazett. The stone age races of Kenya. London, Oxford University Press, H. Milford, 1935. 150p. (AM571.676 L47s)

3873 Leakey, Mary Douglas (Nicol). Excavations at the Njoro River cave; stone age cremated burials in Kenya Colony. Oxford, Clarendon Press, 1950. 78p. (AM571.1L47e)

3874 Leigh, Ione. In the shadow of the Mau Mau. London, W. H. Allen, 1955. 223p. (M967.62 L53)

3875 Leys, Norman Maclean. Kenya. London, L. and Virginia Woolf at the Hogarth press, 1925. 409p. (M967.6 L59k)

3876 Lipscomb, J. F. We built a country. London, Faber and Faber, [1956] 214p. (M967.6 L66)

3877 Loftus, E. A. Gregory; the Great Rift Valley. Nairobi, Thomas Nelson and Sons, ltd., 1952. 63p. (M967.6L82g)

3878 Malo, Shadrak. Dhoudi mag central Nyanza [Clans of Central Nyanza] Kampala, The Eagle Press, 1953. 173p. (M967.62-M29d)

3879 Mann, I. Nyuki ni mali [Bees are wealth] Kampala, The Eagle Press, 1953. 109p. (M967.62 M31n)

3880 Massam, J. A. The cliff dwellers of Kenya. London, Seeley, Service and co., ltd. 1927. 267p. (AM572.676 M38)

3881 Mataamu, Bwana. The beautiful Nyakiemo. London, Thomas Nelson and Sons, ltd. 1951. 39p.

3882 Matheson, J. K., ed. East African agriculture. A short survey of the agriculture of Kenya, Uganda, Tanganyika, and Zanzibar, and of its principal products. London, New York, Oxford University Press, 1950. 332p. (M967M42e)

3883 The Mau Mau in Kenya. Foreword by Granville Roberts. London, Hutchinson, 1954. 47p. (M967.62 M44)

3884 Mayer, Philip. The Lineage principle in Gusii Society. London, Oxford University Press, 1949. 35p. (M967.62 M451)

3885 Mayer, Philip. Two studies in applied anthropology in Kenya. London, H. M. Stationery Office, 1951. 33p. (M967.62 M45t)

3886 Mbotela, James. Uhuru wa watumwa; [The slaves who were brought to Freetown.] Nairobi, The Eagle Press, 1951. 102p.

3887 Mboya, Tom. The Kenya question: An African Answer. London, Fabian Colonial Bureau, 1956. 48p.

3888 Middleton, John. The central tribes of the North-Eastern Bantu (The Kikuyu, including Embu, Meru, Mbere, Chuka, Mwimbi, Tharaka, and the Kamba of Kenya). London, International African Institute, 1953. 107p. (M967.65 M58c)

3889 Mockerie, Parmenas Githendu. An African speaks for his people, with a foreword by Professor Julian Huxley. London, L. and Virginia Woolf at the Hogarth Press, 1934. 95p. (M967.65 M71a)

3890 Mwandia, David. Kilovoo. London, Thomas Nelson and Sons, Ltd., 1952. 44p. (Written in Kamba)

3891 Ngala, Donald G. Nchi na desturi za wagiriama. Nairobi, The Eagle Press, 1949. 41p.

3892 Ngurungu, Sospeter Munuhe. Muceera na Mukundu akundukaga o taguo [V. D. and drunkenness.] Nairobi, The Eagle Press, 1950. 16p.

3893 Northcott, C. H., ed. African labour efficiency survey. London, H. M. Stationery Office, 1949. 123p. (AM331N81)

3894 Nsimbi, M. B. Olulimi Oluganda [Correct Luganda.] Nairobi, The Eagle Press, 1955. 52p.

3895 Orde-Browne, Granville St. John. The vanishing tribes of Kenya, a description of the manners and customs of the primitive and interesting tribes dwelling on the vast southern slopes of Mount Kenya, and their fast disappearing native methods of life. London, Seeley, Service & Co., Ltd., 1925. 284p. (AM-572.96760r2)

3896 Oschinsky, Lawrence. The racial affinities of the Baganda and other Bantu tribes of British East Africa. Cambridge (England), W. Heffer, 1954. 188p. (M967.64 Os2r)

3897 Otiendo, J. D. Habari za azaluyia [The abaluyia of Nyanza Province, Kenya.] Nairobi, The Eagle Press, 1949. 51p.

3898 Oyende, J. P. The ideal African chief; Chifu hodari wa kiafrika. Nairobi, The Eagle Press, 1951. 14p.

3899 Oyende, J. P. Paro mako kuom dohini e Kenya [Some thoughts on native tribunals in Kenya.] Nairobi, The Eagle Press. 1950.

3900 Parker, Mary. How Kenya is governed. Nairobi, The Eagle Press, 1951. 105p. (M967.62 P22h)

3901 Penwill, D. J. Kamba customary law. Notes taken in the Machakos district of Kenya Colony. London, Macmillan and Co., Ltd., 1951. 122p. (M967.62 P38k)

3902 Peristiany, J. G. The social institutions of the Kipsigis, London, George Routledge, [1939.] 288p. (M572.9676 P41)

3903 Place, James B. A School History of Kenya. Kampala, The Eagle Press, 1954. 115p. (M967.62P69s)

3904 Popkin, J. M. Geography, history, civics; lessons for standard three in African primary schools. Kampala, The Eagle Press, 1954. (M967.62 P81g)

3905 Prins, A. H. J. The coastal tribes of the north-eastern Bantu (Pokomo, Nyika, Teita) London, International African Institute, 1952. 138p. (M967.62 P93c)

3906 Rabuku, M. A. Puonjrwok mar nyako [A girl's education.] Nairobi, The Eagle Press, 1950. 23p.

3907 Rawcliffe, Donovan Hilton. The struggle for Kenya. London, Gollancz, 1954. 189p. (M967.6R19)

3908 Ross, William McGregor. Kenya from within; a short political history. London, George Allen and Unwin, [1927.] 486p (M967.6 R73)

3909 Salvadori, Massimo. La colonisation européene au Kenya. Paris, Larose éditeurs, 1938. 227p. (M967.6 Sa3c)

3910 Schapera, Isaac. Some problems of anthropological research in Kenya Colony. London, Oxford University Press, 1949. 43p. (M967.62Sch1)

3911 Simpson, Alyse. Red dust of Africa. London, Cassell [1952.] 200p. (M896.3Si5r)

3912 Slater, Montagu. Trial of Jomo Kenyatta. London, Secker and Warburg, 1955. 255p. (MB9 K42s)

3913 Solly, Gillian. Kenya history in outline. Nairobi, The Eagle Press, 1953. 123p.

3914 Southall, A. Lineage formation among the Luo. London, Oxford University Press, 1952. 43p. (M967.62 So81)

3915 Stoneham, Charles Thurley. Mau Mau. London, Museum Press, [1953.] 159p. (M967.62 St7)

3916 Stoneham, Charles Thurley. Out of barbarism. London, Museum Press [1955.] 190p. (M967.6St71)

3917 Wagner, Gunter. The Bantu of North Kavirondo. London, New York. Published for the International African Institute by the Oxford University Press, 1949. (M796.62 W12b)

3918 Wako, Daniel M. Akabaluyia bemumbo [Customs of the Western Abaluyia people of the Nyanza Province, Kenya.] Kampala, The Eagle Press, 1954. 64p.

3919 Wallbank, T. Walter. American reflections on Kenya. London, Macmillan, 1938. 21p. (M967.6 W15)

3920 White, L. W. Thornton. Nairobi master plan for a colonial capital . . . London, His Majesty's Stationery Office, 1948. 92p. M967.62 W58n)

3921 Whittall, Errol. Dimbill, the story of a Kenya farm. London, Arthur Barker, 1956. 158p.

3922 Wills, Colin. Who killed Kenya? London, D. Dobston, [1953.] 111p. (M867.6W68)

3923 Abedi, K. Amri. Sheria za kutunga mashairi na diwani ya Amri. [The poems of Amri with an essay on Swahili poetry and the rules of versification.] Kampala, The Eagle Press, 1954. 148p. (M967.82 Ab3)

3924 Amri, Daudi. Polisi na raia [The police and the public.] Kampala, The Eagle Press, 1951. 32p.

3925 Baumann, Oscar. Durch Massailand zur Nilquelle. Reisen und Forschungen der Massai-Expedition des deutschen AntisklavereiKomite in der Jahren 1891-1893. Berlin, Geographische verlogshandlung Dietrich Reimer, 1894. 385p. (M967.8B32)

3926 Brady, Cyrus Townsend. Commerce and conquest in East Africa, with particular reference to the Salem trade with Zanzibar. Salem, Essex Institute, 1950. 245p. (M967.8 B72c)

3927 British Information Services. Reference Division. Britain and trusteeship. New York, British Information Services; 1947. 27p. (M940.3141B77b)

3928 Carnochan, Frederic Grosvenar. The empire of the snakes. New York, Frederick A. Stokes Co., 1935. 290p. (M916.78 C21)

3929 Corbin, Iris. The Tanganyika Trail. [Broadway, Livingstone Bookshop, 193?] 16p. (M967.82 C81t)

3930 Cory, Hans. African Figurines; their ceremonial use in Puberty rites in Tanganyika. (AM738.6 C81) London, Faber and Faber, 1956. 176p.

3931 Cory, Hans. The indigenous political system of the Sukuma and proposals for political reform. Nairobi, The Eagle Press for the East African Institute of Social Research, 1954. 130p. (M967.82 C81i)

3932 Cory, Hans. Sukuma law and custom. London, New York, Pub. for the International African Institute by the Oxford University Press, 1953. 194p. (M967.82 C81)

3933 Cory, Hans. Wall-painting by snake charmers in Tanganyika. London, Faber and Faber, 1953. 99p. (AM750 C81)

3934 Cory, Hans and Hartnoll, M. M. Customary law of the Haya tribe. Tanganyika territory, London, P. Lund, Humphries and Co., Ltd., 1954. 299p. (M967.8 C81c)

3935 Eshleman, Merle W. Africa answers. Scottsdale, Pa., Mennonite Publishing House, 1951. 179p. (M967.82 Es3a)

3936 Ford, V.C.R. The trade of Lake Victoria; a geographical study.

Kampala, East African Institute of Social Research, 1955. 65p. (M967.88 F75)

3937 Fortie, Marius. . . . Black and beautiful, a life in safari land. Indianapolis, New York, The Bobbs-Merrill Company, 1938. 344p. (M916.78 F77)

3938 Great Britain. Colonial Office. Report by His Majesty's Government in United Kingdom of Great Britain and Northern Ireland to the General Assembly of the United Nations on the administration of Tanganyika, 1947. London, H.M.S.O. (M-967.82 G79r)

3939 Great Britain. Colonial Office. Report of Tanganyika, 1949. (M-967.82 G79r)

3940 Great Britain. Colonial Office. Development of African local government in Tanganyika. London, H.M.S.O., 1951. 55p. (M-967.82 G79d)

3941 Gulliver, P. H. Labour migration in a rural economy; a study of the Ngoni and Ndendeuli of Southern Tanganyika. Kampala, East African Institute of Social Research, 1955. 48p. (M-967.8 G94)

3942 Hailey, William Malcolm Hailey, baron. East Africa: Uganda, Kenya, Tanganyika. London, H. M. Stationery office, 1950. 358p. (AM354H12n)

3943 Harrison, A. Royden. The occurrence mining and recovery of diamonds. pp. 315-325. Reprinted from the *Journal of Chemical, Metallurgical and Mining Society of South Africa,* April 1952. (AM553.8 H24)

3944 Heckel, Benno. The Yao tribe; their culture and education. Arts and crafts in training of Bemba Youth [by] Griffith Quick . . . London, Oxford University Press, 1935. 53p. (AM572.9678 H35)

3945 Hore, Edward Coode. Tanganyika, eleven years in Central Africa. London, Edward Stanford, 1892. 306p. (M967.82 H78)

3946 Jackson, Mabel V. European powers and south-east Africa. New York, Longmans, Green and Co., 1942. 284p. (AM967.8 J13)

3947 Jacques, Oliver. Tommy goes to Africa. Washington, Review and Herald Publishing Association. [1949.] 128p. (M967.8 J16t)

3948 Joelson, F. S. The Tanganyika Territory (Formerly German East Africa), characteristics and potentialities. New York, Appleton, 1921. 256p. (M967.8 J59)

3949 Johnston, Sir Harry Hamilton. The Kilima-Njaro Expedition. London, K. Paul, Trench, and Co., 1886. 572p. (M967.8 J64)

3950 Kayamba, H. Martin Th. African problems. London, United Society for Christian Literature, 1948. 93p. (M967.82K18a)

3951 Kayombo, Innocent K. Stories of our Tanganyika forefathers. London, Sheldon Press, 1952. 29p. (M967.82 K18s)

3952 Kombo, S. M. Ustaarabu na maendeleo ya Mwafrika. [The civilization and development of the African.] Nairobi, The Eagle Press, 1950. 60p.

3953 Lemenye, Justin. Maisha ya semeni ole kivasis yaani Justin Lemenye. [The life of Justin Lemenye.] Kampala, The Eagle Press, 1953. 71p. (Written in Swahili)

3954 Lennard, T. J. (ed.) How Tanganyika is governed. Nairobi, The Eagle Press, 1955. 111p. (M967.82 L55h)

3955 Leubuscher, Charlotte. Tanganyika territory; a study of economic policy under mandate. London, New York, Printed for the Royal Institute of International Affairs by Oxford University Press, 1944. 217p. (M967.82 L57t)

3956 Loveridge, Arthur. Tomorrow's a holiday (Kesho siku kuu). New York and London, Harper & Brothers [1947.] 278p. (M968.-963L94t)

3957 Macdonald, Sheila Scobie. Tanganyika safari. Sydney, Angus and Robertson, 1948. 237p. (M916.78 M14t)

3958 Malcolm, Donald Wingfield. Sukumaland: an African people and their country; a study of land use in Tanganyika. London, New York, Oxford University Press, 1953. 224p. (M967.8 M29)

3959 Matheson, J. K., ed. East African agriculture. A short survey of the agriculture of Kenya, Uganda, Tanganyika, and Zanzibar, and of its principal products. London, New York, Oxford University Press, 1950. 332p. (M967M42e)

3960 Meyer, Eugen Le "Kirengo" des Wachaga, peuplade bantoue du Kilimanjaro, 1918. Reprinted from Anthropos, Revue Internationale d'Ethnologie et de Linquistique. Tome XIII, 1917-1918. (M967.8M57)

3961 Mnyampala, Mathias E. Historia, milia, na desturi za wagogo wa Tanganyika. [History and customs of the Wagogo of Tanganyika. Kampala.] The Eagle Press, 1954. 116p.

3962 Molitor, Henri. La musique chez les Nègres du Tanganika. 1913. 735p. Reprinted from Anthropos, Revue Internationale d'Ethnologie et de Linguistique. Tome VIII, 1913. (M967.8M73)

3963 Ntiro, S. J. Deaturi za wachagga (Customs and traditions of the Chagga people of Tanganyika.) Nairobi, The Eagle Press, 1953. 50p.

3964 Pelham-Johnson, M. Binti Leo Kwake. [Mrs. Good wife in her home.] Nairobi, The Eagle Press, 1950. 35p.

3965 Riwa, R. L. Hadithi za rafika saba. (Tales told by seven friends.) Nairobi, The Eagle Press, 1951. 45p.

3966 Robert, Shaaban. Kusadikika. London, Thomas Nelson and Sons, Ltd. 57p.

3967 Ryan, C. W. W. Tanganyika, tajiri au maskini? [Tanganyika, rich or poor?] by C. W. W. Ryan and D. A. Omari. Nairobi, The Eagle Press, 1954. 17p.

3968 Silverstand, J. H. Probation. Nairobi, The Eagle Press, 1947. 36p. (M967.82Si3)

3969 The Tanganyika Guide, with a foreword by Sir William Dale Battershil. [Dar es Salaam?] 1948. 160p. (M967.8T15)

3970 Tanganyika Territory. Department of Education. Annual report for 1952. Dar es Salaam, 1953. 112p. (M967.8T15e)

3971 Tanganyika Territory. Medical Department. Annual report for 1950. Dar es Salaam, 1951. 65p. (M967.8T15a)

3972 Tanganyika Territory. Provincial administration. Annual reports of the provincial commissioners, 1953. [Dar es Salaam, 1954.] 161p. (M967.9T15a)

3973 Tanganyika Territory. Tanganyika, a review of its resources and their development. Prepared under the direction of J. F. R. Hill, member for communications, works and development planning and edited by J. P. Moffett, commissioner for social development. [Dar es Salaam? 1955.] 924p. (M967.8T15t)

3974 Ulenge, Yussuf. Nguso ya maji; na hadithi nyingine; [The pillar of water and other stories.] Nairobi, The Eagle Press, 1951. 22p. (M967.82U12)

3975 Uzima, Lenga. (Book series). Matuta ya mashambani katika nchi kavu; [The ridging in dry areas; How and why to do it.] Nairobi, The Eagle Press, 1951. 7p.

3976 Williams, Gordon, John. Mica in Tanganyika territory, by G. J. Williams . . . and A. F. Skerl . . . Dar es Salaam, Printed by the government printer, 1940. 51p. (AM553.9W67)

3977 Wilson, Monica (Hunter) Good company; a study of Nyakyusa age-villages. London, New York, Published for the International African Institute by the Oxford University Press, 1951. 278p. (AM572.967 W69g)

3978 Zani, Z. M. S. Mashairi yangu [My poems] Kampala, The Eagle Press, 1953. 279p.

MOZAMBIQUE

3979 Earthy, Emily Dora. Valenge women; the social and economic life of the Valenge women of Portuguese East Africa; an ethnographic study. London, Oxford University Press, H. Milford, 1933. 251p. (M572.67Ea7)

3980 Hamilton, Genesta Mary (Heath). In the wake of the Da Gama, the story of Portuguese pioneers in East Africa, 1497-1729. London, New York, Skeffington, 1951. 176p. (M967.9H18i)

3981 Livingstone, David. Narrative of an expedition to the Zambesi and its tributaries; and of the discovery of the Lakes Shirwa and Nyassa, 1858-1865. New York, Harper and Bros., 1866. 638p. (M916.67L74)

3982 Maugham, Reginald Charles Fulke. Portuguese East Africa. New York, E. P. Dutton and Co., 1906. 340p. (M967.9M44p)

3983 Mozambique. Repartiçao Tecnica de Estatistica. Anuário estatístico. Annuaire statistique. ano. 1—1926-28, 1943-45. Lourenço Marques, Imprensa Nacional de Mozambique. (M967.-9M87)

3984 Mozambique. Repartiçao Tecnica de Estatistica. Boletim económico e estatístico. Ser. especial. no. 1-2. Lourenço Marques, Imprensa Nacional, 1925-34. (M967.9M87b)

3985 Mozambique. Repartiçao Tecnica de Estatistica. Censo de populaçao em 1940. Lourenço Marques, 1943, 1945. (M967.9M87c)

3986 Peters, Karl. The Eldorado of the ancients. London, C. A. Pearson, Ltd., 1902. 447p. (M967.9P44e)

3987 Spence, C. F. The Portuguese colony of Moçambique; an economic survey. Cape Town, A. A. Balkema, 1951. 133p. (M967.9Sp3)

ZANZIBAR

3988 Baumann, Oscar. Durch Massailand zur Nilquelle. Reisen und Forschungen der Massai-Expedition des deutschen Antisklaverei-Komite in den Jahren 1891-1893. Berlin, Geographische verlagshandlumg Dietrich Reimer, 1894. 385p. (M967.8 B32)

3989 Frank, Cedric N. The life of Bishop Steere; a christian interpreter in East Africa. Nairobi, The Eagle Press, 1953. 55p. (M-967.81 F84L)

3990 Great Britain Colonial Office. Reports on Zanzibar. 1947, 1951, 1952. (M967.81 G81)

3991 Hailey, William Malcolm Hailey, baron. Central Africa: Zanzibar, Nyasaland, Northern Rhodesia. London, H. M. Stationery Office, 1950. 168p. (AM354H12n)

3992 Lyne, Robert Nunez. Zanzibar in contemporary times; a short history of the southern East in the 19th century. London, Hurst and Blackett, Ltd., 1905. (M967.81 L99)

3993 Matheson, J. K., ed. East African agriculture. A short survey of the agriculture of Kenya, Uganda, Tanganyika, and Zanzibar, and of its principal products. London, New York, Oxford University Press, 1950. 332p. (M967M42e)

3994 Osgood, Joseph Barlow Felt. Notes of travel; or, Recollections of Majunga, Zanzibar, Muscat, Aden, Mocha and other eastern ports. Salem, Mass., Creamer, 1854. 253p. (AM916 Os2)

3995 Pearce, Francis Barrow. Zanzibar, the island metropolis of eastern Africa. London, T. F. Unwin, Ltd. [1920.] 431p. (M967.-81 P31z)

3996 Steere, Edward. Swahili tales, as told by natives of Zanzibar. With an English translation. London, Society for Promoting Christian Knowledge, 1922. 501p.

3997 Zanzibar. Provincial Administration. Annual report for 1949. (M-967.81 Z17)

MADAGASCAR

3998 Boyer, Danika. Sa majesté Ranavalo III, ma reine. Paris, Fasquelle Editeurs, 1946. 255p. (M843B69s)

3999 Camboué, Paul. Education et instruction en Madagascar. Reprinted from Anthropos, Tome X-XII. 1915-1916. 844-860p. M969.1C14)

4000 Camboué, Paul. Notes sur quelques moeurs et coutumes malgaches. Reprinted from Anthropos, Tome II, fasc. VI, 1907. 981-990p. (M969.1C14)

4001 Callet, Francois. Un "Sahagun" pour l'ethnologie du peuple malgache de l'Imerina: les documents. Reprinted from Anthropos, V. 19. 194-205p. (M969C13)

4002 Chevalier, Louis. Madagascar: populations et resources. [Paris] Presses Universitaires de France, 1952. 212p. (M969.1C42)

4003 Le Commerce d'Importation à Madagascar. Paris, Depeche Coloniale, n.d. 91p. (M969.1C73)

4004 Congrès de l'Afrique orientale (Madagascar et dépendances—Cote Française des Somalis) tenu à Paris, du 9 au 14 Octobre 1911. Compte Rendu des travaus par Ch. Depince; Paris, Au Siège du Comité D'Organisation du Congrès, 1912. 821p. (M969-C76)

4005 Conte d'Ibonia; essai de traduction et d'interpretátion d'après l'édition Dahle de 1877, par R. Becker. Tananarive, Imprimerie Moderne de L'Emyrne, Pitot de la Beaujardière, 1939. 136p. (M969.1Ac1m)

4006 Cotte, Paul Vincent. Regardons vivre une tribu malgache, les Betsimisaraka. Paris, La Nouvelle Edition, 1947. 236p. (M969.-1C82r)

4007 Doyle, Adrian C. Heaven has claws. New York, Random House, 1953. 245p. (M969D77h)

4008 Dubois, Henri M. Monographie des Betsileo (Madagascar). Ouvrage publie avec le concours de l'Académie Malgache. Paris, Institut d'Ethnologie, 1938. 1510p. (M969.1D85M)

4009 Ellis, William. Three visits to Madagascar during the years 1853-1856. Including a journey to the capital. Philadelphia, J. W. Bradley, 1859. 426p.

4010 Escamps, Henry d'. Histoire et géographie de Madagascar. Paris, Firmin-Didot et cie., 1884. 636p. (M969.1Es1h)

4011 Ferrand, Gabriel. Contes populaires, malgaches, recueillis, traduits et annotés. Paris, Ernest Leroux, Editeur, 1893. 266p. (AM-398.3F41)

4012 Fihirana fanao amy ny Eklesia Malagasy miray amy ny Eklesia Anglikana. Antanarivo, Misiona Anglikana, 1898. 87p.

4013 Gaffarel, Paul Louis Jacques. Les colonies françaises. Paris, F. Alcan, 1899. 552p. (M916G12)

4014 Galliéne, [Joseph Simon] Madagascar; chemins de fer, routes et sentiers; Extrait de l'Année Coloniale (1re Année 1900). Paris, Librairie Charles Tallandier, n.d. 25p. (M969G13m)

4015 Galliéne, [Joseph Simon] La pacification de Madagascar (opérations d'Octobre 1896 à Mars 1899); ouvrage rédige d'après les archives de l'Etat-Major du Corps d'occupation. Paris, Librairie Militaire R. Chapelot, 1900. 524p. (M969.1G13p)

4016 Galliéne, [Joseph Simon] Voyage du Général Galliéni. Paris, Hachette et cie., 1901. 165p.

4017 Jully, M. A. Madagascar, au point de vue économique. Conférence faite à la Société de Géographie de Marseille le 9 Juin 1900. Marseille, Typographie et Lithographie Barlatier, 1900. 39p. (M969J94)

4018 Keller, C. Madagascar, Mauritius and the other East-African islands. London, Swan Sonnenschein and Co., 1901. 238p. (M969K28m)

4019 Madagascar. L'élevage des espèces animales domestiques. Paris, Edité par l'Agence Economique de Madagascar et Dependances. 78p. (M969M26e2)

4020 Madagascar. Gouvernment générale de Madagascar et dépendances. Direction de l'enseignement. L'enseignement à Madagascar en 1931. Madagascar Gouvernment, 1931. 118p. (M969-M26e)

4021 Madagascar; le pays, la production, la via administratif et sociale. Paris, Depeche Coloniale. 156p. (M969M26)

4022 Mangin, Charles Marie Emmanuel. Regards sur la France d'Afrique. Paris, Librairie Plon, 1924. 308p. (M969M31r)

4023 Maude, Frances Cornwallis. Five years in Madagascar, with notes on the military situation. London, Chapman and Hall, [1895] 285p. (M969M44)

4024 Nemours, Charles Philippe. Madagascar et ses richesses. Paris P. Roger, c1930. 294p. (M969.1N34)

4025 Papphenheim, Haupt. Madagascar studien shilderungen und erebnisse. Berlin, Verlag Dietrich Reimer, 1906. 355p. (M-969.1P19)

4026 Paulhan, Jean. Les hain-tenys. Paris, Gallimard, 1939. 216p. (M899.214P28h)

4027 Petit, Gabriel. Madagascar. Paris, Éditions Arts et Métiers Graphiques, [1934] 118p. (M969.1P44)

4028 Pheiffer, Ida (Reyer). The last travels of Ida Pheiffer. New York, Harper & Harper, 1861. 338p. (M916P47)

4029 Saron, Gilbert. Madagascar et les comores, cent quatre-vingt six photographies de Robert Lisan. Paris, Paul Hartman, Éditeur, 1953. 184p. (M969Sa7)

SOUTHERN AFRICA

ANGOLA

4030 Angola. Generalidades sôbre Angola, para a 1. Cruzeiro de Férias às Colónias Portuguesas. Luanda, Imprensa Nacional, 1935. 88p. (M967.3An4g)

4031 Angola. Caixa económica postal. . . . Regulamento da Caixa ecónomica postal, aprovado por Portaria n. 3:514, de 23 de Outubro de 1940, do Govêrno geral de Angola. Luanda, Imprensa nacional, 1940. 49p.

4032 Angola. Repartiçao de Estatistica Geral. Boletim trimestral de Estatistica, 1943. Angola, Imprensa Nacional, 1944. 1v. (M-967.3An4b)

4033 Angola. Repartiçao de Estatistica Geral. Censo geral da populaçao, 1940. Luanda, Imprensa Nacional, 1941-47. (M967.-3An4c)

4034 Angola. Repartiçao de Estatistica Geral. Comércio externo. 1940, 1941, 1943, 1944. Luanda, 1944. (M967.3An4e)

4035 Cerqueira, Ivo Benjamin de. Vida social indígena na colónia de Angola (usos e costumes). Lisboa, Divisao de Publicaçoes e Biblioteca, Agência Geral das Colónias, 1947. 96p. (M967.-3C33v)

4036 Childs, Gladwyn Murray. Umbundu kinship and character; being a description of the social structure and individual development of the Ovimbundu of Angola . . . London, New York, Oxford University Press, 1949. 245p. (M967.33C43u)

4037 Claridge, G. Cyril. Wild bush tribes of tropical Africa; an account of adventure and travel amongst pagan people in southern Africa, with a description of their manners of life, customs, heathenish rites and ceremonies, secret societies, sport and warfare collected during a sojourn of twelve years. London, Seeley Service and Co., Limited, 1922. 314p. (AM572.-673C54)

4038 Coles, S. B. Pestalozzi in Angola. New York, Pestalozzie Foundation, 1952. 41p.

4039 Cushman, Mary Floyd. Missionary doctor, the story of twenty years in Africa. New York and London, Harper & Brothers, [1944] 279p. (MC9C95)

4040 Egerton, F. Clement C. Angola in perspective. Endeavor and Achievement in Portuguese West Africa. London, Routledge & Kegan Paul, 1957. 272p.

4041 Endicott, Mary Austin. Spotlight on Africa. Toronto, Canada, The Committee on Missionary Education. [The United Church of Canada, c1945] 68p. (M967.3En2)

4042 Hambley, Wilfrid Dyson. Anthropometry of the Ovimbundu.

Chicago, 1938. pp. 23-79. (AM572.672M17a)

4043 Hambly, Wilfrid Dyson. The Ovimbundu of Angola. Frederick
H. Rawson-Field Museum Ethnological Expedition to West
Africa, 1929-30. Chicago, 1934. pp. 89-362. (AM572.673-
H17o)

4044 Johnston, Harry Hamilton. The river Congo, from its mouth to
Bólóbo; with a general description of the natural history and
anthropology of its western basin. With three etchings, and
over seventy other illustrations and three maps of the Congo.
London, S. Low, Marston, Searle & Rivington, 1884. 470p.
(M916J64r)

4045 McCulloch, Merran. The Ovimbundu of Angola. London, International African Institute, 1952. 50p. (M967.3M13o)

4046 McCulloch, Merran. The Southern Lunda and related peoples
(Northern Rhodesia, Angola, Belgian Congo). London, International African Institute, 1951. 110p. (M968.94M13s)

4047 Miralles de Imperial y Gómez, Claudio. Angola en riempos de
Felipe II y de Felipe III: los memoriales de Diego de Herrera
y de Jerónimo Castano. Madrid, Instituto de Estudios Africanos, 1951. 79p.

4048 Monteiro, Joachim John. Angola and the river Congo. New York,
Macmillan and Co., 1876. 354p. (M916.73M76)

4049 Nevinson, Henry Woodd. A modern slavery. London and New
York, Harper & Brothers, 1906. 215p. (M916.73N41)

4050 Perira, Joaquim Antonio. Angola, terra Portugueas, acçoes de
guerra, vida no sertao; memórias e commentarios. Lisboa, Ex-
pansao Grafica Livreira, 1947. 252p. (M967.3P41a)

4051 Polinard, Edmond. Les roches alcalines de Chianga (Angola) et
les tufs associés. Bruxelles, 1939. (Institut royal colonial
belge. Section des sciences naturelles et médicales). 27p.
(AM552.8P75)

4052 Portugal. Agência Geral des colónias. Annuário do império colonial Português. 8.A ediçao. Ediçao de Empresa National
de Publicidade por contrato com a Agência Geral das Colónias,
1942. 535p. (M967.9P83)

4053 Serra Frazao, Associaçoes secretas entre os indígenas de Angola
. . . Lisboa, Editora Mantimo-Colonial, 1946. 325p. (M967.-
3Se6a)

4054 Sharman, T. C. Portuguese West Africa; economic and commercial
conditions in Portuguese West Africa (Angola). June, 1953.
London, H.M.S.O., 1954. 61p. (M967.3Sh2)

THE FEDERATION OF RHODESIA AND NYASALAND

4055 Allan, William. Land holding and land usage among the plateau Tonga of Mazabuka District, a reconnaissance survey, 1945. Cape Town, Published for the Rhodes-Livingstone Institute by Oxford University Press, 1949. 192p. (M968.94A15)

4056 Allan, William. Studies in African land usage in Northern Rhodesia. Cape Town, New York. Published for the Rhodes-Livingstone Institute by Oxford University Press, 1949. 85p. (M968.94A15s)

4057 Baines, Thomas. The northern goldfields dairies of Thomas Baines. London, Chatto and Windus, 1946. 3v. (M916.892B16n)

4058 Bate, H. Maclear. Report from the Rhodesias. London, Melrose [1953] 288p. (M968.9B31)

4059 Bent, James Theodore. The ruined cities of Mashonaland; being a record of excavation and exploration in 1891 . . . with a chapter on the orientation and mensuration of the temples, by R. M. W. Swan. London, Longmans, Green and Co., 1893. 427p. (M968.93B44)

4060 Bigland, Eileen. The lake of the royal crocodiles. [London] Hodder and Stoughton [1939.] 299p. (M966.23B481)

4061 Brelsford, William Vernon. The succession of Bemba chiefs; a guide for district officers. Lusaka, Northern Rhodesia, The Government Printer, 1944. 45p. (M968B74)

4062 Brelsford, William Vernon. The succession of Bemba chiefs; a guide for district officers. Lusaka, Printed by the Government Printer, 1948. 48p. (M968.965B74)

4063 Brown, William Harvey. On the South African frontier; the adventures and observations of an American in Mashonaland and Matabeleland. New York, Charles Scribner's Sons, 1899. 430p. (M968B81)

4064 Caton-Thompson, Gertrude. The Zimbabwe culture; ruins and reactions. Oxford, Clarendon Press, 1931. 299p. (M913.-68C29)

4065 Chibambo, Yesaya Mlonyeni. My Ngoni of Nyasaland. London, United Society for Christian literature [n.d.] 64p. (M968.-97C43m)

4066 Clark, John Desmond. The stone age cultures of Northern Rhodesia with particular reference to the cultural and climatic succession in the upper Zambezi Valley and its tributaries. Claremont, Cape, South African Archaeological Society [1950.] 157p. (M968.94C54s)

4067   Clark, John Desmond. Stone age sites in Northern Rhodesia and the possibilities of future research. Livingstone, Northern Rhodesia, The Rhodes-Livingstone Institute, 1939. 27p. (M-913.6894C54)

4068   Coudenhove, Hans. My African neighbors; man, bird and beast in Nyasaland. Boston, Little, Brown and Company, 1925. 245p. (M968.97C83)

4069   Cox, D. L. A bibliography of the federation of the Rhodesias and Nyasaland, up to June 30th, 1949. Cape Town, University of Cape Town, School of Librarianship, 1949. (AMO16C83b)

4070   Culwick, Arthur Theodore. Good out of Africa. Northern Rhodesia, The Rhodes-Livingstone Institute, 1942. 43p. (AM572-C89g)

4071   Davidson, James Wheeler. The Northern Rhodesian Legislative Council. London, Faber and Faber [1948.] 150p. (M968.-94D28n)

4072   Deane, Phyllis. Colonial social accounting. Cambridge, University Press, 1953. 360p. (M968.9D34c)

4073   Deane, Phyllis. The measurement of colonial national incomes, an experiment. Cambridge [Eng.] University Press, 1948. 173p. (M325.342D34)

4074   Doke, C. M. The Lambas of Northern Rhodesia. London, Harrap and Co., Ltd., 1931. 407p. (AM572.68D68)

4075   Duff, Hector Livingstone. African small chop. London, Hodder and Stoughton, Ltd., 1932. 222p. (M916.76D87a)

4076   Federal Information Department. Opportunity in Rhodesia and Nyasaland. Rhodesia and Nyasaland, The Rhodesian Print. and Pub. Co., Ltd., 195? 66p. (M968.9F31o)

4077   Fulleborn, Friedrich. Deutsch-Ost-Afrika. Das Deutsche Njassa und Ruwuma Gebiet, Land und Leute. Berlin, Dietrich Reimer. vol. 9, 1906. (M967.95F95)

4078   Gale, William Daniel. Heritage of Rhodes. Cape Town, New York, Oxford University Press, 1950. 158p. (M968.91G13h)

4079   Gibbs, Peter. A flag for the Matabele; a story of empire-building in Africa. London, F. Muller, [1955] 192p. (M968.92G35)

4080   Gluckman, Max. The Judicial process among the Barotse of Northern Rhodesia. Glencoe, Illinois, The Free Press, 1955. 386p. (M968.951G52)

4081   Great Britain. Colonial Office. Annual report on Northern Rhodesia, 1946, 1947, 1949, 1950, 1953. London, H. M. Stationery Office, 1946-1954. (M968.94G79a)

4082 Great Britain. Colonial Office. Annual report, Nyasaland, 1947. (M968.97Govt. Doc.)

4083 Great Britain. Colonial Office. The British territories in East and Central Africa, 1945-1950. London, H. M. Stationery Office, 1950. 165p. (M967.6G79b)

4084 Great Britain. Colonial Office. Central African territories; comparative survey of native policy. London, H.M. Stationery Office, 1951. 91p. (M968.9G79c)

4085 Great Britain. Colonial Office. Central African territories; geographical, historical and economic survey. London, H.M.S.O., 1951. 47p. (M968.9G79)

4086 Great Britain. Colonial Office. Nyasaland protectorate. Report for the year 1955. London, Her Majesty's Stationery Office, 1956. 143p.

4087 Great Britain. Colonial Office. Report of the commission on the civil services of Northern Rhodesia and Nyasaland, 1947. London, His Majesty's Stationery Office, 1948. (M968.9G79r)

4088 Great Britain. Colonial Office. Southern Rhodesia, Northern Rhodesia and Nyasaland; draft federal scheme prepared by a conference held in London in April and May, 1952. London, H.M.S.O., 1952. 38p. (M968.91G79s)

4089 Hailey, William Malcolm Hailey, Baron. Central Africa: Zanzibar, Nyasaland, Northern Rhodesia. London, H.M. Stationery Off., 1950. 168p. (AM354H12n)

4090 Hall, Richard Nicklin. The ancient ruins of Rhodesia (Monomotapae imperium). London, Methuen and co., 1902. 396p. (M913.68H14)

4091 Hall, Richard Nicklin. Prehistoric Rhodesia; an examination of the historical, ethnological and archaeological evidences as to the origin and age of the rock mines and stone buildings, with a gazetteer of mediaeval south-east Africa, 915 A.D. to 1760 A.D., and the countries of the Monomotapa, Manica, Sabia, Quiteve, Sofala, and Mozambique. London [etc.] T. F. Unwin, 1909. 487p. (M913.32H14p)

4092 Hanna, A. J. The beginnings of Nyasaland and North-eastern Rhodesia, 1859-1895. Oxford, Clarendon Press, 1956. 281p. (M968.97H19)

4093 Harding, Colin. Frontier patrols; a history of the British South

Africa police and other Rhodesian forces. London, G. Bell and sons, ltd., 1938. 372p. (M968.9H21)

4094 Headland, A. R. David Carnegie, or Matabeleland. Broadway, Livingstone Bookshop, 1930. 16p. (MB9C21)

4095 Hensman, Howard. A history of Rhodesia, compiled from official sources . . . Edinburgh and London, W. Blackwood and sons, 1900. 381p. (M968.9H39)

4096 Hinden, Rita. Plan for Africa; a report prepared for the Colonial bureau of the Fabian society. London, G. Allen & Unwin, ltd. [1941] 223p. (M960H58p)

4097 Hole, Hugh Marshall. Lobengula. London, Philip Allan, 1929. 211p. (M968.92H711)

4098 Holleman, J. F. The pattern of Hera kinship. Cape Town, New York, Published for the Rhodes-Livingstone Institute by Oxford University Press, 1949. 58p. (M968.91H72p)

4099 Holleman, J. F. Shona customary law, with reference to kinship, marriage, the family and the estate. Cape Town, New York, Oxford University Press, 1952. 401p. (M968.91H72s)

4100 Hone, Percy Frederick. Southern Rhodesia. London, G. Bell and sons, 1909. 406p. (M968.9H75s)

4101 Jaspan, M. A. The Ila-Tonga peoples of North-western Rhodesia. London, International African Institute, 1953. 72p. (M968.-95J31)

4102 Johnson, Frank William Frederick. Great days; the autobiography of an empire pioneer. London, G. Bell and sons, ltd., 1940. 366p. (MC9J632)

4103 Johnson, William Percival. Nyasa, the Great Water; being a description of the lake and the life of the people. London, Oxford University Press, 1922. 204p. (AM572J63a)

4104 Jones, Arthur Creech. African challenge; the fallacy of federation. London, Africa Bureau [1952] 36p. (M968.9J71a)

4105 Jones, Neville. The prehistory of Southern Rhodesia. Published for the Trustees of the National Museum of Southern Rhodesia at the University Press, 1949. 77p. (M968.91J73p)

4106 Kane, Nora Sophie (Hoffmann). The world's view; the story of Southern Rhodesia. London, Cassell [1954] 294p. (M968.-91K13w)

4107 Keystone, J. E. Regional organisation of research in the Rhodesias and Nyasaland; a report to the Central African Council. Salisbury, Art Printing Works, ltd., 1949. 91p. (M968.9K52)

4108 Kirkwood, Kenneth. The proposed federation of the Central African Territories. Johannesburg, South African Institute of Race Relations, n.d. 26p. (New Africa pamphlet, no. 21) (M968.9K63)

4109 Knight, Edward Frederick. Rhodesia of today; a description of the present condition and the prospects of Matabeleland and Mashonaland. London, and New York, Longmans, Green and co., 1895. 151p. (M968.9K74r)

4110 Langworthy, Emily (Booth). This Africa was mine. Stirling Scot Tract Enterprise [1952] 139p. (M968.97L26t)

4111 Loveridge, Arthur. I drank the Zambexi. New York, Harper 1953. 296p. (M968.97L94)

4112 Lugard, Frederick John Dealtry, baron. The rise of our East African empire; early efforts in Nyasaland and Uganda. Edinburgh and London, W. Blackwood and sons, 1893. 2v. (M960-L96r)

4113 Mair, Lucy Philip. Native administration in Central Nyasaland. London, H.M. Stationery Off., 1952. 17p. (M968.97M28n)

4114 Mansfield, Charlotte. Via Rhodesia; a journey through Southern Africa. London, S. Paul and co. [1911] 430p. (M916.89M31)

4115 Massiye, A. Sylvester. The lonely village. London, Thomas Nelson and sons, ltd., 1951. 48p.

4116 Mathers, Edward Peter. Zambesia, England's El Dorado in Africa, being a description of Matabeleland and Mashonaland, and the less-known adjacent territories, and an account of the gold fiends of British South Africa. London, King, Sell & Railton; Capetown, South Africa [etc.] Juta & co. [1895] 480p. (M-968M42)

4117 Maugham, Reginald Charles Fulke. Africa as I have known it, Nyasaland-East Africa-Liberia-Senegal. London, John Murray, 1929. 372p. (M960M44a)

4118 McCulloch, Merran. The Southern Lunda and related peoples (Northern Rhodesia, Angola, Belgian Congo). London, International African Institute, 1951. 110p. (M968.94M13s)

4119 Melland, Frank H. In witch-bound Africa. London, Seeley Service and co., 1923. 316p. (AM572.968M48)

4120 Mhlagazanhlansi. My friend Kumalo. Bulawayo, Southern Rhodesia, The Rhodesian printing and publishing company, 1945. 54p. (M968.9M57m)

4121 Mitchell, J. Clyde. The Yao Village; a study in the social structure of a Nyasaland tribe. N. Rhodesia, Manchester University Press [1956] 235p. (M968.97M69)

4122   Mnyanda, B. J. In search of truth; a commentary on certain aspects of Southern Rhodesia's native policy. Bombay, Hind Kitabs ltd., 1954. 173p. (M968M711)

4123   Moffat, Robert. The Matabele journals of Robert Moffat, 1829-1860. London, Chatto and Windus, 1945- (M968.92M72m)

4124   The New Federation of . . . Rhodesia and Nyasaland. Prepared by the Federal Information Services, Government of Rhodesia and Nyasaland, 1954. 48p. (M968.9N42)

4125   Nhlagazenhlandi. (Pseud.) Early days and native ways in Southern Rhodesia, a series of short essays on native customs, life and habits. Bulawayo, National War Fund of Southern Rhodesia, 1944. 56p. (M968.9N49e)

4126   Northern Rhodesia. Colonial Office. Colonial reports. London, H.M.S.O., 1954. 1947, 1949, 1950, 1953. (M968.94G79a)

4127   Northern Rhodesia and Nyasaland publications bureau report. Lusaka, Printed by the Government Printer. (Annual) 1949- (M968.94Govt.Doc.)

4128   Ntara, Samuel Yosia. Headman's enterprise; an unexpected page in Central African history, translated and edited with a preface by Cullen Young from the Cewa original. London, Lutterworth Press, 1949. 213p. (M968.97N87h)

4129   Ntara, Samuel Yosia. Man of Africa, translated and arranged from the original Nyanja by T. Cullen Young. Foreword by Professor Julian Huxley . . . London, The Religious Tract Society, 1934. 184p. (M968.97N87m)

4130   Nyasaland. Central African Lakeland; a visitor's guide to Nyasaland Protectorate British Central Africa. Zomba, Published by the Public Relations Department and printed by the Government Printer, 1953. 99p. (M986.97N98)

4131   Nyasaland. Delegation of chiefs and citizens. A petition to Her Majesty Queen Elizabeth II against federation, made by chiefs and citizens of Nyasaland. With a postscript on Central African Federation, by A. Creech Jones. London, Africa Bureau [1953] 20p. (M968.97N98p)

4132   Read, Margaret. Native standards of living and African culture change, illustrated with examples from the Ngoni highlands of Nyasaland. London, Oxford University Press, 1938. 56p. (M-960R22n)

4133   Rhodesia and Nyasaland. Federal Information Services. The new federation of Rhodesia and Nyasaland. Salisbury, S. Rhodesia, 1954. 48p. (M968.9R34)

4134   Rhodesia, Northern. African Representative Council. The proceedings of the first session of the second council, held at the Munali Training Centre, Lusaka, 13th July-16th July, 1949. Lusaka, Printed by the Government Printer, 1949. 183p. (M-968.94R34ano.4)

4135   Rhodesia, Northern. African Representative Council. The proceedings of the second session of the council, held at the Munali Training Centre, Lusaka, July 1947. Lusaka, Printed by the Government Printer, 1947. 215p. (M968.94R34ano.2)

4136   Rhodesia, Northern. African Representative Council. The proceedings of the second session of the second council, held at the Munali Training Centre, Lusaka, 22nd January-27th January, 1951. Lusaka, Printed by the Government Printer, 1951. 263p. (M968.94R34ano.5)

4137   Rhodesia, Northern. African Representative Council. The proceedings of the special session of the second council, held at the Welfare Hall, Lusaka, 12th September, 1951. Lusaka, Printed by the Government Printer, 1951. 66p. (M968.9434ano.7)

4138   Rhodesia, Northern. African Representative Council. The proceedings of the third session of the first council, held at the Munali Training Centre, Lusaka, 5th July-10th July, 1948. Lusaka, Printed by the Government Printer, 1948. 330p. (M968.94R-34ano.3)

4139   Rhodesia, Northern. African Representative Council. The proceedings of the fifth session of the second council, held at the African Secondary School, Lusaka, 3rd December-6th December, 1951. Lusaka, Printed by the Government Printer, 1952. 67p. (M968.94R34ano.8)

4140   Rhodesia, Northern. African Representative Council. The proceedings of the sixth session of the second council, held at the Munali Secondary School, Lusaka, 18th December-20th December, 1952. Lusaka, Printed by the Government Printer, 1953. 198p. (M968.94R34ano.9)

4141   Rhodesia Northern. Committee on Further Second Education for European Children. Report. Lusaka, Printed by the Government Printer, 1946. 12p. (M968.94R34)

4142   Rhodesia, Northern. Committee to Inquire in the Status and Welfare of Coloured Persons. Report. Lusaka, Printed by the Government Printer, 1950. 51p. (M968.94)

4143   Rhodesia, Northern. Committee to Review Native Taxation. Report. Lusaka, Printed by the Government Printer, 1948. 15p. (M-968.94R34r)

4144   Rhodesia, Northern. General list of chiefs. Lusaka, Government Printer, n.d. (M968.94R34g)

4145   Rhodesia, Northern. Record of the first, second meeting of the Western Province African Provincial Council, 1950, 1951. Lusaka, Government Printer, 1950-51. 2v. (M968.94R34r)

4146   Rhodesia, Northern.   Report of the commission appointed to enquire into the advancement of Africans in industry. Lusaka, Government Printer 1948. 47p. (M968.94R34c)

4147   Rhodesia, Northern. Report of the commission appointed to inquire into the administration and finances of native locations in urban areas. Lusaka, Government Printer, 194? 53p. (M968.94R34co)

4148   Rhodesia, Northern. Report of the committee appointed to investigate European education in Northern Rhodesia, May-July 1948. Lusaka, Government Printer, 1948. 69p. (M968.94R34ee)

4149   Rhodesia, Northern. Report of the European housing committee. Lusaka, Government Printer, 1947. 11p. (M968.94R34eh)

4150   Rhodesia, Northern. Report on the census of population of Northern Rhodesia held on 15th October, 1946. Lusaka, Government Printer, 1949.   125p.   (M968.94R34c)

4151   Rhodesia, Northern. Report on the education of women and girls in Northern Rhodesia. August and September, 1947. Lusaka, Government Printer, 1948. 7p. (M968.94R34e)

4152   Rhodesia, Southern. Public Relations Department. Southern Rhodesia, a field for investment. [Salisbury, 1950] 59p. (M968.-91R34s)

4153   Rhodesia, Southern. Rhodesia museum, Bulawayo. First annual report, 1902. Bulawayo, Philpott and Collins, Printers and Stationers, 1902. 14p. (M968.923R34)

4154   Richards, Audrey Isabel. Hunger and work in savage tribes. London, G. Routledge and sons, ltd., 1932. 238p. (AM572.68R39)

4155   Richards, Audrey Isabel. Land, labour and diet in Northern Rhodesia; an economic study of the Bema tribe. London, New York, Oxford University Press, 1939. 423p. (M968.9R391)

4156   Richards, Audrey Isabel. Tribal government in transition; the Babemba of North-Eastern Rhodesia. Supplement to the "Journal of the Royal African Society." October 1935, vol. XXXIV, no. CXXXVII. 26p. (M968.96R39)

4157 Rukavina, Kathaleen (Stevens). Jungle pathfinder; the biography of Chirupula Stephenson. London, New York, Hutchinson, 1951. 252p. (M968.9R34)

4158 Selous, Frederick Courteney. Sunshine and storm in Rhodesia. London, R. Ward and co., ltd., 1896. 290p. (M968.92Se4s)

4159 Shaw, Mabel. God's candlelights, an education venture in Northern Rhodesia. London, Edinburgh House Press, 1933. 196p. (AM-370Sh2)

4160 Smith, Edwin W. The Ila-speaking peoples of Northern Rhodesia ... London, Macmillan and co., ltd., 1920. 2v. (M968.9Sm5)

4161 Spearpoint, F. The African native and the Rhodesian copper mines. [London] Royal African Society, 1937. 56p. (M968.94Sp3a)

4162 Spotlight on Africa. An NBC radio discussion by Lord Hailey and Calvin W. Stillman. Chicago, University of Chicago Round Table, 1953. 16p. (M960Sp6)

4163 Tabler, Edward C. The far interior; chronicles of pioneering in the Matabele and Mashona Countries, 1847-1879. Capetown, A. A. Balkema, 1955. 443p. (M968.92T11)

4164 Tanser, George Henry. Founders of Rhodesia. Cape Town, Oxford University Press, 1950. 80p. (MBT15f)

4165 The Thirty Seven Club. The Thirty Seven Club Organization. Bulawayo, Southern Rhodesia. 1949. 12p. (M968.94T34)

4166 Thompson, Cecil Harry. Economic development in Rhodesia and Nyasaland. London, D. Dobson [1954] 205p. (M968.9T37)

4167 Torrend, J. Specimens of Bantu folk-lore from Northern Rhodesia. London, K. Paul, Trench, Trubner and co., 1921. 187p. (M-398.3T63)

4168 Turner, VX. W. The Lozi peoples of North-western Rhodesia. London, International African Institute, 1952. 62p. (M968.-95T85)

4169 U.S. Bureau of Foreign Commerce (1953-) Near Eastern and African Division. Investment in Federation of Rhodesia and Nyasaland; basic information for United States businessmen. Washington, U.S. Govt. Print. Off. [1956] 158p. (M968.9Un3i)

4170 U.S. Department of Commerce. Investment in Federation of Rhodesia and Nyasaland; basic information for United States businessmen. Washington, D.C., U.S. Government Printing Office, 1956. 158p.

4171 Van der Post, Laurens. Venture to the Interior. New York, Morrow, 1951. 253p. (M968.97V28v)

4172 Von Sicard, Harold. Ngoma lungundu, eine Afrikanische bundeslade. Uppsala, Almquist and Wiksells, 1952. 192p. (M968.91J89n)

4173 Wallis, John Peter Richard. The Matabele mission. London, Chatto and Windus, 1945. 268p. (M968.92W15m)

4174 Whiteley, Wilfred. Bemba and related peoples of Northern Rhodesia ... With a contribution on the Ambo by B. Stefaniszyn. Peoples of the lower Luapula Valley, by J. Slaski. London, International African institute, 1951. 100p. (M968.3W58b)

4175 Wilson, Godfrey. The Constitution of Ngonde. Livingstone, Northern Rhodesia, the Rhodes-Livingstone Institute, 1939. 86p. (AM572W69c)

4176 Wilson, Godfrey. An essay on the economics of detribalization in Northern Rhodesia. Livingstone, Northern Rhodesia, The Rhodes-Livingstone Institute, 1941. (AM572W69e)

4177 Wright, Fergus Chalmers. African consumers in Nyasaland and Tanganyika. London, His Majesty's Stationery Office, 1955. 116p. (M968.97W93)

SOUTH-WEST AFRICA

4178 Baines, Thomas. Explorations in South-west Africa. Being an account of a journey in the years 1861 and 1862 from Walvisch bay, on the western coast, to lake Ngami and the Victoria falls. London, Longman, Green, 1864. 457p. (AM968B16e)

4179 Ballard, Brok B. South West Africa: 1945-50—Union province or United Nations trusteeship territory. Chicago University of Chicago, Department of History, June, 1955. Microfilm (M-966B21)

4180 Frenssen, Gustav. Peter Moor's journey to Southwest Africa. Boston, and New York, Houghton Mifflin Co., 1908. 244p. (AM-916.68F89)

4181 Green, Lawrence G. Lords of the last frontier; the story of South West Africa and its people of all races. London, Stanley Paul and Co., [1953] 237p. (M968.8G82)

4182 International Court of Justice. International status of South-west Africa, advisory opinion of July 11, 1950. Leyden, A. W. Sijthoff's Publishing Co., [1950] 95p. (M968.81n8)

4183 Jones, John David Rheinallt. The administration of South West Africa, welfare of the indigenous population. Johannesburg, South African Institute of Race Relations, n.d. 19p. (M968.-8J71)

4184 Jones, John David Rheinallt. The future of South West Africa.
Johannesburg, South African Institute of Race Relations, 1946.
30p. (M968.8J71f)

4185 Legendre, Sidney Jennings. Okovango, desert river. New York, J.
Messner [c1939] 300p. (M916.88L52)

4186 McCarrol, Vernell. The operation and administration of the mandate system in South West Africa for 1931. (Thesis) Washington, D.C., Howard University, 1944. 80p. (M378.242HM120)

4187 Passarge, Siegfried. Die Buschmänner der Kalahari. Berlin, D.
Reimer, 1907. 144p. (M968.19P26)

4188 South Africa. South West Africa and the Union of South Africa, the
history of a mandate. Published by authority of the government
of the Union of South Africa, dist. in the U.S. by Union of South
Africa Government Information Office. 108p. (M968.8So8)

4189 Steenkamp, W. P. M. Is the South-West African Herero committing
race suicide? Cape Town, Printed by Unie-Volksper Bpk., n.d.
39p. (M968.85St32i)

4190 Vedder, Heinrich. South West Africa in early times; being the story
of South West Africa up to the date of Maharero's death in
1890. London, Oxford University Press, H. Milford, 1938. 525p.
(M968.8V51)

BECHUANALAND

4191 Bechuanaland Protectorate. Education Department. Annual Reports
1946, 1948, 1949, 1950.

4192 Bechuanaland Protectorate. Laws, statutes, etc. High commissioner's proclamations and the more important notices, from [9th
May, 1950] Pretoria, The Government printing and stationery
office, 1950. 1 vol. (M968.1B38)

4193 Bechuanaland Protectorate. Police Report of the Commissioner of
the Bechuanaland Protectorate Police, 1948.

4194 Bechuanaland Protectorate. Proclamations and government notices.
Pretoria, Government printing and stationery office, 1950. (M-
968.1B38)

4195 Debenham, Frank. Development in Bechuanaland. London, The
Anti-Slavery Society, 1951. 7p. (M968.1D35d)

4196 Flavin, Martin. Black and white, from the Cape to the Congo;
with illustrations. 1st ed. New York, Harper [1950.] 332p.
(M968F61b)

4197 Great Britain. Colonial Office. Annual Report on Bechuanaland protectorate, 1946-48.　London, H. M. Stationery Office. 1946-48.　(M968.1G79a)

4198　Great Britain.　Commonwealth Relations Office.　Bechuanaland protectorate.　Succession to the chieftainship of the Bamangwate tribe, presented by the Secretary of State for Commonwealth Relations to Parliament by Command of His Majesty.　London, H.M.S.O., 1950.　(M968.1G79b)

4199　[International African Service Bureau] Hands off the protectorates. London, Headley Brothers [n.d.] 12p.　(M968In8h)

4200　Jennings, A. E.　Shomolekae.　[Broadway, Livingstone Bookshop, 1930.]　15p.　(MB9Sh7j)

4201　Khama, Tshekdi.　Bechuanaland and South Africa.　[London, The Africa Bureau, 1955.]　20p.　(M968.785T78)

4202　Khama, Tshekdi.　A statement to the British parliament and people.　London, Anti-Slavery and Aborigines Protection Society, 1935.　19p.　(M968.1K52s)

4203　Lugard, Lord.　South Africa and the protectorates.　Reprinted from the "Manchester Guardian," Monday 27, 1935; Tuesday, May 28, 1935.　(M968L96s)

4204　Mockford, Julian.　Seretse Khama and the Bamangwato.　New York, Staples Press, 1950.　231p.　(M968.1M71s)

4205　Molema, Silas M.　Life and health, being health lectures delivered to Bechuanaland Bantu Societies.　Lovedale, South Africa, Lovedale Institution Press, 1924.　69p.　(M968M731)

4206　Perham, Margery Freda.　The protectorates of South Africa; the question of their transfer to the Union.　London, Oxford University Press, H. Milford, 1935.　119p.　(M968P41)

4207　Redfern, John.　Ruth and Seretse: "A very disreputable transaction."　London, Gollancz, 1955.　224p.　(M968.1R24)

4208　Schapera, Isaac.　Married life in an African tribe.　New York, Sheridan House, 1941.　364p.　(M572.968Schlm)

4209　Schapera, Isaac.　Migrant labour and tribal life, a study of conditions in the Bechuanaland Protectorate.　London, New York, Oxford University Press, 1947.　248p.　(M968.1Schlm)

4210　Sillery, A.　The Bechuanaland Protectorate.　Cape Town, New York, Oxford University Press, 1952.　236p.　(M968.1Si3b)

SWAZILAND

4212　Doveton, Dorothy M.　The human geography of Swaziland.　London, George Philip and Son, Ltd., 1937.　110p. (M968.34D75)

4213   Edwards, Isobel Eirleys. Protectorates or native reserves? A political and constitutional survey of the High Commission Territories in South Africa—Basutoland, Bechuanaland and Swaziland. London, The Africa Bureau, n.d. 28p. (M968Ed9p)

4214   Great Britain. Colonial Office. Annual report on Swaziland, 1937, 1954. London, H.M.S.O., 1938, 1955. (M968..34G79s)

4215   Johnson, Kathryn M. Stealing a nation; a brief story of how Swaziland, a South African kingdom, came under British control without the knowledge or consent of its people. Chicago, Pyramid publishing Co., [1939.] 50p. (M968.34J63)

4216   Kuper, Hilda. An African aristocracy; rank among the Swazi of Bechuanaland. New York, Pub. for the International African Institute by Oxford University Press, 1947. 251p. (M968.-34K96a)

4217   Kuper, Hilda. The Swazi. London, International African Institute, 1952. 89p. (M968.34K96s)

4218   Kuper, Hilda. The uniform of colour, a study of white-black relationships in Swaziland. Johannesburg, Witwatersrand University Press, 1947. 160p. (M968.34K96u)

4219   Marwick, Brian Allen. The Swazi; an ethnographic account of the Swaziland Protectorate. Cambridge, University Press, 1940. 320p. (AM572.968M36)

4220   O'Neil, Owen Rowe. Adventures in Swaziland. New York, The Century Co., 1921. 381p.

4221   Perham, Margery Freda. The protectorates of South Africa; the question of their transfer to the Union. London, Oxford University Press, H. Milford, 1935. 119p. (M968P41)

4222   Swaziland. Department of Education. Report, 1949. 51p. (M-968.3Sw2e)

4223   Swaziland. Minutes of the first session of the Re-constituted European advisory council of the territory of Swaziland held at MBane, on the 6th, 7th and 8th days of December 1949. 219p. (M968.3Sw2m)

4224   Swaziland. Principal education officer. Annual report, 1954. Swaziland, Government Printer, 1954. 54p. (M968.34Sw2)

4225   Whiteley, Wilfred. Bemba and related peoples of Northern Rhodesia. Peoples of the lower Luapula Valley. London, International African Institute, 1951. 100p. (M968.3W58b)

BASUTOLAND

4226   Ashton, Hugh. The Basuto. London, New York, Pub. for the

International African Institute by the Oxford University Press, 1952. 355p. (AM572.968As3b)

4227 Basutoland. Director of Education. Annual Report of the Director of Education for the year 1949. Maseru, Basutoland, 1949. (M968.6B29a)

4228 Basutoland. Laws, Statutes, etc. Basutoland proclamations and notices, 1950. Pretoria, Printed by the government printer, 1950. (M968.6B29)

4229 Casalis, Eugène Arnaud. Les Bassoutos; ou, Vingt-trois années de séjour et d'observations au sud de l'Afrique. Paris, C. Meyruels et cie, 1859. 370p. (M968.61C26b)

4230 Damne, Mosebi. Peace, the mother of nations. The "Saga" of the origin of the Protestant Church in Basutoland. [Basutoland, Morija Printing Works of the Paris Evangelical Missionary Society] 1947. 54p. (M968D18p)

4231 Edwards, Isobel E. Basutoland enquiry. London, An African Bureau Publication, 1955. 27p. (M968.61Ed9)

4232 Edwards, Isobel E. Protectorates, or native reserves? A political and constitutional survey of the High Commission Territories in South Africa—Basutoland, Bechuanaland, and Swaziland. London, The Africa Bureau n.d. 28p. (M968Ed9p)

4233 Ellenberger, D. Fred. History of the Basuto, ancient and modern. London, Caxton Publishing Co.; 1912. 396p. (M968.61E15)

4234 Franz, G. H. The literature of Lesotho (Basutoland). Johannesburg, The University of Witwatersrand Press, 1930. 38p. (M968.61F851)

4235 Great Britain. Colonial Office. Annual Reports on Basutoland, 1946-1949, 1954. London, H.M.S.O., 1947-1954- (M968.-61G79ba)

4236 Groen, Juliete. Bibliography of Basutoland. Capetown, University of Cape Town, School of Librarianship, 1946. 30 leaves. (MO-16.968G89b)

4237 Hubbard, Margaret Carson. African gamble. New York, Putnam's Sons, 1937. 279p. (M916.894H86)

4238 [International African Service Bureau.] Hands off the protectorates. London, Headley Brothers, [n.d.] 12p. (M968In8h)

4239 Lagden, Godfrey Yeatman. The Basutos; the mountaineers and their country; being a narrative of events relating to the tribe from its formation early in the nineteenth century to the present day. London, Hutchinson & Co., 1909. 2v. (M-968.61L13)

4240 The Laws of Lerotholi in Basutoland. Johannesburg, Witwatersrand University Press, 1953. 20p. Reprinted from Vol. 11,
No. 4, 1952 issue of "African Studies." (M968.6L44)

4241 Martin, Minnie. Basutoland; Its legends and customs. London,
Nichols & Co., 1903. 174p.

4242 Mohapeloa, J. M. Africans and their chiefs; should Africans be
ruled by their chiefs or by elected leaders. Cape Town, The
African Bookman, 1945. 26p. (M968.6M72a)

4243 Norbury, H. F. Naval brigade in South Africa during the years
1877-1879. London, Sampson, 1880. 307p. (M968.6N75)

4244 Perham, Margery Freda. The protectorates of South Africa; the
question of their transfer to the Union. London, Oxford University Press, H. Milford, 1935. 119p. (M968P41)

4245 Sechefo, Justinus. The twelve Lunar months among the Basuto.
Reprinted from Anthropos, Revue International D'Ethnologie
et de Linguistique, 1910. pp. 931-34. (M968.61Se2)

4246 Widdicombe, John. Fourteen years in Basutoland; a sketch of
African mission life. London, The Church printing Co., [pref.
1891.] 306p. (M916.861W63)

4247 Williams, J. Grenfell. Moshesh; The man on the mountain. London, Oxford University Press, 1950. 150p. (MB9M848)

UNION OF SOUTH AFRICA

GENERAL

4248 Adams, M. J. The solution of unemployment by the aid of token
money. Prepared for submission to the National Conference
of Social Work held at Johannesburg, 30th Sept.-3rd Oct.,
1936. Cape Town, 1936. 46p. (AM331Ad1)

4249 African National Congress. South Africa behind bars, Johannesburg, African National Congress, 1950. 16p. (M968Af83s)

4250 Agar-Hamilton, John Augustus Ion. The road to the north: South
Africa, 1852-1886. London, New York, Longmans, Green and
Co., 1937. 458p. (M968Ag1r)

4251 Akeley, Mary L. (Jobe) Restless jungle. New York, R. M. Mc-
Bride & Co., c1936. 313p. (AM916.8Ak3)

4252 Andersson, Karl Johan. Lake Nagmi; or, Explorations and discoveries during four years' wanderings in the wilds of south-
western Africa, with numerous illustrations, representing sporting adventures, subject of natural history, devices for destroy-

ing wild animals, etc. New York, Harper & Bros., 1856. xviii, [19]-521p. (M968An2)

4253　Andersson, Karl Johan. Notes on travel in Southwestern Africa ... New York, G. P. Putnam's Sons, 1875. 318p. (M968An2n)

4254　Andersson, Karl Johan. The Okabango River; A narrative of travel, exploration and adventure . . . with numerous illustrations and a map of southern Africa. New York, Harper & Brothers, 1861. 21-414p. incl. plates, front fold map. (M968-An20)

4255　Ardizzone, Michael. The mistaken land. London, Falcon press, [1951.] 210p. (AM968Ar2m)

4256　Arndt, E. H. D. Die Unie se goudreserwe: The Union's gold reserve. Pretoria, C. T., Ltd., 1956. 63p.

4257　Ashton, E. H. Medicine, magic and sorcery among the southern Sotho. Capetown, School of African Studies, 1943. 32p. (AM968.6As3m)

4258　Ashton, Eric Ormerod. Notes on form and structure in Bantu speech. London, Oxford University Press, International African Institute, 1945. 19p. (M496.3As3)

4259　Aydelotte, William Osgood. Bismarck and British colonial policy. Philadelphia, Univ. of Penn. press, 1937. 179p. (AM968Ay1)

4260　Backhouse, James. A narrative of a visit to the Mauritius and South Africa. London, Hamilton, Adams, and co., 1844. 648p. (AM-916.8B12)

4261　Baines, Thomas. The gold regions of South Eastern Africa. London, Stanford, 1877. 240p. (M968B16)

4262　Ballinger, Williams George. Race and economics in South Africa. London, Leonard and Virginia Woolf; Hogarth Press, 1934. 67p. (M968B21)

4263　Bangeni, Benjamin A. Kupilwa pi. Lovedale, Lovedale press, 1934. 163p. (M896B22k)

4264　Bangeni, Benjamin A. Ukuwela Kwamadodana Nezikhumbuzo wzibini. Lovedale, Lovedale Press, 1952. 113p. (M896B22u)

4265　Bantu. Welfare Trust. Annual report of the trustees. 2nd, 3rd, 1937-38; 1938-1940. Johannesburg, McPherson & Field ltd., 1938, 1940. 2v. (M968B22)

4266　Barnes, James Albert. Politics in a changing society; a political history of the Fort Jameson Ngoni. Cape Town, Oxford University Press, 1954. 220p. (M968.974B26p)

4267 Barnes, L. Caliban in Africa, an impression of colour-madness. London, V. Gollancz, ltd., 1930. 245p. (AM916.8B26)

4268 Barnes, Leopard. The new Boer war. London, L. & Virginia Woolf at the Hogarth press, 1932. 238p. (M968B26)

4269 Barnouw, Adriaan Jacob. Language and race problems in South Africa. The Hague, M. Nijhoff, 1934. 71p. (M960.323B26)

4270 Barry, Charles. South African native studies. South Africa, Central News Agency ltd., 1946. (M968B27s)

4271 Bell, Nancy R. E. (Meugens) and Arthur Bell. Heroes of South African discovery. London, Marcus Ward, 1889. 388p. (AM-968B41)

4272 Bereng, David Cranner Theko. Lithotokiso tsa Moshoeshoe le tse ling. Morija, Sesuto Book Depot, 1931. 114p. (M896.1B451)

4273 Bicknell, Leona Mildred. How a little girl went to Africa, told by herself. Boston, Lothrop, Lee and Shepard Co., c1904. 172p. (M916.8B47)

4274 Bigelow, Poultney. White man's Africa ... New York and London, Harper bros., 1899. 271p. (M968B48w)

4275 Bissett, Murray. The digest of South African Case Law containing the reported decision of the superior courts ... Cape Town, Juta and Co., ltd., 1949. 362p. (AM968B54)

4276 Bixler, R. W. Anglo-German imperialism in South Africa, 1880-1900. Baltimore, Warwick and York inc., 1932. 181p. (AM-968B55)

4277 Blackwell, Leslie. African occasions; reminiscences of thirty years of bar, bench, and politics in South Africa. With a foreword by General J. C. Smuts ... London, Hutchinson & Co., 1938. 287p. (M968B56a)

4278 Bleek, Dorothea. Cave artists of South Africa. Cape Town, A. A. Balkema, 1953. 80p. (AM750B61)

4279 Bleek, Dorothea F. Comparative vocabularies of Bushman languages. Cambridge, England, The University press, 1929. 94p. (M496B61)

4280 Bleek, Dorothea F. The Mantis and his friends. Bushman folklore. Cape Town, T. Maskew Miller, London and Oxford, n.d. 68p. (AM398B61m)

4281 Bleek, Wilhelm Heinrich Immanuel. A brief account of Bushman folklore and other texts ... London, Trubner and company, 1875. 21p. (AM398B61)

4282 Bleek, Wilhelm Heinrich Immanuel. Specimens of Bushman folk-lore, collected by the late W. H. I. Bleek, Ph.D., and L. C. Lloyd; ed. by the latter; with an introduction by George McCall Theal ... Translation into English; illustrations; and appendix. London, G. Allen & company, ltd. 1911. 468p. (M398-B61

4283 Bokwe, John Knox. Ntsikana; the story of an African convert. 2d. ed. [Lovedale, South Africa, Printed at the Mission Press, 1914] 67p. (MB9N879b)

4284 Brady, Cyrus Townsend. Africa astir, a pictorial report on the advancement of Southern Africa. Melbourne, Georgian House, 1950. 100p. (M968B72a)

4285 Brayshaw, E. Russell. The racial problems of South Africa. London, Friends Home Service Committee, 1952. 9-24p. (M-968B73r)

4286 Breuil, Abbe Henri. Rock paintings of Southern Africa. London, The Trianon Press, 1956. 1v. (AM571.72B83)

4287 British Empire. The Union of South Africa. Catalogue, 1924. 392p.

4288 British information service. Not just peanuts ... New York, British information services. 1948. 28p. (AM968B77n)

4289 Brookes, Edgar Harry. The colour problems of South Africa: being the Phelps-Stokes lectures, 1933. Lovedale, South Africa, Lovedale Press; London, K. Paul, Trench, Trubner and co., ltd., 1934. 237p. (AM968B79)

4290 Brookes, Edgar Harry. South Africa in a changing world. Cape Town Oxford University Press, 1953. 151p. (M968B79s)

4291 Broome, M. A. (Stewart) Baker, lady. Life in South Africa. Philadelphia, J. B. Lippincott & co., 1877. 136p. (AM968B78)

4292 Broome, Mary Ann (Stewart) Baker, lady. A year's house keeping in South Africa. London, Macmillan and co., 1879. 355p. (AM916.8B79)

4293 Broomfield, Gerald Webb. Colour conflict; race relations in Africa, London, Edinburgh house, press, 1943. 144p. (AM916.8B791)

4294 Brown, A. S. and Brown, G. G. The guide to South Africa, 1896-97 ed. London, S. Low, Marston and co., ltd.

4295 Brown, John Tom. Among the Bantu Nomads; a record of forty years spent among the Bechuana, a numerous & famous branch of the central South African Bantu, with the first full description of their ancient customs, manners & beliefs ... with an introduction by A. R. Radcliffe Brown ... 1926. London, Seeley, Service & co., ltd. 272p. (Md68.1B813)

4296 Brown, William Harvey. On the South African frontier; the adventures and observations of an American in Mashonaland and Matabeleland. New York, Chas. Scribner's sons, 1899. 430p. (AM968B81)

4297 Browne, John Hutton Balfour. South Africa; a glance at current conditions and politics ... London, New York and Bombay, Longmans, Green and co., 1905. 238p. (M968B817)

4298 Brownlee, Frank. Lion and jackal, with other native folk tales from South Africa. London, G. Allen & Unwin, 1938. 174p. (AM398B821)

4299 Bryant, Alfred T. An abridged English-Zulu word-book. Incwadi yabantu yamazwi esingisi esasiselwe ngesoizulu, 4th ed. (Marianhill, South Africa) Mariannhill Mission Press, 1940. 471p. (AM496.3B84a)

4300 Bryant, Alfred T. The Zulu people, as they were before the white man came. Pietermaritzburg, Shuter and Shooter 1949. 769p. (M968.3B84z)

4301 Bryce, James Bryce. Impressions of South Africa. New York, The Century co., 1897. 499p. (M968B84)

4302 Bud-M-belle, I. Kafir scholar's companion. Lovedale, Lovedale Missionary Press, 1903. 181p. (M496B85K)

4303 Bullock, Charles. The Mashona. Cape Town & Johannesburg, Juta & co., ltd. 1928. 400p. (AM572.68N87)

4304 Burchell, William John. Travels in the interior of Southern Africa. Reprinted from the original ed. of 1822-4, with some additional material. London, Batchworth press [1953] 2v. (AM968B89)

4305 Burger, John, pseud. The black man's burden. London, V. Gollancz ltd., 1943. 252p. (AM968B91)

4306 Burkitt, Miles Crawford. South Africa's past in stone and paint. Cambridge, [England] The University press, 1928, xiv 183, [Ip.] col. front., illus., viii pl., map. (M572.68b91)

4307 Calloway, Henry. Nursery tales, tradition and histories of the Zulus in their words. Natal, John A. Blair, 1896. 375p. (AM-398.3C13n)

4308 Calloway, Henry, bp. The religious system of the Amazulu. London, Trubner and co., 1868-70. (AM290C13)

4309 Calpin, G. H. Indians in South Africa [1st ed.] Pietermaritzburg, Shuter and Shooter, 1949. 310p. (AM968C13i)

4310 Calpin, George Harold. The South African way of life; values and ideals of a multi-racial society. Edited by G. H. Calpin, under the auspices of the South African Institute of International Affairs. New York, Columbia University Press, 1953. 200p. (M968 C135)

4311   Calpin, George Harold. There are no South Africans. London N. Y., Nelson & sons, 1941. 412p. (M968C13t)

4312   Calvin, Ian Duncan. South Africa ... with twelve reproductions in colour of original drawings by G. S. Smithard and J. S. Skelton. London and Edinburgh, T. C. & E. C. Jack [1909] xiii, 327 1p. (Half-title) Romance of empire series. ed. by John Lang (M968C72)

4313   The Cambridge history of the British empire. v.8—South Africa. Cambridge, England, The University Press, 1936. (M968C14)

4314   Campbell, Dugald. In the heart of Bantuland. Philadelphia, J. B. Lippincott co., London, Seeley, Service and co., ltd., 1922. 313p. (AM966C14)

4315   Campbell, John. Travels in South Africa. Undertaken at the request of the Missionary society. Andover, Mass., Flag and Gould, 1916. xv, 16-398p. Front. 6pl. fold. Map. (M968C15t)

4316   Carnegie Corporation of New York. Memorandum, libraries in the Union of South Africa, Rhodesia and Kenya Colony. New York, 1929. 34p. (AM020C21)

4317   Carnegie Corporation of New York. Report of professor Robert Herndon Fife on tendencies in education in East and South Africa with particular reference to language questions. New York, Printed for the information of the Board of Trustees, 1932. 70p. (AM370C21)

4318   Carnegie Corporation of New York. Report of Rev. Anson Phelps Stokes on education; native welfare and race relations in East and South Africa. 1934. 59p. (AM370C21)

4319   Carter, Gwendolen Margaret. South Africa. [New York Foreign Policy Association] 1955 [c1954] 62p. (M968C24s)

4320   Cathrein, Victor. Der Gottesbergriff der Sulus. 1916. 307-322p. (M968.3C28)

4321   Cele, Madikane Quandiyane. Trip to Africa. Durban, n.d. (M968-C33t)

4322   Chadwick, William Sydney. Mother Africa hits back, the native problem and its solution. Stellenbesch, University Publishers and Booksellers, 1950. 219p. (M968C34)

4323   Chalmers, John A. U-Tiyo Soga; incwadi yobom bake, eyabalwa'.

Lovedale Institution Press, 1923. 158p. (AMB9SO2ch)

4324 Chambliss, J. E. The life and labors of David Livingston, L.L.D., D.C.L., covering his entire career in Southern and Central Africa. Carefully prepared from the most authentic sources . . . The whole rendered clear and plain by a most accurate map of the whole region explored and the routes clearly indicated. Philadelphia, Boston and Cincinnati, Hubbard Bros., etc., 1875. 805p. (M968C35)

4325 Chawner, C. Austin. Timhaka ta Manyana. Nelspruit, Emmanuel Press, [n.d.] 43p. (M968.3C35t)

4326 Chilvers, Hedley Arthur. Johannesburg (Out of the crucible), New York, Stockes [1930] 273p. (AM968C43)

4327 Chilvers, Hedley Arthur. The seven lost trails of Africa. London, Cassel and Co., Ltd. [1931.] 241p. (AM968C43)

4328 Chilvers, Hedley Arthur. The seven wonders of Southern Africa. Johannesburg, 1929. 386p. (AM968C43s)

4329 Clairmonte, E. The Africander. London, T. Fisher Unwin, 1896. 272p. (AM968C52)

4330 Clayton, G. H. Who pays for Bantu progress? Johannesburg, South African Institute for Race Relations, 1941. 11p. (M-968.22057)

4331 Clinton, Desmond Kenilworth. The South African melting pot. London, New York, etc., Longmans, Green and Co., 1937. 158p. (AM266C61)

4332 Cole, D. T. Fanagalo and the Bantu languages in South Africa. n.p. 1953. 1-9p. Reprinted from March, 1953. December 1 issue of African Studies. (AM496.3C67f)

4333 Colenso, Frances Ellen. History of the Zulu war and its origin. London, Chapman and Hall, 1880. 491p. (M968.3C67h)

4334 Colenso, Frances Ellen. The ruin of Zululand: an account of British doings in Zululand since the invasion of 1879. By Frances Ellen Colenso. . . . Being a sequel to the History of the Zulu war, by Frances Ellen Colenso and Lieut.-Colonel Edward Durnford. . . . London, W. Ridgway, 1884-85. 2v. (M968.-3C67r)

4335 Comhaire, J. L. L. Aspects of urban administration in tropical southern Africa, [Cape Town University of Cape Town] 1953. 99p. (M968C73)

4336 Conseil Scientifique pour l'Afrique and Sud du Sahara. Mapping and surveying of Africa South of the Sahara. London, Pub-

lished under the sponsorship of the Com. for Technical Cooperation in Africa South of the Sahara, 1954. 22p. (M968-
C76)

4337   Cook, Edward Tyas. Edmund Garrett; a memoir. London, E.
Arnold, 1909. 284p. (AM968C771)

4338   Cook, Peter Alan Wilson. A history of South Africa for native
schools. London, Longmans, Green, 1932. 144p. (M968C77)

4339   Coppin, Levi Jenkins. Letters from South Africa. Philadelphia,
A.M.E. book concern, n.d. 210p. (AM968.94C791)

4340   Coppin, Levi Jenkins. Observations of persons and things in South
Africa, 1900-1904. Philadelphia, A.M.E. Book Concern, n.d.
205p. (AM968C79o)

4341   Cory, Sir George. The rise of South Africa; a history of the origin
of South African colonization and of its development toward
the east from the earliest times to 1857. . . . London, New
York, etc. Longmans, Green & Co., 1910-1926. 4v. (M968-
C81)

4342   Cotton, Walter Aidan. Racial segregation in South Africa. London,
The Sheldon Press, 1931. 158p. (AM916.8C82)

4343   Council on African Affairs. Resistance against fascist enslavement
in South Africa. With a postscript for Americans by Alphaeus
Hunton. New York, 1953. 62u. (AM968C828r)

4344   Council on African Affairs. Seeing is believing. Here is the truth
about the color bar, land, hunger, poverty and degradation,
pass system, labor exploitation, racial oppression in South
Africa. New York, The Council, 1947. 24p. (AM968C83s)

4345   Coupland, Sir Reginald. Zulu battle piece, Isandhlwana. London,
Collins, 1948. 144p. (M968.3C83z)

4346   Crawshaw, C. J. A first Kafir course. 5th ed. Cape Town, J. C.
Juta, 1903. 133p. (M496.3C85f)

4347   Cron, Gretchen. The roaring veldt. New York, London, G. P.
Putnam's Sons, 1930. 286p. (AM799.2C88)

4348   Curtis, Lionel. With Milner in South Africa. Oxford, Blackwell,
1951. 354p. (M968.2C94w)

4349   Daddo, Y. M. The Indian people in South Africa, facts about the
Ghetto Act. Johannesburg, District Committee, 1946. 13p.
(M968D12)

4350   Damne, Mosebi. Moorosi, Morena oa Baphuthi. Morija, Sesuto
Book Depot, 1948. 54p. (M968D18m)

4351 Davidson, Basil. Report on Southern Africa. London, Jonathan
Cape [1952.] 285p. (M968D28r)

4352 Davies, Horton. South African missions, 1800-1950, an anthology
compiled by Horton Davies and R. H. W. Shepherd. London,
New York, Nelson [1954.] 232p. (M968D29s)

4353 Davis, Alexander. The Native problem in South Africa. London,
Chapman & Hall, 1903. 242p. (M968D29n)

4354 Dawbarn, Charles. My South African year. London, Mills and
Boon, Ltd. [1921.] 252p. (M968D32)

4355 Dawson, William Harbutt. South Africa: people, places and problems. London, New York, Longmans, Green & Co., 1925. 448p.
(AM968D32s)

4356 Day, Price. Crisis in South Africa. "Reprinted from Baltimore
Sun, 1948." 37p. (AM968D27)

4357 De Kiewiet, Cornelius William. A history of South Africa, social
and economic. Oxford, The Clarendon Press, 1941. 292p.
(M968D36h)

4358 Desmond, Shaw. African log . . . photographs and verse by the
author; frontispiece from a drawing by Alfred Palmer . . .
London, Hutchinson & Co., Ltd. [1935.] 282p. (M916D46)

4359 Dlokweni, J. I-Ntliziyo yom ntu (The heart of man) Intshumayelo.
Cape Town, The Methodist Book Room, 1930. 89p. (M220-
D65)

4360 Doell, E. W. Doctor against witchdoctor. London, C. Johnson,
1955. 216p. (M968D67)

4361 Dornan, S. S. Pygmies and Bushmen of the Kalahari. London,
Seeley, Service and Co., Ltd., 1925. 80p. (AM968D73p)

4362 Doyle, Conan A. The great Boer war. New York, McClure Phillips, 1900. 478p. (M968D77g)

4363 Doyle, Conan A. The war in South Africa. New York, McClure
Phillips, 1902. 139p. (M968D77w)

4364 Dube, John Langalebalele. Insila ka Tshaka. (Mariannhill) Icin-
dezelwe Ngokwesi tatu, 1933. 80p. (M896D5i)

4365 Dube, John Langalebalele. Jeqe, the body-servant of King Tshaka
Translated from the Zulu by Professor J. Boxwell. Lovedale,
The Lovedale Press, 1951. 84p. (M896D85i)

4366 Dube, John Langalebalele. Ukuziphatha Khale (Goodmanners),
ibalwe ngu John L. Dube. 2nd. ed. Mariannhill, Mariannhill
Mission Press, 1935. 61p. (M896D85u)

4367 Duggan-Cronin, Alfred Martin. The Bantu tribes of South Africa; reproductions of photographic studies. Cambridge, [Eng.] Deighton, Bell, 1928. 4v. (M968D87)

4368 Dvorin, Eugene P. Racial separation in South Africa: An analysis of apartheid theory. Chicago. University of Chicago Press, 1952. 256p. (M968D95r)

4369 Dyafta, D. Z. I kamua lethu, Ibalwe ngu D. A. Dyafta. Lovedale, The Lovedale Press, 1953. 96p. (M896D98i)

4370 Education in the Union of South Africa. Empire exhibition, Johannesburg, Pretoria, Union of South Africa. Government Printer, 1936. 34p. (AM370Ed8)

4371 Edwards, Isobel Eirlys. The 1820 settlers in South Africa. London, New York, Longmans, Green and Co., 1934. 207p. (AM-968Ed9e)

4372 Edwards, Isobel Eirlys. Protectorate or native reserves? A political and constitutional survey of the High Commission Territories in South Africa-Basutoland, Bechuanaland and Swaziland. London, The African Bureau, n.d. 28p. (M968Ed9p)

4373 Ellenberger, V. Un Siècle de Mission su Lessouto, 1833-1933. Paris, Société des Missions Évangéliques, 1932. 131p.

4374 Evans, Ifor Leslie. Native policy in southern Africa; an outline. Cambridge, Eng. The University Press, 1934. 117p. (M968-Ev1)

4375 Facts about South Africa; a reprint from the South African-American survey 1951. New York, Union of South Africa, Government Information Office, 1951. 134p. (AM968F11)

4376 Fairbridge, Dorothea. A history of South Africa ... London, New York, etc., Oxford University press, H. Milford, 1918. 319p. (M968F15h)

4377 Fairbridge, Dorothea. The pilgrim's way in South Africa. London, Oxford University press, 1928. 195p. (M968F15)

4378 Fallers, Lloyd A. Bantu bureaucracy; A study of role conflict and institutional change in the Soga political system. Chicago, University of Chicago Library, Dept. of Phorographic reproduction, 1953. (M968F19b)

4379 Farming in South Africa ... Pretoria, Dept of agriculture and forestry (AM968F22)

4380 Federal Council of the Dutch Reformed Church. European and Bantu being papers and addresses read at the conference on native affairs ... at Johannesburg on 27th-29th Sept., 1923, n.p. [1924] 56p. (AM968F31)

4381 Ferguson, John Henry. American diplomacy and the Boer war ...
[by] John H. Ferguson. Philadelphia, 1939. 240p. (M968.-
2F38a)

4382 Fitzsimons, Frederick William. The monkey folk of South Africa ...
with sixty illustrations. London, New York, etc., Longmans,
Green and Co., 1911. 167p. (M968F58)

4383 Flavin, Martin. Black and white from the Cape to the Congo. New
York, Harper, 1950. 332p. (M968F61b)

4384 Frank, Cedric N. U.M.C.A. and the colour bar. London, Universities' Mission to Central Africa, 1955. 12p. (M968F85)

4385 Franklin, N. N. Economics in South Africa. Cape Town, Oxford
University Press, 1948. 253p. (M968F85c)

4386 Frobenius, Leo. Erythraa, lander und zeiten des heligen konigs-
mordes. Berlin, Zurich, Atlanta Verlag, 1931. 368p. (AM-
968F92)

4387 Fuller, Robert Hart. South Africa at home ... London, G. Newnes,
ltd., 1908. xiii, 235p. (M968F95)

4388 Gandhi, Mohandas Karamchand. Satyagraha in South Africa. Stanford, Calif., Academic Reprints, 1954. 351p. (M968C15s)

4389 Gardiner, Allen Francis. Narrative of a journey to the Zoolu country, in South Africa ... undertaken in 1835. London, William
Crofts, 1836. 412p. (M968G16)

4390 Gatti, Attilio. Here is the veld. New York, C. Scribner's sons, 1948.
154p. (AM916.8G22h)

4391 Gerard, Francis. Springbok Rampant. London, F. Muller, 1951.
249p. (AM968G31s)

4392 Gibbs, Henry. Twilight in South Africa. New York, Philosophical
Library, 1950. 288p. (M968G35t)

4393 Gil, Antonio. Consideraçoes sobre alguns pontos mais importantes
da moral religiosa e systema de jurisprudencia dos pretos do
continente da Africa occidental portugueza alem do equador,
tendentes a dar alguma. Lisboa, Typografia da Academic,
1854. 56p. (AM968G41c)

4394 Gluckman, Max Custom and conflict in Africa. Oxford, Blackwell,
1955. 173p. (M968.3G52)

4395 Gordon-Brown, Alfred. Pictorial art in South Africa during three
centuries to 1875. London, C. J. Sawyer, 1952. 172p. (AM-
709G65)

4396 Gordon-Cumming, Ronaleyn George. A hunter's life among lions, elephants, and other wild animals of South Africa. New York, Derby and Jackson, Cincinnati, H. W. Derby and Co., 1857. 2v. (AM968G65)

4397 Gould, Charles. Author and printer in South Africa. Johannesburg, Imprint Society, 1945. 24p. (M968G72)

4398 Grammar e nyenyana ea ba ithutang se English. Morija, Sesuto Depot, 1940. 30p. (M496.3G76)

4399 Great Brit. British Information Services. The story of the British commonwealth and empire. New York, 1947. (AM330.942G79)

4400 Great Brit. Royal Commission on the war in South Africa ... Minutes of evidences taken before the Royal commission on the war in South Africa ... London, Printed for H. M. Stationery office, by Wyman and sons, ltd., 1903. 415p. (M968G79m)

4401 Great Brit. Royal Commission on the war in South Africa. Report of His Majesty's commissioners appointed to inquire into the military preparations and other matters ... London, Wyman and sons, ltd., 1903. 316p. (AM968G79r)

4402 Green, M. S. The making of the union of South Africa, a brief history, 1487-1939. London, New York, Longmans, Green, 1946. 227p. (M968G82m)

4403 Hamilton-Brown, G. A lost legionary in South Africa. London, T. Werner Laurie [n.d.] 308p. (M968H181)

4404 Hance, Gertrude Rachel. The Zulu yesterday and today; twenty-nine years in South Africa. New York, Chicago, Fleming H. Co., [c1916] 274p. (M968.3H19)

4405 Harmsworth, C. B. Pleasure and problem in South Africa. London, J. Lane; New York, J. Lane Co., 1908. 253p. (M968H22)

4406 Hartshorne, K. B. Native education in the Union of South Africa; A summary of the report of the Commission on Native Education in South Africa—U. G. 53-1951. Johannesburg, South African Institute of Race Relations, 1953. 62p. (M968H25)

4407 Hatch, John Charles. The Dilemma of South Africa. London, D. Dobson [1952] 255p. (M968H28d)

4408 Hattersley, Alan Frederick. South Africa, 1652-1933 ... London, T. Butterworth limited, 1933. 255, 1p. (Half-title: The home university Library of modern knowledge) (M968H28s)

4409 Hawarden, Eleanor. Labour and the new economic policy. A commentary on the 23rd interim report of the industrial and agricultural requirements commission. Johannesburg, South African institute of Race relations, 1942. 18p. (M968H31)

4410 Haythornthwaite, Frank. All the way to Abenab. London, Faber and Faber, 1956. 288p. (M968H33)

4411 Hellmann, Ellen. Handbook on race relations in South Africa; ed. by Leah Abrahams. Pub. for the South African Institute of Race Relations, Cape Town, Oxford University Press, 1949. 778p. (M968H36)

4412 Hellmann, Ellen. Problems of urban Bantu youth. Report of enquiry into the causes of early school-leaving and occupational opportunities amongst Bantu youth in Johannesburg. Johannesburg, South African Institute of Race Relations, 1940. 151p. (M968H36p)

4413 Hepple, Alex. The African worker in South Africa; a study in trade unionism. London, The Africa Bureau, n.d. 36p.

4414 Herbstein, Joseph. The civil practice of the Superior Courts in South Africa, by Joseph Herbstein and others. Cape Town, Juta & Co., ltd., 1954. 736p. (M968H41c)

4415 Hillegas, Howard Clemens. Oom Paul's people; a narrative of the British-Boer troubles in South Africa. New York, D. Appleton & Co., 1899. 308p. (M968.2H550)

4416 Hobman, Daisy Lucie. Olive Schreiner, her friends and times. London, Watts, 1955. 182p. (MC9Sc7)

4417 Hobson, John Atkinson. The war in South Africa; its causes and effects ... New York, The Macmillan company; London, Macmillan and Co., ltd., 1900. 324p. (M968H65w)

4418 Hockly, Harold Edward. Mars, the law of insolvency in South Africa. 4th ed. Cape Town, Juta & Co., ltd., 798p. (AM-968H65m)

4419 Hoernle, R. F. Alfred. South African native policy and the liberal spirit. Being the Phelps-Stokes lectures delivered before the University of Cape Town, May 1939. Cape Town Phelps-Stokes Fund of the University of Cape Town, 1939. (AM968-H78) 190p.

4420 Hofmeyr, Jan Hendrik. Christian principles and race problems. Johannesburg, S. A. Institute of Race Relations, 1945. 31p. (M968H67)

4421 Hofmeyr, Jan Hendrik. South Africa ... New York, C. Scribner's sons, 1931. 331, 1p. (Lettered on cover: The Modern World) (M968H67)

4422 Hofmeyr, Jan Hendrik. South Africa, 2d. rev. ed. by J. P. Cope.

New York, McGraw Hill, 1952. 253p. (AM968H67)

4423   Holden, William Clifford. British rule in South Africa. London. Wesleyan Conference Office, n.d. 218p. (M968.3H71)

4424   Hole, Hugh Marshall. The passing of the black kings. London, P. Allan, 1952. 322p. (M968H71p)

4425   Holt, Basil. Joseph Williams; and the pioneer mission to South-Eastern Bantu. Lovedale, The Lovedale Press, 1954. 186p. (MC9W67h)

4426   Holub, Emil. Sieben Jahre in Sud-Afrika. Erlebnisse, forschungen und jageen auf meinen reisen von den diamantenfeldern zum Zanbesi (1872-1879). Van dr. Emil Holub. Wien, A. Holden, 1881. 2v. (AM968H74)

4427   Honey, James Albert. South-African folk-tales. New York, The Baker & Taylor, 1910. 151p. (AM398H75)

4428   Hooker, LeRoy. The Africanders; a century of Dutch-English feud in South Africa. Chicago and New York, Rand, McNally and Co., 1900. (M968H76)

4429   Horrel, Muriel, comp. A survey of race relations in South Africa 1951-52. Johannesburg, South African Institute of Race Relations, 1952. 80p. (M968H78s)

4430   Houser, George M. (Nonviolent revolution in South Africa. Foreword by Z. K. Matthews. New York, Fellowship publications, 1953. 29p. (M968H81n)

4431   Huddleston, Trevor. Naught for your comfort. New York, Doubleday, 1956. 253p. (M968.22H86)

4432   Huddleston, Trevor. Sport, the arts and the colour bar in South Africa. London, The Africa Bureau. 20p.

4433   Hunter, Monica. Reaction to conquest. London, International Institute of African Language and Culture. 1936. 582p. (M-968H91)

4434   Hunton, William Alpheus. Stop—South Africa's crimes. No annexation of S.W. Africa. New York, Council on African Affairs, 1946. 24p. (M968H92s)

4435   Impey, Samuel Patton. Origin of the bushmen and the rock paintings of South Africa. Cape Town and Johannesburg, Juta & Co., ltd., 1926. 102p. (AM700Im7)

4436   India (Republic) Ministry of External Affairs. Action taken by the government of the Union of South Africa under the Group areas act. 1950. n.p. 1950? 15p. (AM968In3a)

4437   Ireland, William. Historical sketch of the Zulu, Mission in South

Africa. Boston, American board of commissioners for foreign missions, [n.d.] 32p. (AM968Ir2)

4438 Jabavu, Davidson Don Tengo. Bantu literature. Classification and reviews. [n.d.] South Africa, P. P. Lovedale, 1921. 27p. (AM-469.3J11)

4439 Jabavu, Davidson Don Tengo. The black problem. Papers and addresses on various native problems. Lovedale, C. P. the book dept., 1920. 173p. (M968J11b)

4440 Jabavu, Davidson Don Tengo. E-Amerika u-welo luka. Lovedale, Lovedale press, 1932. 52p. (M968J11a)

4441 Jabavu, Davidson Don Tengo. Imbumba jamaNyama. Lovedale, Lovedale press, 1952. 105p. (M968J11im)

4442 Jabavu, Davidson Don Tengo. E-Indiya nase East Africa. Lovedale. Lovedale press 1951. 175p. (M968J11ei)

4443 Jabavu, Davidson D. T. The influence of English on Bantu literature. Lovedale, Lovedale Press, 1943. 26p. (M968J11i)

4444 Jabavu, Davidson Don Tengo. E-Jerusalem u-hambelo luka. Lovedale, Lovedale press, 1929. 124p. (M968J11e)

4445 Jabavu, Davidson Don Tengo. The life of John Tengo Jabavu, editor of Imvo Zabantsundu, 1884-1921. Lovedale, South Africa, Lovedale Institution press, [1922] 156p. (M968J11j)

4446 Jabavu, Davidson Don Tengo. "Native disabilities" in South Africa. [Lovedale, Cape Province, South Africa] The Lovedale Press [1932.] 26p. (M968J11n)

4447 Jabavu, Davidson Don Tengo. The segregation fallacy and other papers (a native view of some South African interracial problems). [Lovedale] Lovedale institution press, 1928. 137p. (M968J11s)

4448 Jackman, Stuart Brooke. The numbered days. London, SCM Press, 1954. 100p. (M968J13)

4449 Jacottet, Edouard. Litsomo tsa Basotho. Buka ea bobeli. Morija, Sesuto Book Depot, 1941. 148p. (AM398J151)

4450 Jagger, John William and Tredgold, Clarkson. The native franchise question. Addresses by J. W. Jagger and Sir Clarkson Tredgold delivered at a public meeting held in Capetown on Wednesday, 15th January, 1930 at 8:15 p.m. Capetown, Non-Racial Franchise Association, [ca.] 1930. 15p. (M968J18)

4451 James, Selwyn. South of the Congo. New York, Random House, 1943. 347p. (M968J23)

4452 Jansen, Ernest George. Native policy of the union of South Africa; statements made on April 20, 1950 and May 19, 1950. Pretoria State Information office, Union of South Africa, 1950. 29p. (M968J26n)

4453 Jeffery, Gladys M. South Africa—fellowship or fear? London, Fellowship of Reconciliation, 1952. 12p. (M968J36s)

4454 Jessett, Montague George. The key to South Africa: Delagoa Bay ... With maps and illustrations. London, T. F. Unwin, 1899. 177[1]p. (M967J49)

4455 Johannesburg, Publicity Association. Johannesburg, a sunshine city built on gold. Johannesburg, Goverm, Dands & co., 1933. 56p. (AM968.21J59j)

4456 Johannesburg. Johannesburg. A sunshine city built on gold. Johannesburg. Publicity Association, 1929. 110p. (M968.22J59)

4457 Johnson, M. P. The stone implements of South Africa. London, New York, Bombay & Calcutta, Longmans Green, and co., 1907. 53p. (AM913.68J63)

4458 Johnson, Kathryn M. Stealing a nation. Chicago, Pyramid publishing co., [1939] 9-50p. (AM968.34J63)

4459 Johnston, James. Reality versus romance in South Central Africa. New York, Chicago, F. H. Revell co., 1893. 353p. (AM916.-7J64)

4460 Jolobe, James J. R. Amavo. Introduction by R. T. Bokwe. Johannesburg, University of Witwatersrand Press, 1945. 72p. (M896J68a)

4461 Jolobe, James J. R. Iintsomi zika-aesop (Isilumko somgrika), Lovedale, The Lovedale Press, 1953. 98p. (M896J68i)

4462 Jolobe, James J. R. Lovedale Xhosa rhymes (IziCengcelezo zose Dikeni azilungele la Mabanga: Sub A, Sub B, Std 1, Std 11, Lovedale, The Lovedale Press, 1952. 44p. (M896J68L)

4463 Jolobe, James J. R. Ukuphakama ukusuka ebukhobokeni. (Up from slavery, by Booker T. Washington) Johannesburgh, Afrikoonse Pers Boekhandel, 1951. 162p. (M896J68uk)

4464 Jolobe, James J. R. U-Zagula, ibalwe. Lovedale, The Lovedale Press, 1944. 80p. (M896J68uz)

4465 Jolobe, James J. R. Xhosa grammatical terminology (amazwi emigaqo yentetho yesizhosa by J. T. Arosi. Lovedale, The Lovedale press, 1951. 20p. (M896J68x)

4466 Jones, John David Rheinallt. The union's burden of poverty. Johannesburg, South African institute of Race Relations, 1942. 44p. (AM968J71)

4467 Jones, Thomas Jesse. The two U.S.A.'s Some aspects of the race question. Johannesburg, South African Institute of Race Relations, n.d. Pamphlet No. 1 n.p. (AM968J72)

4468 Jooste, G. P. South Africa; planned policy or chaos. New York, Union of South Africa Government information Office, 1952. 31p. (M968J74s)

4469 Jordan, A. C. Ingqumbo yeminyanya. Lovedale, Lovedale press, 1946. 250p. (M896.3J76i)

4470 Joshi, P. S. The tyranny of colour: a study of the Indian problem in South Africa. S. Africa, E. P. & Commercial Printing Co., 1942, 318p.

4471 Junod, Henri Alexandre. The life of South African tribe. London, Macmillan Co., 1913. 2v. (AM968J96)

4472 Junod, Henri Alexandre. Moeurs et coutumes de Bantous, la vie d'une tribu Sud-Africaine . . . Paris, Payot, 1936. 2v. (M968-J96m)

4473 Junod, Henri Phillippe. Bantu heritage. Johannesburg, South Africa, Hortors, limited, 1938. 155p. (AM572.96J96)

4474 Junod, Henri Philippe. The wisdom of the Tonga-Shangaan people. Published with the assistance of a grant made by the Cargenie Corporation through the Research Grant Board, Union of South Africa, [n.d.] 285p. (AM968J96w)

4475 Kalane, Thomas B. The customs of my people in their uncivilized state. Wilberforce, Ohio, The Industrial Press, 1909. 12p. (M968K12c)

4476 Kawa, Richard Tainton. I bali lama mfengu. Introduction by D. D. T. Jabavu. Lovedale, Lovedale press, [1929] 116p. (M968K17i)

4477 Kay, Stephen. Travels and researches in Caffrari; describing the character, customs, and moral condition of the tribes inhabiting that portion of southern Africa; with historical and topographical remarks illustrative of the state and prospects of the British Settlement in its borders, the introduction of Christianity, and the progress of civilization . . . New York, Harper & brothers, 1834. [1] [11]-428p. (M968K18)

4478 Kemp, Samuel. Black frontiers; pioneer adventures with Cecil Rhodes in Africa. [New York] Brewer, Warren and Putnam [1931] 287p. (AM968K32)

4479   Kennedy, W. P. M. The law and customs of the South African constitution. London, Oxford University press, H. Milford, 1935. 640p. (AM916.8K38)

4480   Keppel-Jones, Arthur. The dilemma of South Africa. Toronto, Canadian Institute of International Affairs, 1950. 20p. (AM-323K446d)

4481   Keppel-Jones, Arthur. Friends or foes? A point of view and a programme for racial harmony in South Africa. Pietermaritzburg, Shuter and Shooter, 1950. (M968K44)

4482   Keppel-Jones, Arthur. South Africa; a short history. London, New York, Hutchinson's University Library [1949] 21p. (AM-968K44s)

4483   Kgasi, Micah. Thulaganyô dipolêlô. Lovedale, The Lovedale Press, 1951. 69p. (M968K52t)

4484   Kgasi, Micah. Thuto ke eng. Lovedale, Lovedale press, 1945. 44p. (M968K52th)

4485   Khafula, John J. B. This thing has got to stop. Capetown, The African Bookman, 1946. 15p. (M968K53t)

4486   Khaketla, B. Makalo. Moshoeshoe le baruti. E ngotsoe ke B. Makalo Khaketla . . . Morija, Basutoland, Morija Sesuto Book Depot, 1947. 95p. (M896.2K52m)

4487   Kidd, Dudley. The essential Kafir. 2nd. ed. London, A & C. Black, 1925. 435p. (AM968K53e)

4488   Kidd, Dudley. The Kafir socialism and the dawn of individualism; an introduction to the study of the native problem. London, A&C Black, 1908. 286p. (AM968.6K53)

4489   King, Andrew. Gold metallurgy on the Witwatersrand. [Johannesburg, Transvaal Chamber of Mines, 1952] 458p. (AM968K-577)

4490   King, Marisa (Nourse) Woodroffe. Sunrise to evening star. London, g. g. Harrap & Co., ltd. 1935. 314p. (AM968K58)

4491   Kirby, Percival Robson. The musical instruments of the native races of South Africa. London, Oxford University Press, 1934. 285p. (AM781.91K63)

4492   Kirk, John. The economic aspects of native segregation in South Africa . . . with a foreword by Dr. C. T. Loram . . . London, P. S. King & son, ltd., 1929. 148p. (M960.323K634)

4493   Kirkland, Caroline. Some African highways; a journey of two American women to Uganda and the Transvaal . . . with an introduction by Lieutenant General Baden-Powell; with illustrations from photographs and a map. Boston, Dana Estes & Company [c1908] 11-345p. (M968.2K63)

4494 Kolbe, F. W. A language study based on Bantu; London, Trubner & co., 1888. 97p. (AM496.3K83)

4495 Komai, Felicia. Cry, the beloved country. New York, Friendship Press, 1948. 80p.

4496 Kriel, T. The new Afrikaans school dictionary; Afrikaans-English and English-Afrikaans. Capetown, Susseau, 1937. (AM496.-3K89)

4497 Krige, Eileen (Jensen). The realm of a rain queen, a study of the pattern of Lovedu society by J. D. Krige ... with a foreword by the R. Hon. Field-Marshall J. C. Smuts .. London, New York, etc. Pub. for the International Institute of African Languages & Cultures by the Oxford University press, 1943. 1 335p. (M968K89)

4498 Krige, Eileen (Jensen). The social system of the Zulus. 2nd ed. Pietermaritzburg, Natal, East Union of South Africa, Shuter and Shooter, 1950. 420p. (AM968K89s)

4499 Kruger, Stephanue Johannes Paulas. The memoirs of Paul Kruger; four times President of the South African Republic, told by himself. London, T. Fisher Unwin, 1952. 543p. (MC9K93)

4500 Laubscher, Barent Jacob Frederick. Sex, customs and psychopathology; a study of South African pagan natives. New York, R. M. McBride and Co., 1938. 347p. (AM968L36s)

4501 Leask, Thomas. Southern African diaries, 1865-1870. Edited by J. P. R. Wallis. London, Chatto & Windus, 1954. 253p. (M-968L48)

4502 Lecatle, Edward Motsamai. Morena Moshoeshoe mor'a Mokhachane. Morija, Sesuto Book Depot, 1942. 84p. (AMB9L55m)

4503 Letcher, Owen. The gold mines of South Africa. Johannesburg, London, The Author, 1936. 580p. (AM916.8L56)

4504 Lewin, Julius. Studies in African native law. Cape Town, African Bookman; Philadelphia, University of Penn. Press, 1947. 174p. (M968L58s)

4505 Lewis, Stakesby. Kaffir beer halls. The failure of "an experiment." [Fordsburg, South Africa, P. C. Westwood, printer, 1941] 40p. (AMd68L585)

4506 Lichtenstein, Hinrich. Travels in southern Africa in the years 1803, 1804, 1805, and 1806. Translated from the original German by Anne Plumptre. London, Printed for Henry Colburn 1812. 383p. [30p] (M916.8L61t)

4507   Livingstone, David. Livingstone's travels and researches in South Africa; including a sketch of sixteen years' residence in the interior of Africa, and a journey from the Cape of Good Hope to Loanda on the west coast, thence across the continent, down the river Zembezi, to the eastern ocean. From the personal narrative of . . . to which is added a historical sketch of discoveries in Africa . . . Philadelphia, J. W. Bradley, 1858, 2, 5-446p. (M-968L76t)

4508   Livingstone, David. Missionary travels and researches in South Africa. New York, Harper and brothers, 1858. 732p. (AM-916.67L76m)

4509   Loram, Charles Templeman. The education of the South African native. London, New York, Longmans, Green and co., 1917. 340p. (AM370L88)

4510   Lovedale Missionary Institution. South Africa. Report for 1930 . . . Lovedale, Lovedale press, 1930. (AM968L94e)

4511   Lovell, Reginald Ivan. The struggle for South Africa, 1875-1899. New York, Macmillan company, 1934. 438p. (AM968L94)

4512   Lowndes, E. E. K. Everyday life in South Africa. London, S. W. Partridge & Co., 1900. 182p. (AM916.68L95)

4513   Lumb, Subil Victoria Central and southern Africa; a short history, Cambridge (End) University Press, 1954. 119p. (M968L97)

4514   Luyt, R. E. Trade Unionism in African Colonies. Johannesburg, South African Institute of Race Relations, 1949. 42p. (AM-331L97)

4515   McCrone. Ian Douglas. Group conflicts and race prejudices. Johannesburg, South African Institute of Race Relations, 1947. 31p.

4516   MacCrone, Ian Douglas. Race attitudes in South Africa; historical experimental and psychological studies, London, New York, etc. Published on behalf of the University of the Witwatersrand, Johannesburg, by the Oxford University Press, 1937. 317p. (M960.323M13)

4517   Machobane James J. Mahaneng a Matso. Morija, Basutoland, Sesuto Book Depot, 1946. 38p. (M398M18ma)

4518   Machobane,. James J. Mphatlatatsane ea Sekhutlo. Morija, Sesuto Book Depot, 1947. 105p. (M398M18ma)

4519   Mackenzie, William Douglas. South Africa; its history, heroes and wars assisted by Alfred Stead ... Superbly illustrated with original drawings and photographs under direction of George Spiel. Chicago, Philadelphia, Monarch book company, c1899. 7-682p. (M968M19s)

4520 Mackinnon, James. South African traits. Edinburgh, J. Gemmell, 1887. 301p. (M968M21s)

4521 Macmillan, William Miller. Africa beyond the union. Johannesburg, South African Institute of Race Relations, 1949. 20p. (M968-M22a)

4522 Macmillan, William Miller. Bantu, Boer, and Briton. London,, Faber and Gwyer limited, 1929. 328p. (M960.323M22)

4523 Macmillan, William M. Complex South Africa; an Economic Footnote to History. London, Faber and Faber ltd., [1930] 293p. (AM968M22)

4524 MacVicar, Neil. Western civilization and the Bantu. Johannesburg, South African Institute of Race Relations, 1947. 39p. (M968-M25w)

4525 Maile, Mallane L. Ngoanana ha a botsa telejane. Morija, Sesuto Book Depot, 1947. 32p. (M896M28)

4526 Maile, Mallane L. Ramasoabi le potse ("Father of weeping" written in Sotho) Morija, Sesuto Book Depot. 1947. 39p. (M-968,2M28r)

4527 Majeke, Nosopho. The rôle of the Missionaries in conquest. Johannesburg, Society of Young Africa, 1952. 140p.

4528 Makoa, Jeremia. Sefofu Bartimea. Morija, Sesuto Book Depot, 1939. 29p. (M896M29s)

4529 Malan, Daniel Francois. Foreign policy of the Union of South Africa; statements. Pretoria, State Information Office, Union of South Africa, 1950. 52p. (M968M291f)

4530 Malherbe, Ernest Gideon. Handbook on education and social work in South Africa. Pretoria, The New education fellowship. 1934. 120p. (AM968M27)

4531 Malherbe, Ernst Gideon. Race attitudes and education. Johannesburg S. A. Institute of Race Relations, 1946? 29p. (M968M-288)

4532 Malherbe, Janie A. Complex country. London, Longmans, Green and co., ltd., 1944. 80p. (AM968M29c)

4533 Mangoaela, Zekea D. Har'a libatana le linyamatsane. Morija, Sesuto Book Depot 1945. 105p. (M896M31h)

4534 Mangoaela, Zekea D. Lithoko tsa Marena a Basotho, tse Bokelet-

soeng ke, Morija, Sesuto Book Depot, 1928. 246p. (M896M-
31e)

4535   Mangoaela, Zakea D. Tsoelo-pele ea Lesotho. The Progress of the
        Sotho People. Morija, Sesuto Book Depot, 1928. 52p. (M-
        968M31t)

4536   Manyase, L. T. Indlela yokubalwa kwamagama esi-Xhose ngolobalo
        olutsha. Lovedale, Lovedale Press, 1952. 20p. (M496M31)

4537   Mapetla, Joase. Liphoofolo, Linonyana, Li taola le lithoko tsa
        tsona. Morija, Sesuto Book Depot, 1928. 32p. (M896.1M321)

4538   Marais, Ben J. Colour: unsolved problem of the West. Cape Town,
        Harold B. Timmins, 1952. 329p. (M986M32)

4539   Marquard, Leopold. The peoples and policies of South Africa. Lon-
        don, New York, Oxford University Press, 1952. 258p. (AM-
        968M34p)

4540   Marquard, Leopold. The southern Bantu. London, Oxford Univer-
        sity Press, 1939. 262p. (M968M34)

4541   Marwede, Hud H. T. Shall lobolo live or die? Two opposing view-
        points on the passing of gift cattle in Bantu marriage. Cape
        Town, African Bookman, 1945. 30p. (AM968M365)

4542   Mason, Philip. An essay on racial tension. London, New York,
        Royal Institute of International Affairs [1954] 149p. (M-
        968M38)

4543   Mathers, Edward Peter. Zambesia, England's El Dorado in Africa.
        London, King, Sell and Railton; Capetown, South Africa, Juta
        and co., [1895] 480p. (M968M42)

4544   Matthews, Zachariah K. The Crisis in South Africa. Reprinted
        from Christianity and crisis, November 10 and 24, 1952. 8p.
        (AM968M43c)

4545   Matthews, Zachariah K. South Africa: a land divided against itself.
        In: The Yale Review, 1953. 528p.

4546   Maud, John Primatt Redcliffe. City government; the Johannesburg
        experiment. Oxford, The Clarendon Press, 1938. 412p. (M96-
        8.22M44c)

4547   Mauduit, Jacques. Kalahari; la vie des bochimans. Paris, Fernand
        Nathan, 1954. 87p. (M968.19M44)

4548   May, Henry John. The South African Constitution. 3d. ed., with
        chapters by A. V. Dickinson [and others] Cape Town, Juta,
        1955. 678p. (M968M45)

4549   Mayer, Philip. Gusii bridewealth law and custom. Cape Town,

New York, Published for the Rhodes-Livingstone Institute by
Oxford University press, 1950. 67p. (M968M45g)

4550 Mdontswa, A. D. Unkom'ikhal' Inlahlelwa. [Lacks imprint] 1934.
63p. (M968M46u)

4551 Menon, K. N. Passive resistance in South Africa. New Delhi, [The
Author] 1951. 32p. (AM968M52p)

4552 Millin, Sarah Gertrude (Liebson) The people of South Africa. London, Constable 1951. 324p. (M968M62p)

4553 Millin, Sarah Gertrude. The South Africans ... New York, Horace
Liveright, Publisher, 1931. 13-287p. (M968M62)

4554 Mockford, Julian. The golden land, a background to South Africa.
London, Black [1949] 270p. (M968M71g)

4555 Mockford, Julian. Here are South Africans. With a foreword by
Deney Reitz. Third edition. London, Adam & Charles Black,
1949. 11p. (M968M71h)

4556 Mockford, Julian. Overseas reference book of the Union of South
Africa, including South-West Africa, Basutoland, Bechuana-
land Protectorate and Swaziland. London, and New York,
Todd Publishing co., 1945. 567p. (916.8M71o)

4557 Mocoancoeng, Jac. G. Tseleng ea Bophelo. Le lithothokiso tse ncha.
Johannesburg, Witwatersrand University press, 1947. 52p.
(M896M71t)

4558 Moffat, Robert. Missionary labours and scenes in Southern Africa.
8th ed. New York and Pittsburg, Robert Carter, 1845. 406p.
(M967M72)

4559 Mofokeng, Twantyman M. Sek'ona sa joala; papali ea tsa motse,
Morija, Sesuto Book Depot, 1931. 45p. (M896.2M72)

4560 Mofolo, Thomas. Chaka, an historical romance, with an introduction
by Sir Henry Newbolt. Tr. from the original Sesuto by F. H.
Dutton. London, published for the International Institute of
African languages & Cultures by Oxford University press, 1931.
198p. (AM896.3M72)

4561 Mofolo, Thomas. Chaka. Morija. Sesuto Book Depot 1925. 288p.
(M896.3M72)

4562 Mofolo Thomas. Chaka der Zulu; roman. Zurich Manesse verlag,
1953. 268p. (M896.3M72c3)

4563 Mofolo, Thomas. Moeti oa bochegela. (Morija, Sesuto book depot,
1938) 156p. (M896.3M27tm)

4564 Mofolo, Thomas. Pitseng. Morija, Sesuto book depot, 1930. 433p.
(M896.3M72p)

4565   Mofolo, Thomas. The traveller of the East. London, Society for promoting Christian knowledge, n.d. 125p. (M896.3M72t)

4566   Mohapeloa, J. P. Meloli le lithallere tas Afrika. Morija, Sesuto Book Depot, 1945. 79p. (M784M72)

4567   Moikangoa, C. R. Litsomo tsa ma-Afrola (African Folk Tales). Maseru, Basutoland, Macenod Institute, n.d. 78p. (M398M721)

4568   Molema, Silas M. The Bantu, past and present; and ethnographical & historical study of the native races of South Africa. Edinburgh, W. Green & son, limited, 1920. 398p. (M968M73b)

4569   Morris, G. R. A bibliography of the Indian question in South Africa. Cape Town, University of Cape Town, School of Librarianship, 1946. 17p. (AMO16M83)

4570   Morton, Henry Canova Vollam. In search of South Africa. London, Methuen, 1948. 359p. (AM968M46)

4571   Motlamelle, Paulua. Ngaka ea Mosotho Lacks imprint. 1937. 160p. (AM614M85)

4572   Motsamai, Edward. Mehla ea malimo. Morija, Sesuto Book Depot. 143p. (M896.3M85m)

4573   Motsatse, Ratsebe L. Khopotso ea bongoana. Morija, Sesuto Book Depot, 1938. 112p. (M896.3M858)

4574   Mpalele, Ezekial L. Man must live and other stories. Cape Town, The African Bookman, 1946. 46p. (M896.3M87m)

4575   Mpanza, James Sofasonke. Izimpa zendlela yomkrestu. Lovedale, Lovedale Press, 1936. 55p. (M896M87iz)

4576   Mqhayi, Samuel Edward Krune. Imihobe nmeibongo, yokufundwa ezikolweni. Yanziwe. London, The Sheldon press [1927] 116p. (M896M87i)

4577   Mqhayi, Samuel Edward Krune. I-nzuzo. Johannesburg, The University of Witwatersrand press, 1942. 96p. (M896M87in)

4578   Mqhayi, Samuel Edward Krune. Ityala lama-Wele. [Lovedale] Ushicilelo Lwesi-tandatu [1914] 136p. (M896M87it)

4579   Mqhayi, Samuel Edward Krune. Ityala lama-wele. NgamaZwembezwembe akwagzuluwe. Lovedale, The Lovedale press [1931] 167p. (M896M87it)

4580   Mqhayi, Samuel Edward Krune. U-Bom bomOFundsi u John Know Bokwe. Lovedale, Lovedale Institution press, 1925. 92p. (M-896M87u)

4581   Mqhayi, Samuel Edward Krune. U-Don Jadu: "Ukuhamba yi Mfundo." Imbali yokukutaza u Manyano ne nqubela Pambili.

Lovedale Lovedale press 1929. 77p. (M896M87it)

4582 Mqhayi, Samuel Edward Krune. U-Don Jadu: "UkuHamba yim Fundo." Imbali yokukhuthaza uManyano nenkqubela-Phambili. Lovedale, Lovedale Press, 1944. 68p. (M896M87in)

4583 Mqhayi, Samuel Edward Krune. U-Mqhayi wase-Nta6'ozuko. Lovedale, Lovedale press, 1939. 87p. (M896M87um)

4584 Muller, Edward. Isiguqulo sama Protestanti saciteka kanjani namazwe amaningi. Mariannhill Mission Press, 1929. 54p. (M-280M91i)

4585 Muller, Edward. Umlando we Bandhla. Mariannhill Mission Press, 1929. 57p. (M280M91u)

4586 Mzimba, Livingstone Ntibane. Ibali lobomi nomsebenzi womfi umfundishi Pambani Heremiah Mzimba. Libalwe nqunyana wake U-Livingstone Ntibane Mzimba. Lovedale, Lovedale Institution Press, 1923. 93p. (MB9M99)

4587 National coloured-European conference. First National coloured-European conference. Report of proceedings. Cape Town, June 26, 27, 28, 1933. Cape Town Atlas Printing Works, 1933. 116p. (M968N21f)

4588 National European-Bantu conference. Report of the National European-Bantu conference, Cape Town, Feb. 6-9, 1929. Lovedale, Lovedale Institution Press, 1929. 4p. (M968N21r)

4589 National Union of South African Students. The African in the universities. Cape Town, 1951. 40p. (AM378N21)

4590 Ncwana, K. K. Amanqakwana ngeminombo yezizwe zasembo. Lovedale, Lovedale press, 1953. 64p. (M968 N24a)

4591 Ndamase, Victor Poto. Ama-Mpondo. Ibali ne-Ntalo. Lovedale, Ishicilewe e-Lovedale, 1925. 158p. (M968 N23a)

4592 Ndebele, Nimrod N. T. Ugubudele namazimuzimu (Umdlalo osenzosinye esinemiboniso emihlanu). Johannesburg, University of the Witwatersrand Press, 1941. 75p. (M896.2N24u)

4593 Ngani, Alfred Z. Ibali lanagqunukawebe. Lovedale, Lovedale press, [1937] 38p. (M968N51i)

4594 Ngani, Alfred Z. Ubom buka-kama [The life of Kama] Lovedale, The Lovedale press 1952. 55p. (M968N51u)

4595 Ngcobo Selby Bangani. The Bantu Peoples. New York, Columbia University Press, 1953. 49-69p. (M968C135)

4596 Ngubane, Jordon K. Should the natives representative council be abolished? Cape Town, The African Bookman, 1946. 28p. (M-968N51s)

4597 Nhlapo, Jacob M. Bantu babel. Will the Bantu languages live? Cape Town, The African Bookman, 1944. 15p. (M496N51)

4598 Nhlapo, Jacob M. Nguni and Sotho, A practical plan for the unification of the South African Bantu languages. Cape Town, The African Bookman, 1945. 22p. (AM968N49)

4599 Nicholls, G. Heaton. Native policy of the Union of South Africa, New York, South African Govt. Information Office, 1945. 69p. (M968N51n)

4600 Nicholson, Marjorie. Self-government and the communal problem. London, Fabian publication, 1948. 45p. (M968N52s)

4601 Nielsen, Peter. The black man's place in South Africa. Cape Town, Juta & co., ltd., 1922. 149p. (M968N55b)

4602 Nielsen, Peter. The colour bar. Cape Town and Johannesburg, Juta & co., limited [1937] 148p. (M960N55)

4603 Nkomo, Simbini Mamba. The call of Africa; the tribal life of the people of South Africa. Chicago, Institute Place, 1917. unnumbered pages. Autographed by the author. At head of title: "Oration delivered at the College Commencement at Greenville, Ill., in June 1917." (M968N65c)

4604 Norbeth, B. M. Some notes upon technical education 1914. Durban, Pl. Davis & sons, 1915. (AM370.96N16s)

4605 Norton, Conrad. Opportunity in South Africa. London, Rockliff, 1948. 172p. (AM968N82o)

4606 Ntsane, K. E. Masoabi. Ngoan'a Mosotho 'aKajeno. Morija, Basutoland, Sesuto Book Depot, 1947. 139p. (M896N88ma)

4607 Ntsane, K. E. 'Musa-pelo. Morija, Basutoland, Sesuto Book Depot, 1946. 76p. (M896.1N88mu)

4608 Nyembezi, Cyril Lincoln. Siibusiso. Zulu Proverbs. Johannesburg, Witwatersrand University Press, 1954. 238p. (M398.9N98)

4609 Oldham, Joseph Houldsworth. New hope in Africa the aims of Capricorn Africa Society. London, Longmans, Green and Co., 1955. 102p. (M968011n)

4610 Oldham, Joseph Houldsworth. White and black in Africa; a critical examination of the Rhodes lectures of General Smuts. London, New York, Longmans, Green and Co., 1930. 73p. (M968012w)

4611 Olivier, Sydney Haldane Olivier, baron. The anatomy of African misery. London, L. and Virginia Woolf, 1927. 233p. (M-968014a)

4612 Oppenheim, Gladys. Books for the Bantu, a study of library service for the Africans. Pretoria, South Africa, Carnegie Corporation Visitor's grants Committee, 1940. 52p. (M9680p5)

4613 Oppenheimer, H. F. Towards racial harmony. Supplement to Optima, Sept., 1956. 16p. (M968p5t)

4614 Paton, Alan. Cry, the beloved country. New York, Scribner's sons, 1948. 278p. (M896.3P27c)

4615 Paton, Alan. The land and people of South Africa. Philadelphia and New York, J. B. Lippincott, 1955. 143p.

4616 Paton, Alan. Too late the phalarope. New York, Scribner, 1953. 276p. (AM896.3P27t)

4617 Patterson, Sheila. Colour and culture in South Africa. London, Routledge and Kegan Paul, ltd., 1953. 402p. (M968P277c)

4618 Peattie, Roderick. Struggle on the veld. New York, The Vanguard Press, 1947. 264p. (M967P32)

4619 Perham, Margery Freda. The protectorates of South Africa; the question of their transfer to the Union by Lionel Curtis. London, Oxford University Press, H. Milford, 1935. 119p. (M-968p41)

4620 Phillips, Henry Albert. Cape Town to the Mountains of the Moon. New York, M. McBride, 1949. 223p. (M968P54c)

4621 Phillips, Ray Edmund. The Bantu are coming. London, Student Christian movement press, 1930. 238p. (M968P54)

4622 Phillips, Ray Edmund. The Bantu in the city; a study of cultural adjustment on the Witwatersrand. [Lovedale, South Africa.] The Lovedale Press, 1938. 452p. (M968.22p54)

4623 Pienaar, Eduard Christiaan. Dichters unt Zuida-Afrika. Bloem Pretoria, J. H. De Bussey, 1917. 126p. (AM839.36D59d)

4624 Plaatje, Solomon Tshekisho. Dinsthontsho tsa Bo-Juliuse Kesara, Ke William Shakespeare. (Translated by S. T. Plaatje; foreword by G. P. Lestrade). Johannesburg, University of Witwatersrand Press, 1942. 75p. (M968P69d)

4625 Plaatje, Solomon Tshekisho. Mhudi; an epic of South African native life a hundred years ago. Lovedale, Lovedale press, 1930. 225p. (M968P69mh)

4626 Plaatje, Solomon Tshekisho. The mote and the beam. An epic on sex-relationship 'twixt white and black in British South Africa. New York, Young's Book Exchange, n.d. 11p. (M968p69m)

4627 Plaatje, Solomon Tshekisho. Native life in South Africa, before and since the European war and the Boer rebellion. . . . London, P. S. King & Sons, Ltd., 1916. 352p. (M968p69n)

4628 Plaatje, Solomon Tshkisho. Native life in South Africa, before and since the European war and the Boer rebellion. Kimberley, South Africa, New York, The Crisis. 382p. (M968P69m)

4629 Pollack, Walter. The South African Law of Jurisdiction. Johannesburg, Hortors, limited, 1937. 265p. (M916.8P76)

4630 Powell, Oliver. Spotlight on South Africa. New York, Friendship Press, 1952. 48p. (M968P87s)

4631 Pretoria. Department of Agriculture. Annual report, 1948. Pretoria, 1948. (M913.68P92a)

4632 Pretoria University. Archaeological committee. Mapungubwe; ancient Bantu civilization on the Limpopo. Cambridge, The University Press, 1937. 62p. (M913.68P92)

4633 Prussia. Grosser generalstab. Kriegsgeschichtliche abteilung. The war in South Africa, prepared in the Historical section of the Great general staff, Berlin. London, J. Murray, 1904. 280p. (M968P95)

4634 Prussia. Grosser generalstab. Kreigsgeschichtliche abteilung. The war in South Africa; the advance to Pretoria after Paardeberg, the Upper Tugela campaign, etc., London, J. Murray, 1906. 374p. (M968D85w)

4635 Pyrah, G. B. Imperial policy and South Africa, 1902-10. Oxford, at the Clarendon Press, 1955. 272p.

4636 Raditladi, L. D. Motswasele ii. Johannesburg, University of Witwatersrand Press, 1945. 65p. (M896.2R11m)

4637 Reed, Douglas. Somewhere south of Suez. London, Cape, 1950. 428p. (M916.8R25s)

4638 Reeves, Ambrose. Justice in South Africa. London, The Africa Bureau, 1955. 12p. (M968R25)

4638a Reich, Hanns. Portrait of Southern Africa. London, Collins, St. James Place, 1956. 95p.

4639 Reich, Hanns. Südafrika: Text und aufnahem von Hanns Reich. München, H. Reich Verlag [1954, c1955.] unp. (M968R27s)

4640 Reitz, Deneys. Afrikander. New York, Minton, Balch and Co., 1933. 320p. (AM968R27)

4641 Reynolds, Rex. Searchlight on South Africa's native policy, a survey. New York, Union of South Africa State Information Office, 1947. 64p. (M968R33s)

4642 Rey, Charles Fernand. The Union of South Africa and some of its problems. New York, 1947. 60p. (M968R33u)

4643   Roberts, Austin. The birds of South Africa illustrated by Norman C. K. Lighton. Published for the trustees of the South African bird book fund. London, H.F.&G. Witherby, Ltd., [etc., etc.] [1940.] 463p. (M968R54b)

4644   Rogers, Howard. Native administration in the Union of South Africa, being a brief survey of the organization, functions and activities of the department of Native affairs of the Union of South Africa. Johannesburg, University of Witwatersrand, 1933. 372p. (AM354.68R63)

4645   Roscoe, John. The northern Bantu. Cambridge, The University Press, 1915. 305p. (AM968R71)

4646   Rose-Innes, James and others. . . . Native disabilities in the Union of South Africa. Speeches delivered in the city hall. (Banqueting Room) Cape Town at a crowded meeting of citizens on 28th January, 1931, by Rt. Hon. H. Burton . . . Rev. R. B. Douglas . . . Prof. Fremantle and Rev. A. M'Timkulu, n.p. ca.1931. 20p. (968R72n)

4647   Rose-Innes, James. The native franchise question. A speech . . . read at the opening meeting of the Non-Racial Franchise Association, Cape Town, Cape Times, Limited, 1929. 15p. (M-968R72)

4648   Routh, Guy. Industrial relations and race relations. Johannesburg, South African Institute of Race Relations, 1952. 28p. (M968R76)

4649   Roux, Edward. Time longer than rope; a history of the black man's struggle for freedom in South Africa. London, V. Gollancz, 1948. 398p. (M968R76t)

4650   Sachs, E. S. The Choice before South Africa. New York, Philosophical Library, 1952. 220p. (M968Sa1)

4651   St. John, Robert. Through Malan's Africa. [1st ed.] Garden City, N. Y. Doubleday, 1954. 317p. (AM968Sa2)

4652   Saron, Gustav. The Jews in South Africa; a history. London, Oxford University Press, 1955. 422p. (M968Sa7)

4653   Schapera, Isaac. The Bantu-speaking tribes of South Africa. London, G. Routledge & Sons, Ltd., 1937. 453p. (AM572.968-Sch1)

4654   Schapera, Isaac. The ethnic composition of the Tswana tribes. London, London School of Economics and Political Science, 1952. 133p. (M968.1Scle)

4655   Schapera, Isaac. A handbook of Tswana law and custom. London, Oxford University Press, 1938. 326p. (AM916.81Sch1)

4656 Schapera, Isaac. The Khoisan peoples of South Africa, Bushmen and Hottentots. . . . London, G. Routledge & Sons, Ltd., 1930. 450p.

4657 Schapera, Isaac. Select bibliography of South African native life and problems. London, Oxford University Press, 1941. 249p. (AMO16Sch1)

4658 Schapera, Isaac. The Tswana. London, International African Institute, 1953. 80p. (M968Sc1)

4659 Schreiner, Olive. From man to man. London, T. F. Unwin, Ltd., 1926. 483p. (AM896.3Sch7)

4660 Schreiner, Olive. The South African question. Chicago, Charles H. Sergel Co., 1899. 123p.

4661 Scientific Council for Africa South of the Sahara. Reports, 1950. Kikuyu, Kenya, 1950. (M968)

4662 Scott, Michael. Civilization in Africa. London, Fellowship of Reconciliation, [195-] 7p. (AM968c8c)

4663 Scott, Michael. Experiment in time; a sermon preached in New York Cathedral. London, The Africa Bureau, 1954. 15p (M25-2Sc8)

4664 Scott, Michael. Shadow over Africa. London, Union of Democratic Control [1950.] 24p. (M968.8Sc8s)

4665 Scully, William Charles. Kafir stories. New York, Henry Holt & Co., 1895. 194p. (AM810.8Sc4)

4666 Searle, Ernest W. With a policeman in South Africa. New York, London, The Abbey Press, 1900. 130p. (AM916.68Se17)

4667 Segal, Albert. Johannesburg Friday. New York, McGraw-Hill Book Co., 1954. (AM896.3Se3)

4668 Segoete, Everitt Lechesa. Monono. Le moholi, ke mouoane. Morija, Sesuto Book Depot, 1926. 227p. (M896 Se3m)

4669 Segoete, Everitt Lechesa. Raphepheng. Morija, Sesuto Book Depot, 1913. 122p. (M896Se3r)

4670 Sekese, Azariele M. Bukana ea tsomo tsa pitso ea linonyana le tseko ea sefofu le seritsa. Morija, Sesuto Book Depot, 1931. 113p. (M896Se4p)

4671 Sekese, Azariele M. Mekhoa le maele a Ba-Sotho. A Hlalositsoeng ke Azariele Sekese. Morija, Sesuto Book Depot, 1931. 408p. (M896Se4m)

4672 Serpa Pinto, Alexandre Alberto da Rocha de. How I crossed Africa. Hartford, Conn., R. W. Bliss, 1881. 406p. (M916.-8Se6e)

4673 Severinghaus, Whitman J. South Africa: old policies, new leaders. New York, Foreign Policy Association, 1951. 212p. (AM968-Se8s)

4674 Shackleton, Charles Walter. East African experiences, 1916, from the diary of a South African infantryman in the German East African campaign. Durban, South Africa, The Know Publishing Co., 1940. 140p. (AM968Sh1)

4675 Shaw, Barnabas. Memorials of South Africa. London, J. Mason, 1840. 371p. (M968Sh2)

4676 Sheddick, V. G. J. The Southern Sotho. London, International African Institute, 1953. 87p. (AM968Sh3)

4677 Sheldon, Louise (Vescelius) Yankee girls in Zulu land. New York, Worthington Co., 1888. 287p. (M916.8Sh4)

4678 Shepherd, Robert Henry Wishart. African contrasts, the story of a South African people by B. G. Paver. Cape Town, Oxford University Press, 1947. 266p. (M916.8Sh4a)

4679 Shepherd, Robert Henry Wishart. Bantu literature and life. Lovedale, The Lovedale Press, 1955. 198p. (M496Sh4)

4680 Shepherd, Robert Henry Wishart. Children of the veld. London, J. Clarke and Co., Ltd., 1937. 194p. (AM266Sh4)

4681 Shepherd, Robert Henry Wishart. Literature for the South African Bantu. A comparative study of Negro achievement. Pretoria, S. Africa, The Carnegie Corporation, 1936. 81p. (M968Sh4)

4682 Shepherd, Robert Henry Wishart. Lovedale and literature for the Bantu; a brief history and a forecast. Lovedale, The Lovedale Press, 1945. 111p. (M896Sh4)

4683 Shepherd, Robert Henry Wishart. Lovedale, South Africa: the story of a century, 1841-1941. Lovedale, C. P. South Africa, The Lovedale Press [1940.] 531p. (M968Sh41)

4684 Shepherd, Robert Henry Wishart. Where aloes flame. South African missionary vignettes. London, Lutterworth Press, 1948. 171p. (AM266Sh4w)

4685 Shropshire, Denys W. T. The Bantu woman under the Natal code of native law; Lovedale, The Lovedale Press, [1941.] 47p. (M968Sh7f)

4686 Shropshire, Denys W. T. Primitive marriage and European law. London, Society for Promoting Christian Knowledge, 1946. 185p.

4687 Sibiya, Christina. Zulu woman. New York, Columbia University Press, 1948. 281p. (AM572.9Silz)

4688   Simms, Katherine L.   The sun-drenched veld.   London, Evans Bros.,
       1949.   143p.   (M916.8Si48)

4689   Skota, T. D., Complier.   The African yearly register; being an
       illustrated national biographical dictionary (Who's Who) of
       black folk in Africa.   Johannesburg, R. L. Esson & Co., 1932.
       450p.   (MB9Sk5)

4690   Smith, Edwin William. The life and times of Daniel Lindley, 1801-
       80; missionary to the Zulus, pastor of the Voortrekkers, Ubebe
       omhlope.   New York, Library Publishers, [1952.]   456p.   (M-
       968Sm5)

4691   Smuts, Jan Christiaan.   The basis of trusteeship in African native
       policy.   An address delivered under the auspices of the South
       African Institute of Race Relations in City Hall, Cape Town on
       Wednesday, January 21, 1942.   Johannesburg, R. L. Esson &
       Co., 1942.   20p.   (M968Sm8)

4692   Smuts, Jan Christiaan.   Toward a better world.   New York, World
       Book Co., distributed by Duell, Sloan and Pearce.   [1944.]
       308p.   (M916.8Sm8)

4693   Soga, John Henderson.   The Ama-Xosa: life and customs.   Lovedale,
       C. P. South Africa, Lovedale Press; London, K. Paul, Trench,
       Trubner and Co., Ltd., [1932.]   431p.   (M968So2a)

4694   Soga, John Henderson.   Inkonzo zema-bandla ka-krestu; umalatiso
       wokuqutywa kwenkonzo, kunye nezimiselo eziya kuba luncedo
       kubapatiswa be-lizwi lika-tixo, nakuma-handla e-nkosi u Yeso
       Krestu.   Lovedale, Lovedale Press, 1943.   (M968So21i)

4695   Soga, John Henderson.   The south-eastern Bantu (Abe-Naguni, Aba-
       Mbo, Ama-Lala).   Johannesburg, The Witwatersrand University
       Press, 1930.   490p.   (M896So21s)

4696   Soga, Tiyo Burnside.   Intalalo ka Xosa.   Lovedale, Lovedale Uni-
       versity Press, [1927.]   250p.   (M896So2i)

4697   Soga, Tiyo Burnside.   Uhambo lo Mhambi [Translation of The Pil-
       grim's Progress.   Part I translated by Tiyo Soga.   Part II
       translated by J. Henderson Soga.]   Lovedale, Lovedale Insti-
       tution Press. n.d. 190p.   (M896So2u)

4698   Soga, Tiyo Burnside.   U-Tiyo Soga; incwadi yobom bake, eyabalwa
       ngu Mfundise U-John A. Chalmers, Wase Tunxe.   Iguqulelwe
       esi-oseni ngu Mfundise U-Tiyo Burnside Soga.   Lovedale, In-
       stitution Press, 1923.   158p.   (M896So2ch)

4699   South Africa.   Commission on Native Education.   Reports . . . 1949-
       1951.   Pretoria, Government Printers, 1951.   233p.   (M968-
       Gov.Doc.)

4700   South Africa. Commission on technical and vocational education. Report . . . Pretoria, Government Printer, 1948. 310p. (M-968Govt. Doc.)

4701   South Africa. Committee of enquiry into subsidies to university colleges and technical colleges . . . Report of the committee . . . 1933. Pretoria, Government Printers, 1934. 39p. (M968-Sorep)

4702   South Africa. Committee on deviate children. Report . . . (Non-European children). Pretoria, 1950. 162p. (M968Govt. Doc.)

4703   South Africa. Committee on medical training. Report of the committee on medical training in South Africa. Pretoria, Union of South Africa, 1939. 73p. (M968So8r)

4704   South Africa. Conference on rural education. Report of conference on rural education, 1934 . . . Pretoria, Government Printer, 1934. 8p. (AM968So8re)

4705   South Africa. Conference on rural education. Report on rural education, 1934 . . . Pretoria, Government Printer, 1934. 8p. (M968So8re)

4706   South Africa. Department of mines and industries. Industrial development in South Africa. Pretoria, The Government printing and stationery office, 1927. 231p. (M916.8So8i)

4707   South Africa. Education Department. Arts and Sciences. Inter-Departmental Committee on Deviate Children. Report . . . (Non-European children) 162p. (Mimeographed). (M968-Govt.Doc.)

4708   South Africa. Education Department. Committee of inquiry. Native school feeding scheme. Report, 1949. Pretoria, Government Printer, 1949. 142p. (M968Gov.Doc.)

4709   South Africa. Education Department. Committee on adult education. Adult education in South Africa. Pretoria, Printed by the Government Printer, 1946. 186p. (AM374So8a)

4710   South Africa. Farming opportunities in the Union of South Africa. [Cape Town, Townshend. Taylor, and Shashall, printers, 1922.] 334p. (AM916.8So8)

4711   South Africa. Information Office. This is South Africa, edited by Henry M. Moolman. New York, 195-. 91p. (AM968So8t)

4712   South Africa. National bureau of educational and social research. Bulletin of educational statistics, 1940. Pretoria, Government printer, 1940. (AM968So8b)

4713   South Africa. National Council for Social Research. Reports for

1947-1949, 1950. Pretoria. (M968Govt.Doc.)

4714 South Africa. Office Census and statistics. Official year book of the Union of South Africa, 1937. (M968So8o)

4715 South Africa on the Nazi path. New Delhi, Indian Overseas Central Association, 1952. 56p. (AM968So789)

4716 South African-American survey; a publication devoted to the promotion of cultural and trade relationships between the Union of South Africa and the United States of America, and of International understanding. [1st] issue; 1947- New York. (AM968So79)

4717 South African-American survey. New York, Union of South Africa Government information office, 1946. 1950. 1951.

4718 South African Association of European teachers in native educational institutions. Annual conference umtata, 1831. [n.p.n.d.] 11p. (AM370So8)

4719 South African Bureau of Racial Affairs. Oppression or opportunity? Stellenbosch, The South African Bureau of Racial Affairs, 1955. 48p.

4720 South African Institute of International Affairs. Africa library. Books, pamphlets and periodicals, list No. 1, Johannesburg, January 1951. 20p.

4721 South African Institute of International Affairs. Africa south of the Sahara. Cape Town, Oxford University Press, 1951. 286p. (AM966So8a)

4722 South African Institute of Race Relations. Inside our prisons. Johannesburg, S. A. Institute of Race Relations, 1944. 9p. (M968.22So8)

4723 South African Institute of Race Relations. National Conference to study the Report of the Native Education Commission. Record of proceedings. Johannesburg, South African Institute of Race Relations, 1952. 31p. (M968So93nr)

2724 South African Institute of Race Relations . . . Political representation of Africans in the Union. Johannesburg, The Institute, 1942. 38p. (M968So9p)

4725 South African Institute of Race Relations. Report 1937-1940, 1945-1946. (M968So93r)

4726 South African Institute of Race Relations. What it is and what it does, Johannesburg, The South African Institute of Race Relations, 1935. 9p. (M968So8w)

4727 South African Native Races Committee. The South African Natives.

London, J. Murray, 1909. 247p. (AM968So.8)

4728 The South African republics vs. Great Britain. By a True American. New York, n.p. 1900. 37p. (AM968So8)

4729 South Africa's heritage (1652-1952); the story of white civilization in South Africa from the landing of the first Dutch settlers with Jan van Riebeeck to the present day. Pretoria, State Information Office (Union of South Africa) 1952. 100p. (M968So87)

4730 South Africa's people. (unnumbered pages) (M968So8s)

4731 Spencer, Frederick H. A report on the Technical Colleges of South Africa. [New York] Carnegie Corporation of New York, 1937. 15-65p. (AM968Sp3)

4732 Spohr, U. H. Photographic service points in libraries, archives and museums in South Africa. Cape Town, University of Cape Town Libraries, 1949. 20p. (AM968Sp6p)

4733 Stark, James Henry. The British and Dutch in South Africa. Boston, J. H. Stark, 1900. 32p. (M968St2)

4734 Stayt, Hugh Arthur. The Bavenda. London, Oxford University Press, H. Milford, 1931. 392p. (M968.2St2)

4735 Steedman, Andrew. Wanderings and adventures in the interior of southern Africa. Longmans and Co., 1835. (London) 2v. (AM916.68St3)

4736 Steevens, George Warrington. From Capetown of Ladysmith; an unfinished record of the South African war . . . ed. by Vernon Blackburn. New York, Dodd, Mead and Company, 1900. 198p. (M968St3)

4737 Stewart, James. Lovedale; past and present. A register of two thousand names. Lovedale, South Africa, Printed at the Mission Press, 1887. 642p. (AM968St41)

4738 Stockley, Cynthia. Poppy, the story of a South African girl. 7th ed. London, Hurst and Blackett, Limited, 1910. 400p. (M-896St6)

4739 Stout, Benjamin. Narrative of the loss of the ship Hercules. London, Hudson, Reprinted A. Stoddard, 1800. 112p. (M916St7)

4740 Stow, George William. The native races of South Africa. London, S. Sonnenschien and Co., Ltd., New York, The Macmillan Co., 1905. 618p. (AM968St7)

4741 Struggle for Africa, south of the Sahara. New York, The Nation, 1953. 557-576pp. (AM968St8)

4742 Stuart, James. A history of the Zulu rebellion, 1906, and of Dinu-

zulu's arrest, trial and expatriation. London, Macmillan and
Co., Ltd., 1913. 581p. (M968.3St9h)

4743 Stuart, P. A. A Zulu grammar for beginners. Rev. ed. Pietermaritzburg. Shuter & Shooter, 1940. 159p. (AM496St9)

4744 Student Christian Association. Christian students and modern South
Africa. A report of the Bantu-European Student Christian Con-
ference. Fort Hare, June 27-July 3, 1930. Fort Hare, Alice,
C.P. 1930. 243p. (AM968St9)

4745 Sundkler, Bengt Gustaf M. Bantu prophets in South Africa. London, Lutterworth Press, 1948. 344p. (AM267.8Su7)

4746 Suzman, Helen. A digest of the Fagan report, the Native Laws
(Fagan) Commission, prepared by Helen Suzman. Johannes-
burg, South African Institute of Race Relations, 1952. 22p.
(M968Su9)

4747 Swaartbooi, V. N. M. U-Mandisa. Lovedale, Lovedale Press, 1946.
47p. (M896.3Sw1)

4748 Symends, Francis Addington. The Johannesburg story. London,
M. Muller, 1953. (M968.22Sy6)

4749 Tabota, I. B. Eight million demand freedom! What about it, Gen.
Smuts? New York, Council on African Affairs, Inc., 1946.
23p. (AM968T11e)

4750 Taljaard, M. S. A glimpse of South Africa. Stellenbosch, University publishers and booksellers, 1949. 226p. (AM916.8T14g)

4751 Taylor, Alice. South Africa; illustrated by Rafaello Busoni. New
York, Holiday House [1954] 26p. (M968T21)

4752 Taylor, Bayard. Travels in South Africa. New York, Scribner,
1887. 336p. (AM916.68T21)

4753 Taylor, W. P. African treasures. London, J. Long, Ltd., 1932.
288p. (AM916.8T21)

4754 Thomas, E. W. Bushman stories. Cape Town, Oxford University,
1950. 75p. (M398T36b)

4755 Tinley, James Maddison. The native labor problem of South Africa.
Chapel Hill, The University of North Carolina Press, 1942.
281p. (M968T49n)

4756 Torrend, J. A comparative grammar of the South African Bantu
languages, London, Kegan Paul, 1891. 336p. (AM496.5T63)

4757 Tracey, Hugh. African dances of the Witwatersrand gold mines.
Photos. by Marlyn Severn. Johannesburg, African Music Society [distributed by Constantia Booksellers and Publishers,
1952.] 156p. (AM793T67)

4758 Tracey, Hugh. "Lalela Zulu;" 100 Zulu lyrics. Johannesburg, African Music Society, n.d. 121p. (AM784T67a)

4759 Tracey, Hugh. Zulu paradox. Illus. by Ernest Ullmann. Johannesburg, Silver Leaf Books, 1948. 110p. (M968.3T67z)

4760 Troup, Freda. In face of fear; Michael Scott's challenge to South Africa. London, Faber and Faber. [1950.] 227p. (M968T75i)

4761 True, Patrick. Marena a Batho. London, Thomas Nelson and Sons, Ltd., 1944. (M968T76m)

4762 Tyler, Josiah. Forty years among the Zulus. Boston and Chicago. Congregational Sunday-school and publishing society. 1891. 300p. (AM916.68T97)

4763 United Nations. Commission on the Racial situation in the Union of South Africa. Report. New York, 1953. [i.e. 1954.] 166p. (M968Un3)

4764 Van Os, Leonard W. Afrikaans self-taught by the natural method. London, E. Marlborough & Co., 1930. 246p. (AM439.36V34a)

4765 Varley, Douglas Harold. Adventures in Africana. Cape Town, University of Cape Town and Trustees of the South African Library, 1949. 45p. (M960V42a)

4766 Vilakazi, Benedict Wallet. Amal'ezulu. Johannesburg, The University of Witwatersrand Press, 1945. 46p. (M896V71a)

4767 Vilakazi, Benedict Wallet. Inkondlo kazulu, Namazwi ebika alotshwe ngu Dr. Innis B. Gumede. Johannesburg, The University of the Witwatersrand Press, 1935. 100p. (M896V71i)

4768 Vilakazi, Benedict Wallet. Nje-Nempela. Mariannhill, Mariannhill Mission Press, 1955. 218p. (M896V71nj)

4769 Walker, Eric Anderson. The great trek. London, A. & C. Black, Ltd., 1934. 388p. (AM968W15)

4770 Walker, Eric Anderson. A history of South Africa. London, New York, Longmans, Green and Co., 1935. 600p. (M968W15h)

4771 Walker, Eric Anderson. South Africa. Oxford, The Clarendon Press, 1940. 32p. (M968W15s)

4772 Walker, Oliver. Kaffirs are lively. Being some backstage impressions of the South African democracy. London, Victor Gollancz, 1948. 240p. (M968.6W15k)

4773 Walton, James. African village. Pretoria, J. L. Van Schaik, Ltd., 1956. 170p.

4774 Warmelo, N. J. Contributions toward Venda history, religion and tribal ritual. Together with 3 reprinted essays on Venda affinities, Venda political organization and Venda marriage laws. Pretoria, The Government Printer, 1932. 207p. (M968W23)

4775   Waters, M. W. The light—Ukukanya; a drama of the history of the Bantus 1600-1924. Lovedale, Lovedale Institution Press, 1925. 36p. (M968W31)

4776   Webb, Maurice. The Durban riots and after, by Maurice Webb and Kenneth Kirkwood. Johannesburg, South African Institute of Race Relations, 1949. 22p. (M968.47W38)

4777   Wellington, John H. Southern Africa; a geographical study. Cambridge, (Eng.), University Press, 1955. 2v. (M968W46s)

4778   Wells, A. W. History for Bantu schools. London, Thomas Nelson & Sons, Ltd., 1946. 2v. (M968.3W46h)

4779   Wells, A. W. South Africa. Philadelphia, David McKay Co., 1939. 432p. (AM916.8W46)

4780   Wells, A. W. Southern Africa. London, J. M. Dent & Sons, Ltd., 1956. (M968W46)

4781   White, Amos Jerome. Dawn in Bantuland. Boston, Christopher Pub. House, 1953. 297p. (AM266W58)

4782   White, Jennie R. South Africa today. Chicago, A. Flanagan Co., 1907. 133p. (AM916.8W58)

4783   Whyte, Quintin. Behind the racial tensions in South Africa. Johannesburg, South African Institute of Race Relations, 1953. 28p. (M968W62b)

4784   Whyte, Quintin. Native school feeding (Summary of the report of the Native School Feeding Committee published 1949). Johannesburg, South African Institute of Race Relations, 1949. 26p. (M968W62)

4785   Wieschhoff, Heinrich Albert. The Zimbawe-Monomotapa culture in southeast Africa. Menasha, Wis., George Banta Co., 1941. 115p. (AM913.689W63)

4786   Williams, Basil. Botha, Smuts and South Africa. New York, Macmillan Co., 1948. 216p. (AM968W67b)

4787   Williams, Charles. Narratives and adventures of travellers in Africa. London, Ward and Lock, 1859. 340p. (AM967W67n)

4788   Williams, Hugh. Selected official documents of the South African republic and Great Britain. [1900.] 72p. (AM968W67)

4789   Williams, J. Grenfell. Moshesh; the man on the mountain. London, Oxford, 1950. 150p. (AM968.6W67m)

4790   William, J. Grenfell and May, Henry John. Je suis un noir on l'historie de Shabala. Bruxelles, Editions la Boeti, 1950. 230p.

4791 Witten, George. Outlaw trails; a Uankee hobo soldier of the queen.
New York, Minton, Balch and Co., 1929. 252p. (AM968W78)

4792 Witwatersrand Technical College, Johannesburg, South Africa. The
work of the technical colleges in the Union of South Africa.
Johannesburg, Witwatersrand Technical College, 1936. 90p.
(AM370W78)

4793 World opinion on apartheid. New Delhi, India Information Services. 1952. 40p. (AM968W889)

4794 Worsfold, William Basil. Lord Milner's work in South Africa from
its commencement in 1897 to the peace of Vereeniging in 1902
containing hitherto unpublished information. London, J. Murray, 1906. 620p. (M968W89)

4795 Wright, Charlotte (Crogman) Beneath the Southern Cross; the
story of an American bishop's wife in South Africa. [1st ed.]
New York, Exposition Press, [1955.] 184p. (M968)

4796 Xuma, A. B. Bridging the gap between white and black in South
Africa. Paper read before the conference of European and
Bantu Christian Student Associations held at Fort Hare, 27th
June to 3rd July 1930. [n.p. n.d.] 20p. (M968Xu8)

4797 The Year Book and guide to Southern Africa. 1893-7; 1909-10;
1940; 1952. London, S. Low, Marston. (M968Y33)

4798 Yergan, Max. Gold and poverty in South Africa; a study of economic organization and standards of living, . . . The Hague,
New York, International industrial relations institute, with the
co-operation of the International committee on African affairs,
1938. 24p. (M968Y4)

4799 Young, Francis Brett. In South Africa. London, Heinemann 1952.
146p. (AM968Y85i)

4800 Zungu, Andreas Z. Ukuthuthuka kwesizwe esinsundu (Development of the Bantu people). Pietermartizburg, Shuter & Shooter, [1936.] 79p. (M968Z85u)

ORANGE FREE STATE

4801 Baumann, Gustav. The lost republic; the biography of a land-
surveyor. London, Faber and Faber, [1940] 269p. (MC9B321)

4802 Holden, William Clifford. History of the colony of Natal, South
Africa. To which is added, an appendix, containing a brief
history of the Orange-river sovereignty and of the various
races inhabiting it, the great lake N'Gami, commandoes of the

Dutch Boers. London, A. Heylin, 1855. 463p. (M968.4H71)

4803   Orange Free State, South Africa. Education department . . . Report . . . Bloemfontein, A. C. White P. & P. Co., 1939. (M968.-50r1r)

4804   South African Institute of Race Relations. Farm labour in the Orange Free State; report of an investigation undertaken under the auspices of the South African Institute of Race Relations. Johannesburg, South African Institute of Race Relations, 1939. 1v. (Monograph series) (AM331So87)

TRANSVAAL

4805   Fisher, William Edward Garrett. The Transvaal and the Boers, a short history of the South African republic, with a chapter on the Orange Free State. London, Chapman & Hall, 1900. 389p. (M968.2F53t)

4806   Fitzpatrick, James Percy. Jock of the bushveld. London, Bombay and Calcutta, Longmans, Green and Co., 1907. 474p. (M968.2F57j)

4807   Fitzpatrick, James Percy. The Transvaal from within; a private record of public affairs. New York, Frederick A. Stokes Co., 1900. 452p. (M968.2F58)

4808   Hillegas, Howard Clemens. Oom Paul's people; a narrative of the British-Boer troubles in South Africa, with a history of the Boers, the country, and its institutions. New York, D. Appleton and Co., 1899. 308p. (M968.2H55o)

4809   Hubbard, Margaret (Carson). African gamble. New York, G. P. Putnam's Sons, 1937. 279p. (M916.89H86)

4810   Non-European library service. Transvaal report. 1950, 1951, 1952. (M968.2N73)

4811   Phillips, Dorothea Sarah Florence Alexandra (Ortlepp). Some South African recollections. London, New York, Longmans, Green and Co., 1899. 183p. (M968.2P54a)

4812   Stickney, Albert. The Transvaal outlook. New York, Dodd, Mead and Co., 1900. 139p. (M916.82St5)

4813   Transvaal chamber of mines. The native workers on the Witwatersrand gold mines. Transvaal, Transvaal chamber of mines, 1947. 20p. (M968.2T68u)

4814   Transvaal. Education department. Report, 1921, 1922, 1929, 1931, 1935, 1936, 1937, 1939. Pretoria. 7v. (M370.96T68)

4815   Transvaal library advisory committee. Survey of the libraries of the Transvaal. Part I. Urban libraries (excluding those in towns of more than 11,000 inhabitants) Pretoria, 1942. 1312p. (M968.2T68s)

4816 Walker, Eric Anderson. W. P. Schreiner, a South African. London, Oxford University Press, H. Milford, 1937. 386p. (M-C9Sch7w)

4817 Williams, Hugh. Selected official documents of the South African republic and Great Britain. A documentary perspective of the causes of the war in South Africa. [Philadelphia, American academy of political and social science,] [c1900] 72p. (M968W67)

NATAL

4818 Bird, John. The annals of Natal, 1495-1856. Pietermaritzburg, P. Davis & Sons, 1888. 2v. (M968.4B53)

4819 Bryant, Alfred T. Olden times in Zululand and Natal, containing earlier political history of the Eastern-Nguni clans. London, New York, Longmans, Green and Co., 1929. 710p. (M968-B84o)

4820 Burrows, Harry Raymond. Indian life and labour in Natal, a survey . . . Johannesburg, South African Institute of Race Relations, 1952. 64p. (M968.4B94)

4821 Hamilton, Margaret. The mango tree. New York, London, The Century Co., [c1932.] 211p. (M813.5H18)

4822 Hattersley, Alan Frederick. The British settlement of Natal; a study in imperial migration. Cambridge [England] University Press, 1950. 350p. (M968.4H28b)

4823 Hattersley, Alan Frederick. Later annals of Natal. London, New York, Longmans, Green & Co., [1938.] 285p. (M968.4H28)

4824 Hattersley, Alan Frederick. The Natalians; further annals of Natal. Pietermaritzburg, Shuter and Shooter, 1940. 200p. (M968.4H28n)

4825 Hattersley, Alan Frederick. Portrait of a colony; the story of Natal. Cambridge [England.] The University Press, 1940. 233p. (M916.84H28)

4826 Holden, William Clifford. History of the colony of Natal, South Africa. To which is added, an appendix, containing a brief history of the Orange-river sovereignty and of the various races inhabiting it, the great lake N'Gami, commandoes of the Dutch Boers, etc., etc., London, A. Heylin, 1855. 463p. (M968.4H71)

4827   Houghton, D. Hobart. The economy of a native reserve. Pieter-
       maritzburg, Shuter and Shooter, 1952. 194p. (M968.4K26)

4828   Isaacs, Nathaniel. Travels and adventures in eastern Africa. Cape-
       town, The Van Riebeeck Society, 1936. (M916.83Is7)

4829   Keiskammahoek Rural Survey. Pietermaritzburg, Shuter and
       Shooter, 1952. 4v. (M968.4K26)

4830   Loftus, E. A. Elton and the East African coast slave-trade. Being
       extracts from the diary of Captain James Elton. London,
       Macmillan and Co., Ltd., 1952. 61p. (M967.6L82e)

4831   Mills, M. E. Elton. Land tenure. Pietermaritzburg, Shuter and
       Shooter, 1952. 154p. (M968.4K26)

4832   Mountain, Edgar D. The natural history of the Keiskammahoek
       District. Pietermaritzburg, Shuter and Shooter, 1952. 85p.
       (M968.4K26)

4833   Natal regional survey. Cape Town, Published for the University
       of Natal by Oxford University Press, 1954. 3v. (M968.4N196)

4834   Natal. Report of the chief inspector of native education for the
       year, 1930. Pietermaritzburg, The Natal Witness, 1931. 29p.
       (M968.4N19r)

4835   Natal. Report of the expedition sent by the government of Natal
       to install Cetywayo as King of the Zulus, in succession to his
       deceased father, Panda, August, 1873. Pietermaritzburg, Davis
       and Sons, 1874. 34p. (M968N19r)

4836   Natal University. Pietermaritzburg. Archaeology and natural re-
       sources of Natal. Cape Town, New York, Pub. for the Uni-
       versity of Natal by Oxford University Press, 1951. 140p.
       (M968.4N196v.1)

4837   Natal University. Pietermaritzburg. Calendar 1956. Natal, Uni-
       versity of Natal, 1956. 417p. (M968.4N19)

4838   Natal University. Pietermartizburg. Dept. of Economics. The
       African factory worker; a sample study of the life and labour
       of the urban African worker. Cape Town, New York, Oxford
       University Press, 1950. 221p. (M968N19a)

4839   Natal University. Pietermartizburg. Dept. of Economics, Re-
       search Section. The Durban Housing survey, a study of hous-
       ing in a multi-racial community, by the Research Section of
       the Department of Economics and certain specialists in other
       departments, University of Natal. Pietermaritzburg, Univer-
       sity of Natal Press, 1952. 508p. (M968.4N196no.2)

4840   Natal University. Pietermaritzburg. Dept. of Sociology and Social Work. Small towns of Natal, a socio-economic sample survey. [Pietermartizburg] University of Natal Press, 1953. 113p. (M968.4N196no.3)

4841 Natal University. Pietermaritzburg. The Dunn Reserve, Zululand, by a research team of the University of Natal. [Pietermaritzburg] University of Natal Press, 1953. 69p. (M968.4N196-no.4)

4842 Natal University Library. Maurice Webb Collection. Pietermaritzburg. A list of books and journals presented to University of Natal Library (mimeographed). Natal University of Natal Libraries, October 1954. 6p. (Vertical file).

4843 Ringrose, H. G. Trade Unions in Natal. Cape Town, New York, Pub. for the University of Natal by Oxford University Press, 1951. 111p. (M968.4N196v.4)

4844 Smith, R. H. Labor Resources of Natal. Cape Town, New York, Oxford University Press, 1950. 93p. (M968.4Sm6)

4845 Van Garderen, J. Fertilizer experiments in Natal (1933-1950). Union of South Africa, Department of Agriculture, 1952. 38p. (M968.4V29)

4846 Warmelo, N. J. Van. History of Matiwane and the Amangwane Tribe, as told by Msebenzi to his kinsman Albert Hlongwane. Pretoria, Government Printer, 1938. 275p. (M968.4W23)

4847 Wilson, Monica. Social structure. Pietermaritzburg, Shuter and Shooter, 1952. 222p. (M968.4K26)

4848 Woods, Clement A. The Indian Community of Natal; their economic position. Cape Town, New York, Published for the University of Natal by Oxford University Press, 1954. 102p. (M968.4N196v.9)

CAPE OF GOOD HOPE

4849 Barker, Mary. Sir Benjamin D'Urban's administration of the eastern frontier of the Cape of Good Hope during the period, 1834-1838; a bibliography. University of Cape Town, School of Librarianship, 1946. 31p. (AM016B24)

4850 Barnard, Anne (Lindsay). South Africa, a century ago; letters written from the Cape of Good Hope. London, Smith, Elder and Co., 1910. 316p. (M968.7B25)

4851 Barrow, John. An account of travels into the interior of southern Africa, in the years 1797 and 1798; including cursory observations on the geology and geography . . . the natural history of such objects as occurred in the animal, vegetable, and min-

eral kingdoms; and sketches of the physical and moral characters of the various tribes. New York, G. F. Hopkins, 1802.
386p. (M968B27)

4852 Brownlee, Frank [comp.] The Transkeian native territories: historical records. Lovedale, Lovedale institution press, 1923.
135p. (M968.6B82)

4853 Bunbury, Charles James Fox. Journal of a residence at the Cape
of Good Hope; with excursions into the interior, and notes on
the natural history, and the native tribes. London, J. Murray,
1848. 297p. (M916.87B88)

4854 DuPlessis, I. D. The Malay Quarter and its people. Capetown,
A. A. Balkema, 1953. 91p. (M968.711D92)

4855 Kolbe, Pierre. Description du Cap de Bonne-Esperance; Ou l'on
trouve tout ce qui concerne l'histoire-naturelle du pays; la religion, les moeurs & les usages des Hottentots; et l'establissement des Hollandois. Tiree des memoires de Mr. Pierre Kolbe
. . . dresses pendant un sejour de dix annees dans cette colonie,
ou el avoit ete envoye pour faire des observations astronomiques & physiques. Amsterdam Chez Jean Catuffe, 1741. 3v.
(M916.87K83)

4856 Macmillan, William Miller. The Cape colour question; a historical
survey. London, Faber and Gwyer, [1927.] 304p. (M968.-
7M22c)

4857 Marais, Johannes Stephanus. The Cape coloured people, 1652-
1937. London, New York, [etc.] Longmans, Green and Co.,
296p. (M968M32)

4858 Noble, Roderick. The Cape and its people and its people and other
essays by South African writers. Cape Town, J. C. Juta, 1869.
408p. (M968.7N66)

4859 Tait, Barbara Campbell. Cape Cameos the story of Cape Town
in a new way. Cape Town, Stewart, 1948. 263p. (M916.8T13)

4860 Talbot, William John. Swartland and Sandveld; a survey of land
utilization in the western lowland of the Cape Province. Cape
Town, Oxford University Press 1947. 79p. (M968.71T145)

4861 Thompson, L. M. The Cape coloured franchise. Johannesburg,
South African Institute of Race Relations, 1949. 59p. (M-
968.7T37c)

4862 Schapera, Isaac. The early Cape Hottentots. Cape Town, The
Van Riebeeck Society, 1933. 309p. (M916.87Sch1)

4863 Sparrman, Anders. A voyage to the Cape of Good Hope, towards the Antartic polar circle, and round the world: but chiefly into the country of the Hottentots and Caffres, from the year 1772, to 1776. Translated from the Swedish original by George Forester. With plates. London, Printed for G. G. J. and J. Robinson, 1785. 2v. (M968.7Sp25)

4864 Stout, Benjamin. Narrative of the loss of the ship Hercules, commanded by Captain Benjamin Stout, on the coast of Caffraria, the 16th of June, 1796; also, a circumstantial detail of his travels through the southern deserts of Africa, and the colonies, to the Cape of Good Hope. London, Hudson, 1800. 112p. (M916St7)

4865 Ziervogel, C. Brown South Africa. Cape Town, M. Miller, 1938. 95p. (M968Z64)

PERIODICALS

4866 Abolition de L'Esclavage, 1848-1948. Evidence de la Culture Negre. Special Issue of—Le Musée Vivant, Nov. 1948.

4867 L'Actualité Congolaises. Leopoldville, Le Bureau de Presse du Gouvernement General du Congo Belge à Leopoldville.

4868 Africa. London, International Institute. Quarterly.

4869 Africa. Madrid, Instituto de Estudios Africanos. Monthly.

4870 Africa Bulletin. London, The Association for African Freedom. Monthly.

4871 Africa Digest. London, Africa Bureau. 6 times a year.

4872 Africa Special Report; Bulletin of the Institute of African American Relations. Washington, D. C. Monthly.

4873 Africa South. Cape Town, Africa South Publications. Quarterly.

4874 Africa South of the Sahara. Paris, Agence France Presse. Biweekly.

4875 Africa Today. New York, American Committee on Africa. 6 times a year.

4876 Africa, Today and Tomorrow. London, Special Commemoration Issue of the Academy of Arts and Research. April 1945.

4877 Africa Weekly. New York, 336 E. 43rd Street.

4878 Africa X-Ray Report. Johannesburg, Investors Intelligence. Monthly.

4879 The African, Journal of African Affairs. New York, African Magazine Co. Monthly.

4880   African League. Buchanan, Grand bassa, Liberia.

4881   African Abstracts. London, International African Institute. Quarterly.

4882   African Affairs. London, Royal African Society. Quarterly. (formerly Journal of Royal African Society.)

4883   The African-American Bulletin. Washington, D. C., Institute of African American Relations. See also, Africa Special Report.

4884   The African and Colonial World. London, Independent Publishing Co. Monthly.

4885   The African Angelus. Tenafly, New Jersey, Society of African Missions in the U. S. A. Quarterly.

4886   African Challenge. Lagos, Nigeria. Monthly.

4887   The African Drum. See Drum.

4888   The African Eagle. New York, African Academy of Arts and Research. Monthly.

4889   The African Interpreter. New York, African Students Association of the United States and Canada. Monthly.

4890   The African Listener. Lusaka, Central African Broadcasting Stations.

4891   African News. Washington, D. C., Ruth Sloan Association, Inc. 10-12 times a year.

4892   The African News, Information from and about Africa. Vineland, New Jersey. Monthly.

4893   The African Newsletter. See African Students Newsletter.

4895   The African Observer. Philadelphia, J. Ashmead. Monthly.

4896   African Opinion. New York, African Picture and Information Service. Bi-monthly.

4897   The African Parade. Salisbury, Southern Rhodesia.

4898   African Repository. Washington, D. C., The American Colonization Society. Monthly.

4899   African Students Newsletter. Washington, D. C., All African Students' Union of the Americas. Monthly.

4900   African Studies (formerly Bantu Studies). Johannesburg, University of Witwatersrand. Quarterly.

4901   African Times and Orient Review. London, Metropolitan Publishers. Monthly.

4902   African Transcripts. Philadelphia, University of Pennsylvania. Bi-monthly.

4903 African Women. London, University of London Institute of Education. Bi-annual.

4904 The African World. London, African Publications, Ltd. Monthly.

4905 The African World Annual. London, African Publications, Ltd. Annual.

4906 The African World and Cape Cairo Express. London, Salisbury House.

4906a Africana Notes and News. Johannesburg, The African Society.

4907 Afrika-Institut. Rotterdam. Monthly.

4908 Afrique. Paris, C. G. O. T. Trimestrielle.

4909 L'Afrique au Sud du Sahara. Bulletin Bi-Hedomodaire d'Information. Paris, Agence France Presse.

4910 L'Afrique et l'Asie. Paris, Centre des Hautes Etudes d'Administration Musulmane. Quarterly.

4911 L'Afrique et Le Monde. Bruxelles, 35, rue de Ruysbroeck. Weekly.

4912 Afrique Equatorial Francais. Paris, A. Tournon et Cie.

4913 L'Afrique Explorée et Civiliseé, Journal Mensuel. Geneve, J. Sandoz.

4914 L'Afrique Française. Bulletin Mensuel. Paris, Comité de l'Afrique Française et du Comité du Maroc.

4915 L'Afrique Noire Française. Numèro spécial de la Revue des Vivvants, Jan. 1930. Paris, 85, Faubourg Saint-Honoré.

4916 Afrique Occidentale Française. Dakar, Edition Inter-Press. (Special Number).

4917 Afro-Asian Torchlight. (formerly "African Torchlight") Glasgow, William Maclellan Publishers.

4818 Agronomia Angolana. Luanda, Reportiçao Central dos Serviços de Agricultura de Angola. Semi-annual.

4919 Agueda: Revue Marocaine des Lettres et des Arts, Images et Doctrines. Rabat, Morocco.

4920 Algeria et l'Afrique du Nord. Algers, Edition de l'Office Algerien D'Action Economique et Touristique. 5 times a year.

4921 L'Algeria—Revue Economique Franco-Suisse. Paris, Chambre de Commerce Suisse en France.

4922 Ambassade de France. New York, Service de Presse et D'Information.

4923 Americans for South African Resistance. Bulletin. New York,

513 W. 166th Street. Irregular.

4924　Ancient Egypt. London and New York, Macmillan. Quarterly.

4925　Angola; Revista Mensal de Doutrina, Estudo e Propaganda Instrutiva. Luanda, Liga, Nacional Africana.

4926　Angola. Mensário administrativo. Luanda, Publiçacoes de Asunto de Interesse.

4927　Anti-Slavery Reporter and Aborigines' Friend. London, The Anti-Slavery Society.

4928　Arquivos de Angola. Luanda, Editada Pelo de Museu de Angola.

4929　Arquivos del Instituto de Estudios Africanos. Madrid. Quarterly.

4930　Artes Africanae. Brussels, Imprimerie Typ'art. Publication de la Commission pour la Protection des Arts et Metiers Indigenas. Irregular.

4931　Background Facts. London, The Africa Bureau, Denison House.

4932　Background to Uganda; News Sheet. Kampala, Department of Information. Weekly.

4933　Bantoe Bantu. Pretoria, Department of Native Affairs. Monthly.

4934　Bantu. Pretoria, Department of Native Affairs. Special edition.

4935　Bantu Studies; a Journal Devoted to the Scientific Study of Bantu, Hottentot, and Bushman. Johannesburg, The University of Witwatersrand Press. Quarterly. See also African Studies.

4936　The Belgian Congo Today. Brussels, F. Van der Linden. Monthly.

4937　Boletim Cultural de Guiné Portuguesa. Bissau, Portuguese Guinea, Centro de Estudos de Guiné Portugesa, Museu da Guiné Portuguesa. Quarterly.

4938　Boletim Geral Das Colónias. Lisboa, Agencia Geral du Colonias.

4939　Boletim Geral Do Ultramar. Lisboa, Agencia Geral do Ultramar. Monthly.

4940　Books For Africa. London, Edinburgh House. Quarterly.

4941　Bulletin Agricole du Congo Belge. Belgium, Ministere des Colonies. Direction de l'Agriculture et de l'Elevage. Quarterly.

4942　Bulletin de l'Institut d'Études Centrafricaines. Brazzaville, Institut d'Études Centrafricaines. Bi-annual.

4943　Bulletin de l'Institut Français d'Afrique Noire. Dakar, IFAN. Quarterly.

4944　Bulletin de Lîaison des Instituteurs et des Institutrices. Alger, Service des Cours d'Adultes.

4945 Bulletin de Recherches Soudanaises. Koulouba, Imprimerie du
Gouvernement.

4946 Bulletin du Centre d'Études des Problemes Sociaux Indigene. Elisabethville, Congo Belge, Centra d'Études des Problemes Sociaux
Indigenes. Irregular.

4947 Bulletin du Comité d'Études Historiques et Scientiques de L'Afrique
Occidentale Française. Paris, Librairie Larose.

4948 Bulletin Économique et Social de la Tunisie. Tunis, Direction de
l'Information de la Résidence Generale de la France. Monthly.

4949 Bulletin de l'Office Colonial du Ministère des Colonies. Bruxelles.
Monthly except August and September.

4950 Bulletin Officiel de la Direction de l'Instruction Publique. Tunis.

4951 Les Cahiers de l'Afrique Occidentale Française. Paris. Bi-monthly.

4952 Chroniques d'Outre Mer. Paris, La Documentation Française.
Monthly.

4953 Colonial Development. London, Colonial Development Corporation. Quarterly.

4954 Colonial Plant and Animal Products. London, His Majesty's Stationery Office. Quarterly.

4955 The Colonial Review. London, Department of Education in Tropical Areas. Quarterly.

4956 The Comet; a Weekly News Magazine of West Africa. Lagos, The
Comet Press.

4957 Common Sense Historical Reviews; African-American Edition.
Chicago, Ira O. Guy, ed. Monthly.

4958 Community Development Bulletin. London, Community Development Clearing House. Quarterly.

4959 Concord. Salisbury, Southern Rhodesia, Rhodesia Printing and
Publishing Co.

4960 Confluent; Revue Morocaine. Rabat, C.C.P. Jeune Press.

4961 Congo Mission News. Leopoldville, Conseil Protestant du Congo.
Quarterly.

4962 Congo; Revue Générale de la Colonie Belge. Bruxelles, Goemaere.

4963 Cuadernos de Estudios Africanos. Madrid, Instituto de Estudios
Politicos. Quarterly.

4964 The Daystar. London. The United Society for Christian Literature and the Society for Promoting Christian Knowledge.
Quarterly.

4965 Department of Labour Quarterly Review. Lagos, Department of Labour.

4966 Drum. (formerly the African Drum) Johannesburg, Drum Publishing Co. Monthly.

4967 The Drum Call. Elat, Ebolewa, Cameroun, Halsey Memorial Press. Quarterly.

4968 East Africa and Rhodesia. London, East Africa, Ltd. Weekly.

4969 The East African Agricultural Journal of Kenya, Tanganyika, Uganda, and Zanzibar. Nairobi, East Africa High Commission. Nairobi, Government Printer. Quarterly.

4970 The East African Medical Journal. Nairobi, Kenya, East African Medical Society. Monthly.

4971 The East African Teachers Journal. Nairobi, Eagle Press. Twice yearly.

4972 East African Trade and Industry. Nairobi, D. A. Hawkins, Ltd. Monthly.

4973 L'Éducation Africaine. Dakar, Service Pedagogique, Direction Général de l'Enseignement. Quarterly.

4974 The Education Gazette of the Province of the Cape of Good Hope. Capetown, Union of South Africa. Bi-monthly.

4975 Egypt News. Press Department, Egyptian Embassy. 2310 Decatur Place, Washington, D. C.

4976 The Egyptian Economic and Political Review. Cairo, The Egyptian Economic and Political Review. Monthly.

4977 Encyclopédie Mensuelle d'Outre Mer. Paris, 3, rue Blaise-Desgoffe. Monthly.

4978 Equipes Nouvelles de l'Union Française. Paris, Le Conseil de la Jeunesse de l'Union Française. Quarterly.

4979 Études Camerounaises. Douala, French Cameroons, IFAN Centrifan Cameroun. Irregular.

4980 Études Dahoméennes. Dahomey, Institut Français d'Afrique Noire, Gouvernement du Dahomey Centre IFAN.

4981 The Federation of Rhodesia and Nyasaland Newsletter. London, Federal Information Department. Weekly.

4982 Folia Scientifica Africae Centralis. Bukavu, Congo Belge, l'Institut pour la Recherche Scientifique en Afrique Centrale. Quarterly.

4983 The Forum. Johannesburg, 170 Main Street. Monthly.

4984 Fortnightly Digest of South African Affairs. Pretoria, State Information Office.

4985 France. Ministère de la France d'Outre-mer, Bulletin Bibliographique. Paris, Ministère de la France d'Outre-mer. Bimonthly.

4986 France Export Colonies. Paris, Production Française et de ses Débouchés dans le Monde. Monthly.

4987 Free Morocco. Washington, D. C., Moroccan Office of Information and Documentation.

4988 The Friend of Africa; Society for the Extinction of the Slave Trade, and for the Civilization of Africa. London, J. W. Parker. Semi-monthly.

4989 Ghana Today. (formerly Gold Coast Today) London, Information Section of the Ghana Office. Bi-monthly.

4990 The Ghana Woman. Accra, West African Graphic Co., Ltd. Quarterly.

4991 Gold Coast Bulletin. Accra, Government Public Relations Department. Monthly.

4992 The Gold Coast Today. See Ghana Today.

4993 Hi-Note; South Africa's Story Magazine. Johannesburg, Proprietors, Hi-Note (Pty.) Ltd. Monthly.

4994 L'Illustration Congolaise. Bruxelles, 34, rue de Stassart. Monthly.

4995 Industries et Travaux d'Outremer. Paris, La Société René Mareux et Cie. Monthly.

4996 Information Digest. London, The Africa Bureau. Bi-monthly.

4997 Initiatives. Yaoundé, Bureau d'Education de Base au Cameroun. Quarterly.

4998 Institut Français d'Afrique Noire. Mémoires. Dakar, Senegal, French West Africa, IFAN. Irregular.

4999 Inter-African News Bulletin. Johannesburg, Agence France-Presse.

5000 International African Opinion. London, International African Publishing Bureau. Monthly.

5001 International Review of Missions. London, Edinburgh House. Quarterly.

5002 Iso Lomuzi. Natal, Amanzemtote Institute Press.

5003 Itinerário, Arte e Divulgaçao. Lourenco Marques, Sociedad Cooperativa de Publicidade. Bi-monthly.

5004 Jana: News Magazine of Resurgent Asia and Africa. Ceylon, Associated Newspapers of Ceylon, Ltd. Monthly.

5005 Jeune Afrique. Elisabethville, Union Africaine des Arts et des Lettres. Quarterly.

5006 Journal de la Société des Africanistes. Paris, Musée de L'Homme. Annual.

5007 Journal for Social Research. Pretoria, Transvaal, National Council for Social Research. Semi-annual.

5008 Journal Mensuel de Propaganda Coloniale. Brussels.

5009 Journal of African Administration. London, Great Britain, Colonial Office. Quarterly.

5010 Journal of East Africa and Uganda Natural History Society. London, East African Standard, Ltd. Quarterly.

5011 Journal of Egyptian Archaeology. London, The Egypt Exploration Society. Quarterly.

5012 Journal of the African Society. London, Macmillan and Co., Ltd. Quarterly.

5013 Journal of the East African Swahili Committee. Tanganyika, Beauchamp Printing Co.

5014 Journal of the Royal African Society. London, Macmillan and Co., Ltd. Quarterly. See African Affairs.

5015 Journal of the Royal Anthropological Institute. London, Royal Anthropological Institute of Great Britain and Ireland. Annual.

5016 Journal of the West African Institute for Oil Palm Research. London, The Institute.

5017 Kenya Calling: Monthly News Digest. Nairobi, Department of Information. Quarterly.

5018 Kenya Today. Nairobi, Department of Information. Quarterly.

5019 Kenya Weekly News. Nakuru, The Nakuru Press, Ltd.

5020 The Leech. Johannesburg, University of Witwatersrand. Annual.

5021 Liaison. Brazzaville, Des Cercles Culturels d'A. E. F. Bi-monthly.

5022 Liberia. Washington, D. C., American Colonization Society. Bi-annual.

5023 Liberia and West Africa. Monrovia, Printing Department of the College of West Africa. Monthly.

5024 The Liberia Educational Outlook. Monrovia, Department of Public Instruction and of the Advisory Committee on Education in Liberia. Monthly.

5025 Liberia Today. Washington, D. C., The Embassy of Liberia. Monthly.

5026 Liberian News. Monrovia. Monthly.

5027 The Liberian Patriot. Monrovia, The Montserrado Printing and Publishing Co. Weekly.

5028 The Liberian Review. Monrovia and Accra, West African Graphic Co. Quarterly.

5029 Library Record. Ibadan, University College. Irregular.

5030 Listen. London, The International Committee on Christian Literature for Africa. Monthly.

5031 Lumu Lua Bena Kasai. Luebo (Congo Belge) American Presbyterian Congo Mission. Monthly.

5032 Makerere. Kampala, Makerere College. Quarterly.

5033 Man; a Monthly Record of Anthropological Science. London, Royal Anthropological Institute of Great Britain and Ireland. Monthly.

5034 Manpower (Volkskragte) A Mi-annual Scientific Journal. Pretoria, Government Printer.

5035 Marchés Coloniaux du Monde. Paris, Haussmann. Weekly.

5036 Maroc; Bulletin d'Information. Rabat, Imprimeries Françaises et Marocaines.

5037 Moçambique; Documentário Trimestral. Lourenco Marques, Imprensa Nacional de Moçambique. Quarterly.

5038 Modernisation. Paris, 21, rue d'Armaille. Monthly.

5039 Moroccan News Bulletin. New York, Moroccan Information Office.

5040 Le Musée Vivant. Paris, Imprimerie L. Hémery.

5041 Nada, The Southern Rhodesia Native Affairs Department; Annual. Salisbury, W. T. Nesham.

5042 Native Teachers' Journal. Pietermaritzburg, The Natal Education Department. Quarterly.

5043 New Africa. New York, Council on African Affairs. Monthly. See also, Spotlight on Africa.

5044 The New African. London, The West African National Secretariat. Monthly.

5045 New Commonwealth. London, Tothill Press. Fortnightly.

5046 New Times and Ethiopian News. Woodford Green, Essex, Sylvia Pankhurst. Weekly.

5047   News from the Gold Coast; Press Release. Accra, Department of Information Services.

5048   News from Nigeria. Lagos, Federal Information Service.

5049   News of Africa. New York, Council on African Affairs. See, New Africa.

5050   Newsletter; Moroccan Studies and Surveys. Rabat, Postal Box 511. Monthly.

5051   Nigeria. Lagos, Government of Nigeria, Exhibition Centre. Quarterly.

5052   Nigeria Liaison Letter. Washington, D. C., Nigeria Liaison Office.

5053   The Nigeria Marketing Board Journal. London, Marketing Section of the Public Relations Department.

5054   Nigeria Review. Lagos, Government Public Relations Department. Weekly.

5055   Nigeria Trade Journal. Lagos, Department of Commerce and Industries. Quarterly.

5056   Nigerian Department of Labour Quarterly Review. Lagos, Department of Labour.

5057   The Nigerian Field. Woodchester, England, Nigerian Field Society. Quarterly.

5058   Northern Rhodesia and Nyasaland Publications Bureau. Lusaka.

5059   Nos Images. Leopoldville, Bureau de l'Information pour Indigènes. Monthly.

5060   Notes Africaines; Bulletin d'Information et de Correspondance. Dakar IFAN. Quarterly.

5061   Noticias de Portugal. Lisboa, Boletim Semanal do Secretariado Nacional da Informaçao.

5062   Odù; Journal of Yoruba and Related Studies. Ibadan, General Publications Department, Ministry of Education.

5063   Les Oeuvres Sociales et l'Enseignement en A. E. F. (Supplément illustré du Courrier Colonial. Dec. 31, 1933.) Paris, 33, rue de Turin.

5064   Optima. Johannesburg, Anglo-American Corporation of South Africa. Quarterly.

5065   Outre-Mer; Revue Générale de Colonisation. Paris, Librairie Larose. Quarterly.

5066   Overseas Education. London, Great Britain Colonial Office, The Church House. Quarterly.

5067 Pages Congolaises. Bruxelles, Le Bureau de Presse du Gouvernment Général du Congo Belge á Leopoldville.

5068 Pan-Africa; Journal of African Life and Thought. Manchester, 58 Oxford Road. Monthly.

5069 La Présence Africaine dans le Monde. Special Issue of Le Musée Vivant, No. 8, 1956.

5070 Présence Africaine. Paris, 17 rue de Chaligny. Bi-monthly.

5071 Problèmes d'Afrique Centrale. Brussels, Association des Anciens Etudiants de l'Institut Universitaire des Territoires d'Outre-Mer. Quarterly.

5072 Quarterly Bulletin of the South African Library. Cape Town, Cape Province, South African Public Library. Quarterly.

5073 Race Relations Journal. Johannesburg, South African Institute of Race Relations. Quarterly.

5074 Race Relations News. Johannesburg, South African Institute of Race Relations. Monthly.

5075 Radio Post; The Magazine of Southern Rhodesian African Broadcasting. Causeway, Box 8030. Monthly.

5076 La Revue Coloniale Belge. Bruxelles, 34, rue de Stassart. Monthly.

5077 Revue d'Afrique. Paris, 23, rue Fontaine. Six times a year.

5078 Revue de l'Aucam. Louvain, le Secretariat de l'Aucam. Ten times a year.

5079 La Revue des Monde Noir. Paris, Editions de la Revue Mondiale. Monthly.

5080 Revue des Vivants. Paris, 85, Faubourg Saint-Honoré.

5081 Revue d'Histoire des Colonies. Paris, Société de l'Histoire des Colonies Françaises. Quarterly.

5082 Sierra Leone Royal Gazette and Supplement. Freetown, Government Printer.

5083 Sierra Leone Studies. Freetown, Government of Sierra Leone. Bi-annual.

5084 Sociedade Cultural de Angola, Boletim. Luanda, Edificio da Uniao Nacional.

5085 South Africa. London, South Africa, Ltd. Weekly.

5086 South Africa Reports—Economic Review. New York, Union of South Africa Government Information Office.

5087 The South African Builder. Johannesburg, National Federation of Building Trade Employees in South Africa.

5088   The South African Health Society Magazine. Lovedale, Central Office of the South African Health Society. Quarterly.

5089   The South African Journal of Economics. Johannesburg, Transvael, Economic Society of South Africa. Quarterly.

5090   South African Libraries. Cape Town, South African Library Association. Quarterly.

5091   South African Medical Journal. Cape Town, Medical Association of South Africa. Weekly.

5092   The South African Outlook. Lovedale, Cape Province, Lovedale Press. Monthly.

5093   South African Scene. Pretoria, State Information Office.

5094   The South African Sugar Journal. Durban, Francis and Graham, Ltd. Monthly.

5095   Southern Cameroons Gazette. Nigeria, The Federal Government Printer.

5096   Spotlight on Africa. New York, Council on African Affairs. Monthly. See also, New Africa.

5097   Statistical and Economic Review. London, United Africa Company. Quarterly.

5098   Sudan Notes and Records. Khartoum, Sudan Printing Press. Semi-annual.

5099   Togo-Cameroun. Magazine Trimestriel. Paris, L'Agence Économique des Territoires Africains sous Mandat.

5100   Trek. Johannesburg, Central News Agency. Monthly.

5101   Tropical Abstracts. Amsterdam, Royal Tropical Institute. Fortnightly.

5102   Ubersee Rundschau; Overseas Review. Hamburg, Ubersee-Verlag.

5103   The Uganda Journal. Kampala, Uganda Society. Semi-annual.

5104   Universitas. Accra, The University College of the Gold Coast. Triannual.

5105   University College of the Gold Coast; Library Bulletin. Accra, The University College of the Gold Coast.

5106   University of Natal Gazette. Pietermaritzburg. Quarterly.

5107   Venture; Journal of the Fabian Colonial Bureau. London, Fabian Society, Colonial Bureau. Monthly.

5108   La Voix du Congolais. Leopoldville, Bureau de l'Information pour Indigènes. Monthly.

5109   WASU; The Journal of the West African Students' Union of

Great Britain. London, West African Student's Union of Great Britain and Ireland.

5110 Weekly Bulletin—Sierra Leone. Freetown, Public Relations Office.

5111 West Africa. London, West African Newspapers, Ltd. Weekly.

5112 West African Advent; Messenger. Accra, West African Union Mission of Seventh-Day Adventists.

5113 West African Press Survey. London, Export Advertising Service, Ltd. Fortnightly.

5114 West African Review. London, West African Newspapers, Ltd. Monthly.

5115 Western Nigeria Illustrated. Western Region, Ibadan, Western Nigeria Information Services. Quarterly.

5116 Zaire; Revue Congolaise. Bruxelles, Editions Universitaires. Ten times a year.

5117 Zonk. Johannesburg, Zonk Publications. Monthly.

NEWSPAPERS

GENERAL

5118 African Times. (New York)

BELGIAN CONGO

5119 Le Front du Travail. (Leopoldville)

5120 Temps Nouveraux d'Afrique. (Usumbru)

CAMEROUN

5121 Le Cameroun Libre. (Yaoundé)

ETHIOPIA

5122 The Ethiopian Herald. (Addis Ababa)

5123 The Voice of Ethiopia. (New York)

FRENCH EQUATORIAL AFRICA

5124 Islam—A. E. F. (Brazzaville)

FRENCH WEST AFRICA

5125 Abidjan-Matin. (Abidjan)

5126 Afrique Noire. (Dakar)

GOLD COAST

5127 African Morning Post. (Accra)

5128 The Ashanti Pioneer. (Kumasi)

5129 The Ashanti Times. (Obuasi)

5130 The Daily Echo. (Accra)

5131 The Daily Graphic. (Accra)

5132 Ghana Evening News. (Accra)

5133 Gold Coast Bulletin. (Accra)

5134 Gold Coast Commercial Guardian. (Accra)

5135 The Gold Coast Observer. (Cape Coast)

5136 The Gold Coast Weekly Review. (Accra)

5137 Spectator Daily. (Accra)

5138 West African Monitor. (Cape Coast)

LIBERIA

5139 Africa's Luminary. (Monrovia)

5140 Liberia Herald. (Monrovia)

5141 The Liberian Age. (Monrovia)

5142 Liberian Register. (Monrovia)

5143 Listener. (Monrovia)

5144 The Weekly Mirror. (Monrovia)

5145 West African Worker. (Accra and Liberia)

MOROCCO

5146 Tangier Gazette and Morocco Mail. (Tangier)

5147 La Voix du Maroc. (Tangier)

NATAL

5148 Ilanga Lase Natal (The Natal Sun). (Durban)

NIGERIA

5149 The Daily Service. (Lagos)

5150 Daily Times. (Lagos)

5151 Eastern Nigeria Guardian. (Port Harcourt)

5152 Eastern Outlook. (Enugu)

5153 Nigeria Review. (Lagos)

5154 The Nigerian Children's Own Paper. (Lagos)

5155 The Nigerian Daily Record. (Enugu)

5156 The Nigerian Daily Standard. (Calabar)

5157 The Nigerian Eastern Mail. (Calabar)

5158 Nigerian Spokesman. (Onitsha)

5159 The Nigerian Statesman. (Lagos)

5160 Nigerian Tribune. (Ibadan)

5161 The Truth. (Lagos)

5162 West African Examiner. (Port Harcourt)

5163 West African Pilot. (Lagos)

RHODESIA AND NYASALAND

5164 African Eagle. (Salisbury)

5165 Bwalo la Nyasaland. (Salisbury)

5166 East Africa and Rhodesia. (Rhodesia and Nyasaland)

SIERRA LEONE

5167 Advance. (Bo)

5168 The African Standard. (Freetown)

5169 The African Vanguard. (Freetown)

5170 The Daily Guardian. (Freetown)

5171 Daily Mail. (Freetown)

5172 Evening Dispatch. (Freetown)

5173 The Gospel Bells. (Freetown)

5174 The Hurricane. (Freetown)

5175 The Renascent African. (Freetown)

5176 The Sierra Leone Observer. (Bo)

5177 Sierra Leone Weekly News. (Freetown)

5178 The Ten Daily News. (Freetown)

5179 Weekly Bulletin. (Freetown)

UNION OF SOUTH AFRICA

5180 New Age. (Capetown)

5181 Umthunywa. (Umtata)

INDEX

WITHDRAWN